PRENTICE HALL

SCIENCE EXPLORER

Integrated Science
Laboratory Manual

Teacher's Edition

PRENTICE HALL
Needham, Massachusetts
Upper Saddle River, New Jersey
Glenview, Illinois

Safety Reviewers

W. H. Breazeale, Ph.D.
Department of Chemistry
College of Charleston
Charleston, South Carolina

Ruth Hathaway, Ph.D.
Hathaway Consulting
Cape Girardeau, Missouri

Field Testers

Tom Barner
F. A. Day Middle School
Newton, Massachusetts

Nikki Bibbo
Russell Street School
Littleton, Massachusetts

Rose-Marie Botting
Broward County School District
Fort Lauderdale, Florida

Tom Messer
Cape Cod Academy
Osterville, Massachusetts

Carol Pirtle
Hale Middle School
Stow, Massachusetts

Pasquale Puleo
F. A. Day Middle School
Newton, Massachusetts

Anne Scammell
Geneva Middle School
Geneva, New York

PRENTICE HALL
Needham, Massachusetts
Upper Saddle River, New Jersey
Glenview, Illinois

Teacher's Edition ISBN 0-13-436370-1
5 6 7 8 9 10   06 05 04 03 02

Laboratory Investigations

Guidelines for Laboratory Safety

This section on laboratory safety is included as a resource for the teacher. Rather than providing definitive rules and regulations, the information is intended to be the basis for the establishment of safe laboratory practice. Prentice Hall, Inc., and its consultants make no claims as to the completeness of this material. Not all the precautions necessitated by the use, storage, and disposal of materials are covered here. Additional steps and safeguards may be required.

Responsibilities of the Teacher and the School

Laboratory safety is a shared responsibility. Both the school and the teacher need to be sure that all educational activities protect and promote the health and safety of students and the environment. To accomplish this goal, teachers need to understand the hazards, precautions, and emergency procedures associated with laboratory activities. When schools or teachers fail to live up to this responsibility, their behavior may be considered negligent. As a result, they may be liable for resulting injuries.

The best way to avoid being considered negligent is to ask yourself four simple questions:

1. What are the hazards?
2. What are the worst things that could happen?
3. What do I need to do if they do happen?
4. What are the prudent practices, protective facilities, and protective equipment needed to minimize the risk?

Be sure that you can answer all four of these questions before starting any science activity or demonstration. Then you can reduce the risks to an acceptable level—a level where the educational benefits of the activity outweigh the risks.

General Safety Strategies

Teachers should promote a "safety first" philosophy through personal example and by the careful planning and implementation of safety strategies.

The following strategies will help create an enjoyable, instructional, and safe environment. Specific safety rules are listed on pages v–vi.

1. Set up a safety committee made up of both teachers and administrators. Arrange to meet regularly to set safety policy for the school, discuss any safety problems that might arise, and organize periodic inspections of classrooms and laboratory equipment.

2. Establish a safety and health reference shelf in a resource center.

3. Develop detailed plans explaining what to do in case of emergency, including spills, cuts, burns, electric shock, poisoning, and fire. Review the procedures periodically throughout the school year.

4. Inform students of these emergency plans and carry out unannounced drills.

5. Explain to students how to use the intercom or other available means of communication to get help during an emergency.

6. Keep up to date in first aid and CPR (cardiopulmonary resuscitation) training.

7. Post emergency phone numbers for ambulance, fire, police, hospital, and the poison control center next to the telephone.

8. Perform laboratory investigations before assigning them to students. Take note of any potential hazards; devise plans for dealing with any possible mishaps or emergencies.

9. Emphasize safety considerations in pre-lab discussions. Hang posters dealing with safety issues in the classroom as reminders.

10. Keep classroom aisles and exits free of obstructions.

11. During an investigation, move about the classroom to keep a constant watch for potentially dangerous situations.

12. Curtail inappropriate behavior immediately. Wild play and practical jokes are forbidden during labs. Once students realize that the practice of safety is a required part of the course, they will accept a serious approach to laboratory work.

13. Never leave students unattended while they are engaged in science activities.

14. Require proper clothing at all times. Insist that long hair, dangling jewelry, and loose clothing be restrained; do not allow students to wear open shoes.

15. Insist that students wear safety goggles when the lab requires it.

16. Encourage students to keep lab work space neat and clear of extraneous objects, such as books and jackets.

17. Make sure that investigations utilizing toxic, fuming, or flammable materials are performed under a fume hood.

18. Keep the fume hood clear of unnecessary chemicals and equipment. Have the fume hood checked periodically to ensure that it is operating safely and efficiently.

19. Demonstrate to students the proper handling of glass materials, such as beakers and graduated cylinders.

20. Only wastepaper should be discarded in wastepaper receptacles. Keep a separate container for broken glass.

21. Substitute plastic containers for glass ones whenever possible, including graduated cylinders and beakers.

22. Consider the use of dispensing containers for liquids. They help prevent spills, skin contact with chemicals, and waste.

23. Use hot plates in place of open flames whenever possible. Never use open flames or hot plates when flammables are present in the room.

24. Use only nonmercury thermometers in investigations that call for the measurement of temperature.

25. Do not permit students to insert glass tubing or thermometers into rubber stoppers. If necessary, do this task yourself. When inserting these items into rubber stoppers, use safety stoppers, which have holes with beveled edges and are easier to use. Use glycerin or water to lubricate the glass.

26. All electrical equipment used in the lab should have GFI switches.

27. Do not leave equipment that is operating or plugged in unattended.

28. When working with live animals or plants, check ahead of time for students who may have allergies to the specimens.

29. Students should wear disposable nitrile, latex, or food-handling gloves when handling live animals or nonliving specimens.

30. Wear all safety equipment required of students.

31. Report in writing all unsafe conditions to the department head, maintenance director, and principal.

32. Have clearly defined penalties for violations of safety rules. Have these penalties approved and supported by the principal.

33. Document safety training, rules violations, and penalties in your records.

34. Keep a record of injuries and incidents (close calls), no matter how minor they may seem. Discuss these events at a department meeting to avoid similar occurrences.

35. As a class, review the safety rules and symbols listed on pages v–vii. Then assign the Student Safety Test on pages ix–xii. Discuss the test results to make sure students understand the safety rules.

36. Require students to sign a safety contract (provided on page viii). Also ask parents or guardians to sign this agreement.

37. Conduct quarterly inspections of the class-rooms and storage areas to maintain safe conditions.

Safety Equipment

Any classroom where laboratory investigations are performed should contain at least one each of the following pieces of safety equipment: (1) fire extinguisher, (2) fire blanket, (3) fire alarm, (4) phone or intercom to the office, (5) eyewash station, (6) safety shower, (7) safety hood, and (8) first-aid kit. If any of these basic pieces of safety equipment are not available, you may need to modify your laboratory program until the situation is remedied.

Make sure students know the location and proper use of all safety equipment. Where appropriate and practical, have students handle or operate the equipment so that they become familiar with it. Make sure all safety equipment is in good working order. All malfunctions should be promptly reported in writing to the proper school or district administrator.

Fire equipment At the beginning of the school year, you may wish to give each student the opportunity to actually operate a fire extinguisher, as the sound and action of a CO_2 fire extinguisher can be quite alarming to those who have never used one. You may also want to have students practice smothering imaginary flames on one another with the fire blanket.

Eyewash station The eyewash station should be used if chemicals are splashed onto the face or eyes. The exposed area should be left in the running water for five to ten minutes.

Safety shower The shower is used when chemicals have been spilled on a student's body or clothing. The student should stand under the shower until the chemical is completely diluted. Have a bathrobe or some type of replacement clothing handy in case the student's clothing is so badly contaminated that it must be removed.

You may want to set up one or two spill kits in your laboratory. The contents of a spill kit are used to neutralize chemicals, such as acids and bases, so that they can be cleaned up more easily. Baking soda (sodium bicarbonate) can be used to neutralize acids. Vinegar (acetic acid) can be used to neutralize bases. Commercial spill kits for acids, bases, and a number of other chemicals are available from supply houses.

Safety hood Use a safety hood whenever students are working with volatile or noxious chemicals. Make sure that the room is well ventilated when students are using any kind of chemicals or are working with preserved speci-mens. Warn students of the flammability and toxicity of various chemicals.

First-aid kit A typical first-aid kit contains an assortment of antiseptics, bandages, gauze pads, and scissors. Most also contain simple instructions for use. Be sure to read the instruc-tions if you are not familiar with basic first-aid procedures. A first-aid kit should be taken on all field trips. For field trips, you may wish to add such items as a bee-sting kit, meat tender-izer, tweezers, and calamine lotion. Do not dispense medication (including aspirin).

Guidelines for the Use and Care of Animals

Animals are an essential part of a science curriculum. The judicious use of live or preserved animals can help students realize that the study of science is relevant, fascinating, and rewarding. It is important to be aware of and sensitive to ethical and practical concerns when studying animals. The purpose of this section is to discuss some realistic guidelines for using animals in the classroom.

1. Whenever possible, live animals should be observed in their natural habitats or in zoos, parks, and aquariums.

2. Check the state and federal codes regarding animal welfare that apply in your area. You may also wish to refer to guidelines published by the National Science Teachers' Association, the National Association of Biology Teachers, and the International Science Fair. Make students aware of all safety rules and regulations regarding animals.

3. Before bringing a live animal into the classroom, determine whether a proper habitat can be maintained in the classroom situation. Such a habitat includes temperature, space, and type of food. Students should have a clear understanding of the appropriate care needed by the live animals brought into the classroom. Do not allow students to tap on animal enclosures or otherwise disturb the animals.

4. No wild vertebrate animals should be brought into the classroom. Purchase animals from a reputable dealer only.

5. Live animals should be nonpoisonous and healthy. Any mammals used in the classroom should be vaccinated against rabies unless the animals were purchased recently from a reliable scientific supply company. Quarantine any animal to make sure it is disease-free before bringing it into the classroom.

6. Make sure that the living quarters of classroom animals are clean, located away from stressful situations, appropriately spacious, and secure enough to confine the animal. You may wish to lock cages to prevent the accidental release of animals; the small padlocks used on luggage are good for this purpose.

7. Remove wastes from animal living quarters daily. Thoroughly clean animal living quarters periodically to ensure that they are odor and germ-free. Provide a daily supply of fresh water and any other need specific to the particular animal.

8. Provide for the care of animals during weekends and school vacations. Inform the custodial staff of the presence of animals and warn them of any special requirements. For example, turning off the aquarium pump to save electricity or spraying the classroom for insects can be fatal to animals.

9. Students should be instructed how to handle each species brought into the classroom. Make students aware that they can receive painful wounds from the improper handling of some animals.

10. Animals should be handled only if necessary. If an animal is frightened or excited, pregnant, feeding, or with its young, special handling is required.

11. Students should thoroughly clean their hands after handling animals or the quarters containing animals.

12. Animals should be returned to their natural habitat after an observation period of not longer than 14 days. However, laboratory-bred animals or species that are not native to an area should not be released into the environment.

13. If an animal must be euthanized, do not allow students to watch. Contact the local humane society for advice.

14. Before performing any experiment involving live animals, check local and state regulations. In some states, certification is required before a teacher is permitted to experiment with animals.

15. No animal studies involving anesthetic drugs, pathogenic organisms, toxicological products, carcinogens, or radiation should be performed.

16. Any experiment requiring live animals should have a clearly defined objective relating to the teaching and learning of some scientific principle.

17. No experimental procedures that will cause pain, discomfort, or harm to animals should be done in the classroom or at home.

18. Surgical procedures should not be performed on live animals.

19. If fertilized bird eggs are opened, the embryo should be destroyed humanely two days before it would have hatched, at the latest.

20. When working with preserved animals, make sure that students maintain a serious and respectful attitude toward the specimens.

Handling Ethical Issues

There is much controversy regarding the use of animals in scientific research. This controversy extends to preserved animals in dissections as well as to live animals in experiments. Although the debate over what uses of animals are appropriate in a science classroom can be emotionally charged, it can also provide an opportunity for students to closely examine a current issue. You may wish to have students read current literature on the subject and contact groups and individuals with varying points of view.

Stress that it is important to make a rational, informed decision before taking a stand on any issue. Point out that it is vital to know and understand the arguments on all sides of an issue. Help students analyze the sources they find in terms of bias and the reliability and objectivity of the author(s). Help them to distinguish between fact and opinion. Encourage them to question what they read and hear. Challenge them to discover the hidden assumptions and implications of different points of view.

If dissections are a part of your curriculum and a student chooses to avoid dissections because of ethical concerns, respect that student's opinion. Point out, however, that no simulation or videotape can completely replace hands-on, firsthand experience.

Additional guidelines for the use of live animals are available from the National Association of Biology Teachers (NABT) 11250 Roger Bacon Drive, Suite 19, Reston, VA 20190 (703)471-1134. See the NABT Web site *nabter@aol.com* for additional information.

Guidelines for Safe Disposal of Laboratory Wastes

Every effort should be made to recover, recycle, and reuse materials used in the laboratory. When disposal is required, however, specific procedures should be followed in order to ensure that your school complies with local, state, and federal regulations.

1. Discard only dry paper into ordinary wastebaskets.

2. Discard broken glass into a separate container clearly marked "For Broken Glass Only."

3. Acidic or basic solutions need to be neutralized before disposal. Slowly add dilute sodium hydroxide to acids and dilute hydrochloric acid to bases until pH paper shows that they are no longer strongly acidic or basic. Then flush the solutions down the drain with a lot of water.

4. Before each investigation, instruct your students concerning where and how they are to dispose of chemicals that are used or produced during the investigation. Specific teacher notes addressing disposal are provided on each lab as appropriate.

5. Keep each excess or used chemical in a separate container; do not mix them. This allows for possible recycling or reuse. It also eliminates unexpected reactions or the need for expensive separation by a contractor if the wastes must be disposed of professionally.

6. Only nonflammable, neutral, nontoxic, nonreactive, and water-soluble chemicals should be flushed down the drain.

7. When growing bacteria cultures, use only disposable petri dishes. After streaking, the dishes should be sealed and not opened again by students. After the lab, students should return the unopened dishes to you and wash their hands with antibacterial soap.

8. Two methods are recommended for the safe disposal of bacteria cultures. *First method:* Autoclave the petri dishes and discard without opening. *Second method:* If no autoclave is available, carefully open the dishes (never have a student do this) and pour full-strength bleach into the dishes and let stand for a day. Then pour the bleach from the petri dishes down a drain and flush the drain with lots of water. Tape the petri dishes back together and place in a sealed plastic bag. Wrap the plastic bag with a brown paper bag or newspaper and tape securely. Throw the sealed package in the trash. Thoroughly disinfect the work area with bleach.

9. To grow mold, use a new, sealable plastic bag that is two to three times larger than the material to be placed inside. Seal the bag and tape it shut. After the bag is sealed, students should not open it. To dispose of the bag and mold culture, make a small cut near an edge of the bag and cook in a microwave oven on high setting for at least 1 minute. Discard the bag according to local ordinance, usually in the trash.

Laboratory Materials and Equipment

Consumables					
Item	**Quantity Per Group**	**Laboratory Investigation**	**Item**	**Quantity Per Group**	**Laboratory Investigation**
bag, plastic lunch	1	C-1	culture, euglena	1	A-3
bags, plastic resealable	4	A-2	culture, paramecium	1	A-3
bags, reclosable, plastic, 1-L size	2	E-4	cups, 8-oz paper	2 or 3	A-1, F-3, G-3, L-4, O-1
balloons	several	M-3	cups, 8-oz plastic	2 or 3	A-5, C-1, E-4, E-5, H-1, I-2, L-4
barley	1 bag	G-4			
Benedict's solution	1 container	D-3	cups, small plastic-foam	3	H-4
biuret solution	1 container	D-3	dry cell, 1.5-V	1	N-1, N-2, N-4
box, small cardboard	1	N-3	eggs, hard-boiled	2	E-4
bulbs, fluorescent, 15-watt	1	O-3	envelope	1	F-1
bulbs, fluorescent, 25-watt	1 per class	O-3	ethanol	30 mL	K-1
bulbs, incandescent, 15-watt	1 per class	O-3	event cards	1 set	E-3
bulbs, incandescent, 60-watt	1	O-3	fish, Betta	1 male and 1 female	B-5
bulbs, light, 1.5-V with socket	3	N-2, N-4	fish food, Betta	1 container	B-5
bulb packaging, 15-watt fluorescent and 60-watt incandescent light	1	O-3	fishing line, nylon	1 meter	M-4
			flour	1 container	D-3
candle, large birthday	1	K-2, M-6	foil, aluminum,	1 roll	J-2, O-3
card, 10 cm × 15 cm	1	J-2	foil, aluminum, small piece	1	N-1
card, 20 cm × 25 cm	1	J-2	food coloring, blue	1 bottle	H-1, H-3, H-4
cardboard	1	M-5	food coloring, red	1 bottle	H-1, H-3, H-4
cardboard, 6 cm × 10 cm piece	1	D-7	food products, various	1 of each	D-3
cardboard, 20 cm × 30 cm piece	1	I-2	gauze, 10-cm strip	1	G-2
cardboard, 30 cm × 30 cm square	1	O-4	gauze, 8 cm × 8 cm square	4	I-2
			gelatin	1 box	D-3
cheesecloth, 8 cm × 8 cm	4	G-2	glue, white	1 container	M-5
clay	1 ball	M-3	glycerin	1 bottle	D-5
clay, loose	1 container	G-4	goldfish	1	B-3
clay, modeling, blocks	2	H-3	granite chips	1 bag	E-5, G-3
clay mixed with soil	1 container	G-2	granite, small samples	2	I-1
cornstarch	25 mL	F-3	grass	1 container	G-4
cotton	1 piece	A-3	gravel	1 container	F-5
couscous	1 bag	B-4	gravel, aquarium	1 bag	B-5
cover, cloth	1	C-4	gravel mixed with soil	1 container	G-2
coverslip	3	Skills Lab 1, A-3, A-4, B-3, C-2	high-density polyethylene (HDPE)	3 pieces	L-4
			honey	1 container	D-3
craft sticks	several	C-3	hydrogen peroxide, 3%	1 container	L-1
crayons, different	4	I-4	ice	several cubes	L-3, M-6
culture, amoeba	1	A-3	index cards, large	several	F-4, I-2
			iodine solution	1 container	C-2, D-3
			iodine solution	3 strengths	C-1

LABORATORY MATERIALS AND EQUIPMENT *(continued)*

Item	Quantity Per Group	Laboratory Investigation
isopropyl (rubbing) alcohol, 91%	1 container	L-4
leaf, floating water plant	1	A-4
leaves, ground-up	1 container	G-4
leaves, land plant, different species	2	C-2
leaves, land plant, same species	10	A-4, C-5
lemon	1	N-3
lemon juice	1 container	I-1
lettuce leaf	1	C-2
lima beans, large	10	C-5
limestone, small samples	2	I-1
limestone chips	1 bag	G-3, E-5
limewater solution	(see lab)	K-2
manganese dioxide	1 bottle	L-1
marble, small samples	2	I-1
marker, glass	1	I-1, K-1, L-1
markers, permanent, colored	9	C-2, C-3, D-7, D-8, F-1, G-2, O-1
matches	1 box	J-3, K-2, L-1, M-6
metal cleaner	1 can	N-3
microscope slides	several	Skills Lab 1, A-3, A-4, B-3, C-2
molasses	20 mL	F-3
mouthwash, 2 types	3 oz each	D-6
mud	1 container	G-4
newspapers	3	Skills Lab 1, F-3, F-5, G-3
notebook	1	D-1, E-2
oil, corn	1 container	K-4
oil, olive	1 container	K-4
oil, safflower	1 container	K-4
oil, soybean	1 container	K-4
oil, sunflower	1 container	K-4
packing material, biodegradable	about 1-L volume	E-4
packing material, nonbiodegradable	about 1-L volume	E-4
paper	several sheets	A-1
paper, 15 cm × 15 cm	1 piece	L-3
paper, colored construction, one color	8 sheets	E-3

Item	Quantity Per Group	Laboratory Investigation
paper, construction, black	1 sheet	E-6
paper, construction, white	1 sheet	E-6
paper, filter	1 sheet	A-5, D-6
paper, graph	1 sheet	C-5, G-3, O-3
paper, lined	1 sheet	J-1
paper, notebook	1 sheet	E-3
paper, plain brown	1 sheet	O-1
paper, plain white	several sheets	F-4, G-4, L-4, O-4
paper, weighing		Skills Lab 2
paper clips, large	20	M-2, M-5, N-1
pen	1	A-2, C-4, D-6, E-2, E-3, F-1, F-2
pencil, colored	9	B-5, C-5, E-2, E-6, F-1, F-4, H-5, I-3, I-4, J-3
pencil, glass-marking	1	A-5, C-1, K-4
pencil, soft graphite	1	A-2, E-1, E-3, F-1, F-2, G-1, I-3, I-4, O-1
pencil, wax	1	G-2, H-1
pens, colored	9	E-6
perch, preserved	1	B-3
petri dishes, plastic	30	A-5, B-4
petri dishes, plastic with agar	4	D-6, H-2
pH indicator paper	1 roll	E-5, H-2, I-1
pH test chart	1	E-5, I-1
pins, straight, push	several	J-2, M-5, O-4
plants, floating aquatic	1 clump	B-5
plaster of paris	1 container	F-5
polyethylene terephthalate (PETE)	3 pieces	L-4
polypropylene	3 pieces	L-4
polystyrene	3 pieces	L-4
poster board	1	M-5
potassium nitrate	25 g	L-3
potato cubes	3	C-1
potato, baked	2 slices	A-2
powdered chalk	1 container	F-5
rice	1 bag	G-4
rock salt	1 bag	G-3
rubber bands	4	G-2, O-2
salad oil	1 container	K-1

Item	Quantity Per Group	Laboratory Investigation	Item	Quantity Per Group	Laboratory Investigation
salt solutions: calcium chloride, potassium chloride, sodium chloride, strontium chloride, and two unknown	6 g each	J-3	tape, transparent	1 roll	A-2, C-4, D-6, E-6, F-1, F-4, H-4, I-2, J-1, J-2, M-3, M-5, N-3
salt, table	1 container	Skills Lab 2, F-5, H-1, H-4, K-1	test kits, water quality	4	H-2
			thread	1 spool	I-2, J-1, M-5
			thumbtacks	several	M-5
salt water	1 container	K-1	tincture of iodine	1 container	K-4
sand	1 container	F-5, G-2	tomatoes	2 or more varieties	A-5
sand, coarse	2 cups	H-3			
sand, red-colored	1 container	G-4	toothpicks	9	D-7, H-4
sand, white-colored	1 container	G-4	towel, cloth	1	D-5
sandpaper	1 sheet	M-5, N-3	towel, paper	1 roll	Skills Lab 1, A-3, A-5, B-2, B-3, C-2, D-2, D-3, D-5, F-3, F-5, G-3, H-1, H-3, J-3
sandstone, small samples	2	I-1			
sea star, preserved	1	B-2			
seeds, bean	1 bag	G-4			
seeds, black-eyed pea	1 bag	A-1			
seeds, kidney bean	1 bag	A-1			
seeds, lentil	1 bag	G-4	twist tie	1	C-1
seeds, lima bean	1 bag	A-1, B-4	vinegar, white	1 container	E-5, I-1
seeds, millet	1 bag	G-4	water, aged in 2-liter soda bottles	2	B-5
seeds, navy bean	1 bag	A-1			
seeds, pea	1 bag	G-4	water, carbonated	1 container	I-1
seeds, pinto bean	1 bag	A-1	water, distilled	1 container	H-1, I-1, L-2
seeds, popcorn	1 bag	B-4	water, hard, sample, standard	1	L-2
seeds, split pea	1 bag	A-1			
seeds, sunflower	1 bag	B-4	water, lake	1 container	H-2
seeds, unpopped popcorn	1 bag	G-4	water, pond	1 container	H-2
soap, bar	1	L-2	water, river	1 container	H-2
soap, liquid hand	1 bottle	L-2	water, stream	1 container	H-2
soil, potting	1 container	F-5, G-2, G-4	water, tap		Skills Lab 1, A-5, C-1, C-2, D-2, D-3, D-8, E-4, F-3, F-5, G-3, H-1, H-4, I-2, L-2, L-3, L-4, M-6, O-1, O-2
splints, wooden	2	L-1			
starch solution	1 container	C-1			
steel wool	1 piece	N-3			
straws, plastic	1 box	G-4, H-3, M-3, M-5			
string	1 ball	D-8, E-2, M-3, M-5, O-1			
swabs, cotton	2	A-2	water, aged in 1-gallon container	1	B-5
tape, electrical	1 roll	O-3			
tape, masking	1 roll	A-2, D-6, M-1, M-5, O-1, O-3	water from an aquarium	1 beaker	B-3

LABORATORY MATERIALS AND EQUIPMENT *(continued)*

Nonconsumables

Note: Safety equipment has not been listed. It is recommended that a laboratory apron, safety goggles, and heat-resistant gloves are worn when required.

Item	Quantity Per Group	Laboratory Investigation	Item	Quantity Per Group	Laboratory Investigation
air pump, hand-held	1	M-3	can lid	1	M-6
ammeter, 0–1 A range	1	N-2	can opener	1	M-6
aquarium	1	M-3	cardboard carton, 25 cm x 25 cm x 30 cm	1	O-3
balance	1	E-4, G-3, H-4, I-1, K-1, K-3, K-4, L-3, M-3, M-5, M-6	clamp	1	M-2
			clamps, burette	2	J-1
balance, triple-beam	1	Skills Lab 2	clips or screws for connecting wires	12	N-4
ball, rubber, 2.5–4.0 cm diameter	1	D-8	clock with second hand	1	B-4, C-1, D-2, E-6, G-3, O-1, O-3
beakers, 100-mL	8	I-1, L-2			
beakers, 150-mL	4	K-2	cloth	1	M-5
beakers, 200-mL	1–4	Skills Lab 2, C-1, F-3	coins, dime	8	N-1, N-3
			coins, nickel	8	N-1, N-3
beakers, 250-mL	4	A-5, E-5, H-1, H-2, H-4, L-3	coins, penny	8	C-4, K-3, N-1, N-3
beakers, 400-mL	4	D-3, O-2	compass, drawing	1	J-2
beakers, 1000-mL	4	B-3, H-4	container, plastic, 1-L	1	G-2
blindfold	1	D-7	containers, metal with plastic lids	2	E-6
board, wood, at least 45 cm long	1	J-1	containers, plastic with lids	2	E-6
books, heavy	several	E-4	cookie sheet	1	F-3
boots, waterproof	1	H-2	cups, transparent plastic	3	D-2
bottle, 2-L plastic	1	D-5	dish, shallow metal	1	K-2
bottle opener	1	M-6	dowel, 40-cm wooden	1	J-1
bottles, plastic 2-L soft-drink with bottom removed	4	G-2, D-8	dowels, 6-cm wooden	4	K-1
			dowel, 15-cm wooden	1	M-6
bottles, plastic 2-L soft-drink with top removed and hole in side	4	G-2	droppers, plastic	3	Skills Lab 1, A-3, A-4, B-3, C-2, D-3, H-3, I-2, K-4, L-2
bowl, plastic, mixing	1	A-5, E-5, G-4	fan, electric	1	M-5
brush	1	A-5	fishing float	1	D-8
bucket, large	1	D-8, I-2, M-3	fishing sinkers, at least 110 g	several	J-1
burner, Bunsen	1	J-3			
calculator	1	E-1	fishnet	1	B-3
can, large, open at both ends	1	M-6	flask, 500-mL Erlenmeyer	1	K-2
can, small, open at one end	1	M-6	forceps	1	Skills Lab 1, B-3, C-1, C-2, D-6, K-3, L-4, M-3
can, soda, or other container that floats when empty	1	M-3			
			fossils	several	F-5, G-4

Item	Quantity Per Group	Laboratory Investigation	Item	Quantity Per Group	Laboratory Investigation
funnel	1	A-5	pan, transparent glass loaf, 5 inches × 9 inches	1	H-3
glass jar, large	1	B-3	pans	several	F-5
globe, world	1	F-1	pegboard	1	N-4
gloves, hot	1	E-6	pitcher, large	1	D-8
graduated cylinder, 10-mL	1	L-1, L-2, L-3	plate, streak	1	F-5
graduated cylinders, 100-mL	4	Skills Lab 2, C-1, D-5, E-4, F-3, G-2, G-3, H-2, H-4, K-1, L-4, M-3, M-6	probe	1	B-3
			protractor	1	O-4
			pulleys, double	2	M-4
			pulleys, single	2	M-4
hand lens	1	E-2	rain gutter, vinyl, 30–40 cm	1	E-5
hot pad	1	H-1	resonance box	1	O-2
hot plate	1	D-3, H-1, L-3	ring, large	1	M-2, M-4, M-6
igniter	1	J-3	ring stands	2	J-1, M-2, M-4, M-6
jars, large, with cover	4	G-3, H-2			
jars, small	2	D-6, G-3	rods, plastic to fit inside straw	several	G-4
lens, hand	2	A-1, B-2, B-3, B-5, E-4, H-2	rods, wooden to fit inside straw	several	G-4
light socket	1	O-3	ruler, metric	1	A-1, C-1, C-2, C-5, D-6, D-7, E-1, E-4, F-4, G-1, G-4, H-3, H-4, K-1, M-6, O-1, O-4
map, world	1	F-1			
maps, outline, world showing latitude and longitude	2	F-1			
mass standard, 100-g	1	M-2			
mass standard, 500-g	1	M-4	scale, spring, 1000-g	1	M-4
materials of known hardness	several	F-5	scissors	1	Skills Lab 1, A-4, D-6, D-7, D-8, E-3, E-6, F-1, F-4, H-1, J-1, J-2, M-5, N-3, O-3
measuring cup, 100-mL	1	G-2			
meterstick	1	E-2, F-3, J-1, J-2, M-1, M-2, M-5, O-1			
microscope, compound	1	Skills Lab 1, A-3, A-4, B-1, C-2, D-1, D-2, H-5	scoop, small	1	Skills Lab 2
			screen, fine wire	1	G-3
			screening, metal window, 3-cm square	1	H-1
milk carton, 1-L	1	G-4	screw eyes	2	D-8
mirror, small and support	1	O-4	screws, machine	several	N-4
nails, iron, 10-cm long	5	N-1	slide, human bone, cross-section	1	D-2
net, plankton	1	H-2			
nuts, metal, at least 110 g	several	J-1	slide, muscle, cardiac	1	D-2
objects, test (small toys, desk items, etc.)	several	Skills Lab 2, K-3, N-1	slide, muscle, skeletal	1	D-2
			slide, muscle, smooth	1	D-2
pan, plastic loaf, 5 inches × 9 inches	1	H-3	slide, planaria	1	B-1
			slide, pork-tapeworm	1	B-1

LABORATORY MATERIALS AND EQUIPMENT *(continued)*

Item	Quantity Per Group	Laboratory Investigation
slide, trichina-worm	1	B-1
slide, vinegar-eel	1	B-1
slides, human tissue	several different	D-1
slides, marine plankton, prepared	several	H-5
spatula	1	A-2, L-3
spectroscope, hand-held	1	J-3
spoon, plastic	1	G-3, L-4
spoon, wooden	1	A-5
spoons, metal	12	A-5, F-3, F-5, H-1, H-4
spring	1	M-2
stakes	4	E-2
stirring rods, glass	2	E-4
stopper, rubber, 2-hole	1	D-5
stopper, solid rubber	1-10	K-2, K-4
stopwatches	3	M-1, M-5, O-1
strainer	1	A-5
switches, knife, double pole-single throw	1	N-4
switch, knife, single pole-single throw	3	N-2, N-4
tablespoon	1	L-4
tape measure	1	M-1
test tubes	3 or 4	C-1, D-3, L-1, L-2, L-3
test tubes, large, with stoppers	4	H-2
test tubes with stoppers	2-10	K-4
test-tube holder	1	D-3
test-tube rack	1	C-1, K-4, L-1, L-2

Item	Quantity Per Group	Laboratory Investigation
thermometers, Celsius, identical	2	E-6, H-1, H-2, I-2, L-3, M-6, O-3
timer	1	D-5, G-2
tongs	1	E-6, K-2, L-1, L-3, M-3
tools, hand	6 different	B-4
tray	1	A-1
tray, dissecting	1	B-2, B-3
tubing, glass, long	1	D-5
tubing, glass, short	1	D-5
tubing, plastic or rubber, various lengths	several	D-5, M-3
tuning forks, 320 Hz	2	O-2
voltmeter, 0–3 V range	1	N-2, N-3
washers	15	M-2
washers, metal, at least 110 g	several	J-1
watch with second hand	1	B-4, C-1, D-2, E-6, F-3, G-2
watch glass	1	K-3
watering can	1	H-3
windmill base	1	M-5
wire, bell	several	N-1, N-3
wires, connecting	17	N-2, N-4
wire loops, nichrome with handles	6	J-3
wood, balsa	1	M-5
wood block, about 7 cm high	1	E-5
wood block, about 10 cm high	1	E-5
yam, baked	2 slices	A-2

Suppliers of Laboratory Materials and Equipment

Consumable and nonconsumable kits for the **Science Explorer** program are produced by

Science Kit and Boreal Laboratories
777 East Park Drive
Tonawanda, NY 14150
1-800-828-7777
sciencekit.com

Other suppliers of laboratory materials and equipment follow.

Carolina Biological Supply
Company
2700 York Road
Burlington, NC 27215
336-584-0381
carolina@carolina.com

Central Scientific Company
11222 Melrose Ave.
Franklin Park, IL 60131
847-451-0150
cenconet.com

Connecticut Valley Biological
Supply Company, Inc.
82 Valley Road
Southampton, MA 01073
800-628-7748
fax: 800-355-6813

Delta Biologicals
P.O. Box 26664
Tucson, AZ 85726-6664
520-745-7878
deltabio@flash.net

Edmund Scientific Company
101 E. Gloucester Pike
Barrington, NJ 08007
609-547-3488
edsci.com

Fisher Scientific Educational
Materials Division
485 S Frontage Road
Burr Ridge, IL 60521
800-955-1177
fisheredu.com

Frey Scientific Company
905 Hickory Lane
Mansfield, OH 44905
419-589-1900
beckleycardy.com

Hubbard Scientific
1120 Halbleib
Chippewa Falls, WI 54729
800-289-9299
amep.com

Lab-Aids, Inc.
17 Colt
Ronkonkoma, NY 11779
516-737-1133

Lab Safety Supply Inc.
401 S. Wright Rd.
Janesville, WI 53546-8729
800-356-0783
labsafety.com

Nasco
901 Janesville Ave.
Fort Atkinson, WI 53538
800-558-9595
nascota.com

Nasco West Inc.
P.O. Box 3837
Modesto, CA 95352-3837
800-558-9595
nascota.com

Nebraska Scientific
A Division of Cygus
Company Inc.
3823 Leavenworth Street
Omaha, NE 68105
402-346-7214
nebraskascientific.com

Sargent-Welch Scientific Co.
911 Commerce Ct.
Buffalo Grove, IL 60089
800-727-4368
sargentwelch.com

Ward's Natural Science
Establishment Inc.
5100 West Henrietta Road
Henrietta, NY 14467
716-359-2502
customer_service@wardsci.com

PRENTICE HALL

Integrated Science
Laboratory Manual

Student Edition

PRENTICE HALL
Needham, Massachusetts
Upper Saddle River, New Jersey
Glenview, Illinois

Safety Reviewers

W. H. Breazeale, Ph.D.
Department of Chemistry
College of Charleston
Charleston, South Carolina

Ruth Hathaway, Ph.D.
Hathaway Consulting
Cape Girardeau, Missouri

Field Testers

Tom Barner
F. A. Day Middle School
Newton, Massachusetts

Nikki Bibbo
Russell Street School
Littleton, Massachusetts

Rose-Marie Botting
Broward County School District
Fort Lauderdale, Florida

Tom Messer
Cape Cod Academy
Osterville, Massachusetts

Carol Pirtle
Hale Middle School
Stow, Massachusetts

Pasquale Puleo
F. A. Day Middle School
Newton, Massachusetts

Anne Scammell
Geneva Middle School
Geneva, New York

PRENTICE HALL
Needham, Massachusetts
Upper Saddle River, New Jersey
Glenview, Illinois

Student Edition ISBN 0-13-436369-8
3 4 5 6 7 8 9 10   06 05 04 03 02 01 00

TABLE OF CONTENTS *(continued)*

To prepare yourself to work safely in the laboratory, read over the following safety rules. Then read them a second time. Make sure you understand and follow each rule. Ask your teacher to explain any rules you do not understand.

Dress Code

1. To protect yourself from injuring your eyes, wear safety goggles whenever you work with chemicals, flames, glassware, or any substance that might get into your eyes. If you wear contact lenses, notify your teacher.

2. Wear an apron or coat whenever you work with corrosive chemicals or substances that can stain.

3. Tie back long hair to keep it away from any chemicals, flames, or equipment.

4. Remove or tie back any article of clothing or jewelry that can hang down and touch chemicals, flames, or equipment. Roll up or secure long sleeves.

5. Never wear open shoes or sandals.

General Precautions

6. Read all directions for an experiment several times before beginning the activity. Carefully follow all written and oral instructions. If you are in doubt about any part of the experiment, ask your teacher for assistance.

7. Never perform activities that are not assigned or authorized by your teacher. Obtain permission before "experimenting" on your own. Never handle any equipment unless you have specific permission.

8. Never perform lab activities without direct supervision.

9. Never eat or drink in the laboratory.

10. Keep work areas clean and tidy at all times. Bring only notebooks and lab manuals or written lab procedures to the work area. All other items, such as purses and backpacks, should be left in a designated area.

11. Do not engage in horseplay.

First Aid

12. Always report all accidents or injuries to your teacher, no matter how minor. Notify your teacher immediately about any fires.

13. Learn what to do in case of specific accidents, such as getting acid in your eyes or on your skin. (Rinse acids from your body with plenty of water.)

14. Be aware of the location of the first-aid kit, but do not use it unless instructed by your teacher. In case of injury, your teacher should administer first aid. Your teacher may also send you to the school nurse or call a physician.

15. Know the location of the emergency equipment such as fire extinguisher and fire blanket.

16. Know the location of the nearest telephone and whom to contact in an emergency.

Heating and Fire Safety

17. Never use a heat source, such as a candle, burner, or hot plate, without wearing safety goggles.

18. Never heat anything unless instructed to do so. A chemical that is harmless when cool may be dangerous when heated.

19. Keep all combustible materials away from flames. Never use a flame or spark near a combustible chemical.

20. Never reach across a flame.

21. Before using a laboratory burner, make sure you know proper procedures for lighting and adjusting the burner, as demonstrated by your teacher. Do not touch the burner. It may be hot. Never leave a lighted burner unattended. Turn off the burner when not in use.

22. Chemicals can splash or boil out of a heated test tube. When heating a substance in a test tube, make sure that the mouth of the tube is not pointed at you or anyone else.

23. Never heat a liquid in a closed container. The expanding gases produced may shatter the container.

24. Before picking up a container that has been heated, first hold the back of your hand near it. If you can feel heat on the back of your hand, the container is too hot to handle. Use an oven mitt to pick up a container that has been heated.

Using Chemicals Safely

25. Never mix chemicals "for the fun of it." You might produce a dangerous, possibly explosive substance.

26. Never put your face near the mouth of a container that holds chemicals. Many chemicals are poisonous. Never touch, taste, or smell a chemical unless you are instructed by your teacher to do so.

27. Use only those chemicals needed in the activity. Read and double-check labels on supply bottles before removing any chemicals. Take only as much as you need. Keep all containers closed when chemicals are not being used.

28. Dispose of all chemicals as instructed by your teacher. To avoid contamination, never return chemicals to their original containers. Never pour untreated chemicals or other substances into the sink or trash containers.

29. Be extra careful when working with acids or bases. Pour all chemicals over the sink or a container, not over your work surface.

30. If you are instructed to test for odors, use a wafting motion to direct the odors to your nose. Do not inhale the fumes directly from the container.

31. When mixing an acid and water, always pour the water into the container first then add the acid to the water. Never pour water into an acid.

32. Take extreme care not to spill any material in the laboratory. Wash chemical spills and splashes immediately with plenty of water. Immediately begin rinsing with water any acids that get on your skin or clothing, and notify your teacher of any acid spill at the same time.

Using Glassware Safely

33. Never force glass tubing or a thermometer into a rubber stopper or rubber tubing. Have your teacher insert the glass tubing or thermometer if required for an activity.

34. If you are using a laboratory burner, use a wire screen to protect glassware from any flame. Never heat glassware that is not thoroughly dry on the outside.

35. Keep in mind that hot glassware looks cool. Never pick up glassware without first checking to see if it is hot. Use an oven mitt. See rule 24.

36. Never use broken or chipped glassware. If glassware breaks, notify your teacher and dispose of the glassware in the proper broken-glassware container.

37. Never eat or drink from glassware.

38. Thoroughly clean glassware before putting it away.

Using Sharp Instruments

39. Handle scalpels or other sharp instruments with extreme care. Never cut material toward you; cut away from you.

40. Immediately notify your teacher if you cut your skin when working in the laboratory.

Animal and Plant Safety

41. Never perform experiments that cause pain, discomfort, or harm to animals. This rule applies at home as well as in the classroom.

42. Animals should be handled only if absolutely necessary. Your teacher will instruct you as to how to handle each animal species brought into the classroom.

43. If you know that you are allergic to certain plants, molds, or animals, tell your teacher before doing an activity in which these are used.

44. During field work, protect your skin by wearing long pants, long sleeves, socks, and closed shoes. Know how to recognize the poisonous plants and fungi in your area, as well as plants with thorns, and avoid contact with them. Never eat any part of a plant or fungus.

45. Wash your hands thoroughly after handling animals or a cage containing animals. Wash your hands when you are finished with any activity involving animal parts, plants, or soil.

End-of-Experiment Rules

46. After an experiment has been completed, turn off all burners or hot plates. If you used a gas burner, check that the gas-line valve to the burner is off. Unplug hot plates.

47. Turn off and unplug any other electrical equipment that you used.

48. Clean up your work area and return all equipment to its proper place.

49. Dispose of waste materials as instructed by your teacher.

50. Wash your hands after every experiment.

These symbols alert you to possible dangers in the laboratory and remind you to work carefully.

Safety Goggles Always wear safety goggles to protect your eyes in any activity involving chemicals, flames or heating, or the possibility of broken glassware.

Lab Apron Wear a laboratory apron to protect your skin and clothing from damage.

Breakage You are working with materials that may be breakable, such as glass containers, glass tubing, thermometers, or funnels. Handle breakable materials with care. Do not touch broken glassware.

Heat-Resistant Gloves Use an oven mitt or other hand protection when handling hot materials. Hot plates, hot glassware, or hot water can cause burns. Do not touch hot objects with your bare hands.

Heating Use a clamp or tongs to pick up hot glassware. Do not touch hot objects with your bare hands.

Sharp Object Pointed-tip scissors, scalpels, knives, needles, pins, or tacks are sharp. They can cut or puncture your skin. Always direct a sharp edge or point away from yourself and others. Use sharp instruments only as instructed.

Electric Shock Avoid the possibility of electric shock. Never use electrical equipment around water, or when the equipment is wet or your hands are wet. Be sure cords are untangled and cannot trip anyone. Disconnect the equipment when it is not in use.

Corrosive Chemical You are working with an acid or another corrosive chemical. Avoid getting it on your skin or clothing, or in your eyes. Do not inhale the vapors. Wash your hands when you are finished with the activity.

Poison Do not let any poisonous chemical come in contact with your skin, and do not inhale its vapors. Wash your hands when you are finished with the activity.

Physical Safety When an experiment involves physical activity, take precautions to avoid injuring yourself or others. Follow instructions from the teacher. Alert the teacher if there is any reason you should not participate in the activity.

Animal Safety Treat live animals with care to avoid harming the animals or yourself. Working with animal parts or preserved animals also requires caution. Wash your hands when you are finished with the activity.

Plant Safety Handle plants in the laboratory or during field work only as directed by the teacher. If you are allergic to certain plants, tell the teacher before doing an activity in which those plants are used. Avoid touching harmful plants such as poison ivy, poison oak, or poison sumac, or plants with thorns. Wash your hands when you are finished with the activity.

Flames You may be working with flames from a lab burner, candle, or matches. Tie back loose hair and clothing. Follow instructions from the teacher about lighting and extinguishing flames.

No Flames Flammable materials may be present. Make sure there are no flames, sparks, or other exposed heat sources present.

Fumes When poisonous or unpleasant vapors may be involved, work in a ventilated area. Avoid inhaling vapors directly. Only test an odor when directed to do so by the teacher, and use a wafting motion to direct the vapor toward your nose.

Disposal Chemicals and other laboratory materials used in the activity must be disposed of safely. Follow the instructions from the teacher.

Hand Washing Wash your hands thoroughly when finished with the activity. Use antibacterial soap and warm water. Lather both sides of your hands and between your fingers. Rinse well.

General Safety Awareness You may see this symbol when none of the symbols described earlier appears. In this case, follow the specific instructions provided. You may also see this symbol when you are asked to develop your own procedure in a lab. Have the teacher approve your plan before you go further.

I, _____ , have read
(please print full name)

the Science Safety Rules and Safety Symbols
sections on pages v–vii of this manual,
understand their contents completely, and agree
to demonstrate compliance with all safety rules
and guidelines that have been established in each
of the following categories:

(please check)

☐ Dress Code

☐ General Precautions

☐ First Aid

☐ Heating and Fire Safety

☐ Using Chemicals Safely

☐ Using Glassware Safely

☐ Using Sharp Instruments

☐ Animal and Plant Safety

☐ End-of-Experiment Rules

_____
(signature)

Date _____

STUDENT SAFETY TEST

Recognizing Laboratory Safety

Time Required:
40 minutes

◆ Pre-Lab Discussion

An important part of your study of science will be working in a laboratory. In the laboratory, you and your classmates will learn about the natural world by conducting experiments. Working directly with household objects, laboratory equipment, and even living things will help you to better understand the concepts you read about in your textbook or in class.

Most of the laboratory work you will do is quite safe. However, some laboratory equipment, chemicals, and specimens can be dangerous if handled improperly. Laboratory accidents do not just happen. They are caused by carelessness, improper handling of equipment, or inappropriate behavior.

In this investigation, you will learn how to prevent accidents and thus work safely in a laboratory. You will review some safety guidelines and become acquainted with the location and proper use of safety equipment in your classroom laboratory.

◆ Problem

What are the proper practices for working safely in a science laboratory?

◆ Materials *(per group)*

science textbook
laboratory safety equipment (for demonstration)

Be sure to show the location of all safety equipment in your laboratory. Also give instructions on its proper use. Guidelines pertaining to the use of special equipment, fire-drill procedures, or penalties for misbehavior in the lab might also be discussed at this time.

◆ Procedure

Part A. Reviewing Laboratory Safety Rules and Symbols

1. Carefully read the list of laboratory safety rules listed on pages v and vi of this lab manual.

2. Special symbols are used throughout this lab book to call attention to investigations that require extra caution. Use page vii as a reference to describe what each symbol means in numbers 1 through 8 of Observations.

Part B. Location of Safety Equipment in Your Science Laboratory

1. The teacher will point out the location of the safety equipment in your classroom laboratory. Pay special attention to instructions for using such equipment as fire extinguishers, eyewash fountains, fire blankets, safety showers, and items in first-aid kits. Use the space provided in Part B under Observations to list the location of all safety equipment in your laboratory.

Name _____ Date _____ Class _____

RECOGNIZING LABORATORY SAFETY *(continued)*

◆ Observations

Part A

 1. Student is working with materials that can easily be broken, such as glass containers or thermometers. They should be handled carefully, and broken glassware should not be touched.

 2. Student is working with a flame and should tie back loose hair and clothing.

_____

_____

 3. Student should use oven mitts or other hand protection to avoid burning hands.

_____

_____

 4. Student is working with poisonous chemicals and should not let the chemical touch the skin or inhale its vapors. Student should wash hands after the lab.

_____

_____

 5. Student is performing an experiment in which the eyes and face should be protected by safety goggles.

_____

_____

 6. Student is working with a sharp instrument and should direct the sharp edge or point away from himself or herself and others.

_____

_____

 7. Student is using electricity in the laboratory and should avoid the possibility of electric shock. Electrical equipment should not be used around water, cords should not be tangled, and equipment should be disconnected when not in use.

_____

 8. Student is working with plants and should handle them according to the teacher's instructions. Student should tell the teacher if he or she is allergic to certain plants. Students should wash hands after the lab.

_____

RECOGNIZING LABORATORY SAFETY *(continued)*

Part B

Student responses will depend on the specific safety features of your classroom laboratory.

Locations might include such directions as above the sink, to the right of the goggles case, near the

door, and so on.

_____

_____

◆ Analyze and Conclude

Look at each of the following drawings and explain why the laboratory activities pictured are unsafe.

1. Safety goggles should always be worn whenever a person is

working with chemicals, lab burners, or any substance that

might get into the eyes.

_____

2. When diluting an acid, pour the acid into water. Never

pour water into the acid. Also, safety goggles and a lab

apron should be worn when working with chemicals.

_____

3. Never heat a liquid in a closed container. The expanding

gases produced may shatter the container.

_____

_____

RECOGNIZING LABORATORY SAFETY (continued)

◆ Critical Thinking and Applications

In each of the following situations, write *yes* if the proper safety procedures are being followed and *no* if they are not. Then give a reason for your answer.

1. Gina is thirsty. She rinses a beaker with water, refills it with water, and takes a drink.

No; you should never drink from laboratory glassware. The last substance in it may have been

poisonous and traces of the poison may remain.

2. Bram notices that the electrical cord on his microscope is frayed near the plug. He takes the microscope to his teacher and asks for permission to use another one.

Yes; electrical appliances with frayed cords or broken insulation may present a hazard and

should not be used.

3. The printed directions in the lab book tell a student to pour a small amount of hydrochloric acid into a beaker. Jamal puts on safety goggles before pouring the acid into the beaker.

Yes; safety goggles should always be worn when working with dangerous chemicals.

4. It is rather warm in the laboratory during a late spring day. Anna slips off her shoes and walks barefoot to the sink to clean her glassware.

No; shoes should always be kept on while working in the laboratory in case glassware breaks

or chemicals are spilled onto the floor.

5. While washing glassware, Mike splashes some water on Evon. To get even, Evon splashes him back.

No; misbehaving is never acceptable in a laboratory.

6. During an experiment, Lindsey decides to mix two chemicals that the lab procedure does not say to mix, because she is curious about what will happen.

No; never mix chemicals unless directed to do so. The mixing might produce an explosive

substance.

Name _____ Date _____ Class _____

Following Directions

This skills sheet helps reinforce students' appreciation of the need to read all directions before beginning an investigation. Use this skills sheet before your students begin work in the laboratory.

1. Read all of the following directions before you do anything.

2. Print your name, last name first, then your first name and middle initial (if you have one), at the top of this page.

3. Draw a line through the word "all" in direction 1.

4. Underline the word "directions" in direction 1.

5. In direction 2, circle the words "your first name."

6. In direction 3, place an "X" in front of the word "through."

7. Cross out the numbers of the even-numbered directions above.

8. In direction 7, cross out the word "above" and write the word "below" above it.

9. Write "Following directions is easy" under your name at the top of this page.

10. In direction 9, add the following sentence after the word "page": "That's what you think!"

11. Draw a square in the upper right corner of this page.

12. Draw a triangle in the lower left corner of this page.

13. Place a circle in the center of the square.

14. Place an "X" in the center of the triangle.

15. Now that you have read all the directions as instructed in direction 1, follow directions 2 and 16 only.

16. Please do not give away what this test is about by saying anything or doing anything to alert your classmates. If you have reached this direction, make believe you are still writing. See how many of your classmates really know how to follow directions.

Name _____ Date _____ Class _____

Defining Elements of a Scientific Method

Laboratory activities and experiments involve the use of the scientific method.
Listed in the left column are the names of parts of this method. The right column
contains definitions. Next to each word in the left column, write the letter of the
definition that best matches that word.

____A____ **1.** Hypothesis

____E____ **2.** Manipulated Variable

____B____ **3.** Responding Variable

____G____ **4.** Controlling Variables

____F____ **5.** Observation

____C____ **6.** Data

____D____ **7.** Conclusion

A. Prediction about the outcome of an experiment

B. What you measure or observe to obtain your results

C. Measurements and other observations

D. Statement that sums up what you learn from an experiment

E. Factor that is changed in an experiment

F. What the person performing the activity sees, hears, feels, smells, or tastes

G. Keeping all variables the same except the manipulated variable

LABORATORY SKILLS CHECKUP 3

Analyzing Elements of a Scientific Method

Read the following statements and then answer the questions.

1. You and your friend are walking along a beach in Maine on January 15, at 8:00 AM.

2. You notice a thermometer on a nearby building that reads −1°C.

3. You also notice that there is snow on the roof of the building and icicles hanging from the roof.

4. You further notice a pool of sea water in the sand near the ocean.

5. Your friend looks at the icicles and the pool and says, "How come the water on the roof is frozen and the sea water is not?"

6. You answer, "I think that the salt in the sea water keeps it from freezing at −1°C."

7. You go on to say, "And I think under the same conditions, the same thing will happen tomorrow."

8. Your friend asks, "How can you be sure?" You answer, "I'm going to get some fresh water and some salt water and expose them to a temperature of −1°C and see what happens."

◆ Questions

A. In which statement is a **prediction** made? 7 _____

B. Which statement states a **problem**? 5 _____

C. In which statement is an **experiment** described? 8 _____

D. Which statement contains a **hypothesis**? 6 _____

E. Which statements contain **data**? 1, 2, 3, 4 _____

F. Which statements describe **observations**? 2, 3, 4 _____

Performing an Experiment

Read the following statements and then answer the questions.

1. A scientist wants to find out why sea water freezes at a lower temperature than fresh water.

2. The scientist goes to the library and reads a number of articles about the physical properties of solutions.

3. The scientist also reads about the composition of sea water.

4. The scientist travels to a nearby beach and observes the conditions there. The scientist notes the taste of the sea water and other factors such as waves, wind, air pressure, temperature, and humidity.

5. After considering all this information, the scientist sits at a desk and writes, "If sea water has salt in it, it will freeze at a lower temperature than fresh water."

6. The scientist goes back to the laboratory and does the following:

   a. Fills each of two beakers with 1 liter of fresh water.

   b. Dissolves 35 grams of table salt in one of the beakers.

   c. Places both beakers in a freezer at a temperature of $-1°C$.

   d. Leaves the beakers in the freezer for 24 hours.

7. After 24 hours, the scientist examines both beakers and finds the fresh water to be frozen. The salt water is still liquid.

8. The scientist writes in a notebook, "It appears that salt water freezes at a lower temperature than fresh water does."

9. The scientist continues, "I suggest that the reason sea water freezes at a lower temperature is that sea water contains dissolved salts, while fresh water does not."

◆ Questions

A. Which statement(s) contain **conclusions**? _8, 9_

B. Which statement(s) contains a **hypothesis**? _5_

C. Which statement(s) contain **observations**? _4, 7_

D. Which statement(s) describe an **experiment**? _6 a–d_

E. In which statement is the **problem** described? _1_

F. Which statement(s) contain **data**? _4, 6 a–d, 7_

G. Which is the **manipulated variable** in the experiment? _the amount of salt in water_

H. What is the **responding variable** in the experiment? _the temperature at which water freezes_

LABORATORY SKILLS CHECKUP 5

Identifying Errors

Read the following paragraph and then answer the questions.

Andrew arrived at school and went directly to his earth science class. He took off his cap and coat and sat down at his desk. His teacher gave him a large rock and asked him to find its density. Realizing that the rock was too large to work with, Andrew got a hammer from the supply cabinet and hit the rock several times until he broke off a chip small enough to work with. He partly filled a graduated cylinder with water and suspended the rock in the water. The water level rose 2 cm. Andrew committed this measurement to memory. He next weighed the rock on a balance. The rock weighed 4 oz. Andrew then calculated the density of the rock as follows: He divided 2 cm by 4 oz. He then reported to his teacher that the density of the rock was .5 cm/oz.

◆ Questions

1. What safety rule(s) did Andrew break?

   He didn't put on his safety goggles. Also, he didn't obtain permission from his teacher before
   obtaining the hammer and breaking the rock.

2. What mistake did Andrew make using measurement units?

   He used linear units (centimeters) instead of volumetric units (milliliters).

3. What should Andrew have done with his data rather than commit them to memory?

   He should have kept a written record.

4. What is wrong with the statement "He next weighed the rock on a balance"?

   A balance is used to determine mass, not weight.

5. Why is "4 oz" an inappropriate measurement in a science experiment?

   Metric units (grams) should be used.

6. What mistake did Andrew make in calculating density?

   Density is expressed in mass per unit volume (g/mL), not length per unit weight.

SKILLS LAB 1   LABORATORY INVESTIGATION

How to Use a Microscope

Key Concept: You can use a microscope to identify and study organisms and objects that are not visible to the unaided eye.

◆ Pre-Lab Discussion

Skills Focus: Observing, calculating

Time Required: 40 minutes

As you explore the natural world in science labs, you will be doing something you do every day—making observations. You use your senses to make observations, but sometimes your senses need help. For several labs in this book, you will be using a microscope to examine organisms and objects that are too small to be seen with the unaided eye. Refer to Figure 1 throughout this lab and other labs that use a microscope.

When you view an object through a microscope, you place the object on a glass slide. The slide may be either a dry-mount or a wet-mount slide. In a dry-mount slide, the object to be examined is placed on the slide and covered with a small square of plastic called a coverslip. In a wet-mount slide, a drop of liquid is placed over the object before being covered with a coverslip. In this investigation, you will learn how to correctly prepare a wet-mount slide and how to observe an object under the microscope.

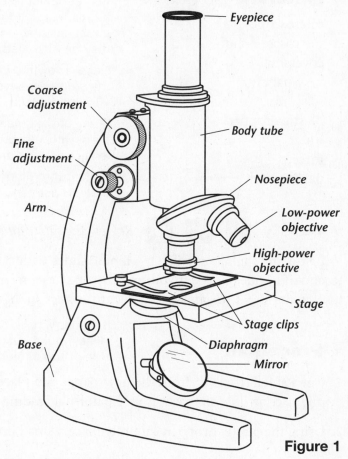

Eyepiece

Coarse adjustment

Fine adjustment

Arm

Body tube

Nosepiece

Low-power objective

High-power objective

Stage

Stage clips

Base

Diaphragm

Mirror

Figure 1

1. When you carry a microscope, why should you carry it with one hand on the arm of the microscope and the other hand under the base?

   This is a stable way to carry the microscope, so that it doesn't knock anything and so that

   sensitive parts of the instrument are not subject to damage.

2. Why should you hold a microscope slide by its edges?

   Holding the slide by its edges prevents fingerprints and smudges from getting onto the slide,

   thus interfering with the view of the object under the microscope.

Advance Preparation: Have microscopes set up at student stations.

Alternate Materials: A pin or a dissecting probe can be used instead of forceps.

HOW TO USE A MICROSCOPE *(continued)*

◆ Problem

How do you prepare an object to be viewed under the microscope, and how do you use the microscope to observe the object?

◆ Materials *(per group)*

microscope
microscope slide
coverslip
newspaper
scissors
plastic dropper
water
forceps
paper towel

Teaching Tips:

For an object to be visible under a light microscope, it must be thin enough for light to pass through it. That is why thin paper, such as newspaper, is required. Any asymmetrical letter may be observed, such as a lowercase "e," "f," or "g."

Never allow the clips to come in contact with the opening in the stage because they will scratch the lens and interfere with viewing objects.

If any of the lenses are dirty, have students carefully clean them with lens paper. Using cloth or other materials instead of lens paper can damage the lenses.

Point out to students that if the letter is in perfect focus as is, they do not need to focus with the fine-adjustment knob.

◆ Safety   *Review the safety guidelines in front of your lab book.*

Wipe up any spills immediately. Handle slides with care to avoid breakage. Tell the teacher if a slide breaks. If your microscope has a mirror, do not tilt it directly toward the sun. Eye damage can occur if direct sunlight is used as a light source.

◆ Procedure

If students have difficulty finding the magnification of the lenses, point out that this is the number before the "X" on the side or top of each objective.

1. Cut a small letter "d" from the newspaper and place it in the center of a clean microscope slide so that it is in the normal reading position.

2. Using the plastic dropper, carefully place a small drop of water over the letter.

3. Place one side of a clean coverslip at the end of the drop of water at a 45° angle. See Figure 2. Use forceps to carefully lower the coverslip over the letter "d" and the drop of water. Do not press on the coverslip. It should rest on top of the water. Try not to trap any air bubbles under the coverslip because these will interfere with your view of the specimen. If you have trapped air bubbles, make a new wet-mount slide.

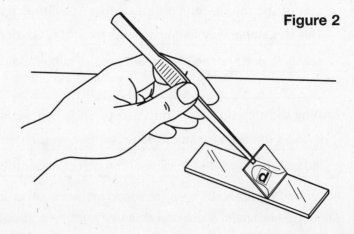

Figure 2

4. Absorb excess water by touching a folded piece of paper towel to the water that comes out around the edges of the coverslip.

HOW TO USE A MICROSCOPE *(continued)*

5. In Observations, draw a picture of the letter "d" just as you see it on the slide, without the aid of the microscope.

6. Place the slide under the clips on the stage of the microscope. Position the slide so that the letter "d" is directly over the center of the stage opening.

7. Turn the nosepiece so that the low-power objective is facing downward, toward the slide. Use the coarse-adjustment knob to slowly lower the low-power objective until it almost touches the slide. **CAUTION:** *To prevent damage to the microscope and the slide, do not let the lens actually touch the slide.*

8. Tilt the mirror and adjust the diaphragm until you get the best light for viewing the specimen. **CAUTION:** *Do not aim the mirror at direct sunlight.*

9. Looking through the eyepiece, use the coarse-adjustment knob to slowly raise the lens until the letter comes into view. **CAUTION:** *To prevent damage, do not lower the coarse adjustment while looking through the eyepiece.*

10. Use the fine-adjustment knob to focus the letter clearly. You should only need to turn the knob one-quarter of a turn or less.

11. Look at the objectives and the eyepiece of your microscope. Then answer question 1 in Observations.

12. Find the total magnification power of your microscope by multiplying the magnification of the eyepiece lens by the magnification of the objective lens you are using. Then answer questions 2 and 3 in Observations.

13. In Observations, draw a picture of the letter "d" as viewed through the microscope. Record the magnification you are using.

14. While looking through the eyepiece, move the slide to the left. Notice which way the letter seems to move. Now move the slide to the right. Again notice which way the letter seems to move.

15. Switch to the high-power objective lens by revolving the nosepiece so that the high-power lens clicks into place. **CAUTION:** *The high-power objective is longer than the low-power objective; it may easily touch and damage the slide. Look at the side of the microscope when switching to the high-power objective to make sure it clears the slide.* Using the fine-adjustment knob only, bring the specimen into focus.

16. In Observations, draw a picture of the letter "d" as seen with the high-power objective lens. Record the magnification you are using.

HOW TO USE A MICROSCOPE *(continued)*

◆ Observations

1. What is the magnification of each objective of your microscope? What is the magnification of your eyepiece?

Answers will vary with the type of microscope used. Usually, low power = 10X,

high power = 40X, and eyepiece = 10X.

2. What is the total magnification power using the low-power objective?

Answers will vary with the type of microscope used but should equal eyepiece objective

magnification × low-power objective magnification. Usually, 10X × 10X = 100X

3. What is the highest magnification of your microscope?

Answers will vary with the type of microscope used but should equal eyepiece objective

magnification × high-power objective magnification. Usually, 10X × 40X = 400X

Letter "d" Without Microscope

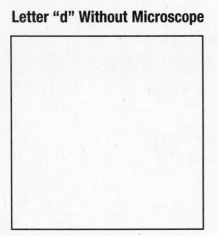

Low-Power Objective

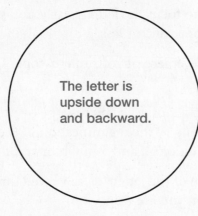

The letter is upside down and backward.

Magnification: _____

High-Power Objective

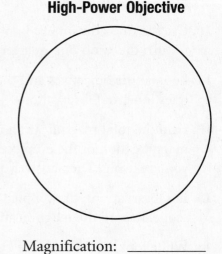

Magnification: _____

◆ Analyze and Conclude

1. How does the letter "d" as seen through the microscope differ from the way a "d" normally appears?

The letter "d" is upside down and backward. It is also, of course, larger.

2. When you move the slide to the left, in what direction does the letter "d" appear to move?

The letter "d" appears to move to the right.

HOW TO USE A MICROSCOPE *(continued)*

3. When you move the slide to the right, in what direction does the letter "d" appear to move?

The letter "d" appears to move to the left.

4. How does the ink that was used to print the letter differ in appearance when you see it with the unaided eye compared with the way it appears under the microscope?

The ink appears solid when you see it with the unaided eye and speckled under the microscope.

5. Briefly explain how to make a wet-mount slide.

Place the object to be viewed in the center of a clean microscope slide. Using the dropper, place

a small drop of water on the object. Hold a coverslip at a 45° angle at the edge of the drop of

water and, using forceps, slowly lower the coverslip over the specimen and the drop of water.

Soak up any excess water.

◆ Critical Thinking and Applications

1. Why should you always use the low-power objective lens to locate objects mounted on the slide first, even if you want to observe them with the high-power objective lens?

The lower magnification of the low-power objective lens allows you to see a larger area under the

microscope, enabling you to get the object in view under the microscope.

2. Suppose you were observing an organism through the microscope and noticed that it moved toward the top of the slide and then it moved right. In what directions did the organism actually move?

Specimens viewed through the microscope appear to move in a direction exactly opposite to

that of their actual movement on the slide. In this case, the organism actually moved toward the

bottom of the slide and then to the left.

HOW TO USE A MICROSCOPE *(continued)*

◆ More to Explore

New Problem What do other objects look like under a microscope?

Possible Materials Small, common objects or thin pieces of material to observe. Consider which materials you should use from the previous part of this lab.

Safety Follow the safety guidelines in the lab.

Procedure Write your procedure on a separate sheet of paper. Have the teacher approve of your procedure and your list of objects to observe.

Observations Draw what you see when using the microscope. Record the magnifications you used.

Analyze and Conclude Evaluate the objects you observed. What objects worked well? What other kinds of objects would you choose?

Objects that are observed easily using a microscope are thin enough for light to pass through. They

are also small enough to manipulate under the lenses.

Help students choose appropriate common objects to observe. Materials must be thin enough to allow light to shine through them. Such objects could include a piece of cotton, a piece of nylon, a human hair, a section of *Elodea*, or a small piece of a color photograph from a magazine. Remind students to view objects under low-power first before using the high-power objective.

SKILLS LAB 2   LABORATORY INVESTIGATION

How to Use a Balance

Key Concept: Using a triple-beam balance allows students to measure mass accurately.

Skills Focus: Observing, measuring, calculating, forming operational definitions

Time Required: 40 minutes

◆ Pre-Lab Discussion

The ability to measure accurately the mass of an object is an important skill in the science laboratory. You can use a triple-beam balance to measure mass. As you can see in Figure 1, the balance has several parts. The pan is the flat surface on which you place the object to be measured. The three beams show the mass of the object. Notice that each beam has a different scale. The scale of the middle beam is from 0–500 grams and measures an object to the nearest 100 grams. The scale of the beam in back is from 0–100 grams and measures an object to the nearest 10 grams. The scale of the beam in front is from 0–10 grams and measures an object to the nearest tenth of a gram.

Notice that each beam carries a weight called a rider. You find the mass of an object by placing it on the pan and moving the riders until the pointer on the right of the balance stays pointed to zero.

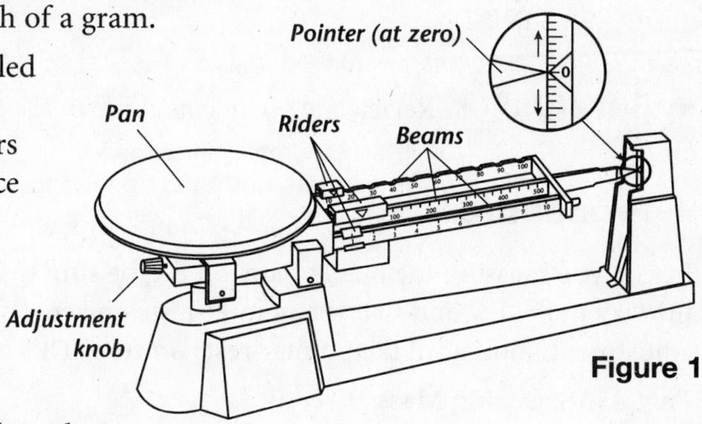

Figure 1

There are three ways you can use the triple-beam balance to find mass:

Method 1. Measure mass directly. Place the object on the pan and move the riders until the pointer points to zero. Add up the numbers on the beams where the riders are positioned to find mass.

Method 2. Find mass by difference. How could you find the mass of a liquid? First, measure the mass of an empty container that can hold the liquid. Then, measure the combined mass of the container and the liquid. Finally, subtract the mass of the container from the combined mass.

Method 3. Measure out a chemical substance. Suppose you need to obtain 50 g of a powdered chemical. How could you do it? First find the mass of a piece of paper or empty container that will hold the chemical. Then, add this amount to the desired mass of the chemical and preset the riders to this number. Finally, add the chemical to the paper a little at a time until the pointer points to zero.

In this investigation, you will learn how to measure accurately the mass of various objects by using the three methods described above.

1. What does it mean when the pointer of the balance reads "zero"?

When the balance pointer reads "zero," it means that the mass of the object being measured

and the mass shown by the riders are equal.

HOW TO USE A BALANCE *(continued)*

2. Suppose a rock is balanced on a triple-beam balance. The riders on the three beams point to 60 g, 300 g, and 3.5 g. What is the mass of the rock?

363.5 g

Advance Preparation: Have triple-beam balances set up at student stations.

◆ **Problem**

Alternate Materials: Any small object can be measured, such as a coin, a paper clip, or a rubber stopper.

What is the proper way to use the triple-beam balance to measure the mass of different objects?

Teaching Tips: Inform students that chemicals should never be placed directly on a balance pan. Therefore, it is necessary to use paper or a container as described in Method 3.

◆ **Materials** *(per class)*

triple-beam balance
100-mL graduated cylinder
3 different small, solid objects
weighing paper

small scoop
table salt
200-mL beaker

[Part A, Step 1] Have students measure some objects with a standard weight as a check of their measuring accuracy.

◆ **Safety** *Review the safety guidelines in the front of your lab book.*

[Part C, Step 1] Filter paper may be used as weighing paper. It can be folded in quarters and then opened to form a "cup" before placing it on the pan.

◆ **Procedure**

[Part C, Step 4] Caution students not to put solids into the sink.

Before you measure the mass of any object, be sure that the riders are moved all the way to the left and that the pointer rests on zero. If necessary, slowly turn the adjustment knob until the pointer rests on zero. This is called zeroing the balance.

Part A: Measuring Mass Directly

1. Place a small, solid object on the balance pan. The beams will rise and the pointer will point above zero.

2. Move the rider on the middle beam one notch at a time until the pointer drops and stays below zero. Move the rider back one notch.

3. Move the rider on the back beam one notch at a time until the pointer again drops and stays below zero. Move the rider back one notch.

4. Slide the rider along the front beam until the pointer stops at zero. The mass of the object is equal to the sum of the readings on the three beams.

5. Record the mass to the nearest tenth of a gram in Data Table 1.

6. Remove this object and repeat steps 1–5 twice, using two other solid objects.

Part B: Finding Mass by Difference

1. Find the mass of an empty 250-mL beaker. Record the mass in Data Table 2.

2. Using the graduated cylinder, obtain 50 mL of water.

3. Pour the water into the beaker and find the mass of the beaker and water. Record the mass in Data Table 2.

HOW TO USE A BALANCE *(continued)*

Part C: Measuring Out a Chemical Substance

1. Place a piece of weighing paper on the balance pan and find its mass. Record the mass in Data Table 3.

2. Add 5 g to the mass of the weighing paper and move the riders to this number.

3. Obtain a sample of table salt from the teacher. Using the scoop, add a small amount of salt at a time to the paper on the balance until the pointer rests on zero. Record the total mass of the weighing paper and salt in Data Table 3.

4. Dispose of the table salt in the container provided by the teacher.

◆ Observations

Data Table 1   Sample Data

Object	Mass (g)
Nickel	5.0
Large paper clip	1.3
Rubber stopper	12.5

Data Table 2

Mass of Empty Beaker (g)	Mass of Beaker with 50 mL of Water (g)
103.7	153.7

Data Table 3

Mass of Weighing Paper (g)	Mass of Weighing Paper and Table Salt (g)
0.5	5.5

◆ Analyze and Conclude

1. What is the mass of 50 mL of water? How did you find this mass?

   50 g; by subtracting the mass of the empty beaker from the mass of the beaker with 50 mL of water in it

2. Which rider on the balance should always be moved first when finding the mass of an object? Why?

   The middle (heaviest) rider should be moved first. This rider measures the largest unit of mass used.

3. What is the mass of the largest object your balance is able to measure?

   Answers may vary. Generally, 610 g is the largest mass that can be measured using a standard triple-beam balance.

4. What is the mass of the smallest object your balance is able to measure accurately?

   The smallest mass that can be measured accurately is 0.1 g.

5. After using your balance, how should it always be left?

   All the riders should be to the left, which should bring the pointer to zero.

HOW TO USE A BALANCE *(continued)*

◆ Critical Thinking and Applications

1. Suppose you did not zero the balance before finding the mass of an object. How might that affect your measurement?

The reading would be inaccurate because you would be starting from a point below or above

zero.

2. In this lab, you found the mass of 50 mL of water. Calculate the mass of 1 mL of water. (Do not use the balance.)

By dividing the mass of 50 mL of water by 50 g, students will find that the mass of 1 mL of

water is 1 g.

3. Describe how you could find the mass of a certain quantity of milk that you poured into a drinking glass.

First find the mass of the empty drinking glass. Then pour in the milk and find the combined

mass. Subtract the mass of the empty glass from the combined mass.

4. If you were baking a dessert and the recipe called for 250 g of sugar, how could you use the triple-beam balance to obtain this amount?

Place a piece of paper or a light food container on the balance and find its mass. Add 250 g to

the mass of this object and set the riders for that amount. Slowly add sugar until the pointer

balances on zero.

◆ More to Explore

Design a balance that finds mass by comparing the mass of a known object to the mass of an unknown object. Study the triple-beam balance used in this activity and think about how you could balance two or more objects. Construct your balance and use it to find the mass of an object. How could you improve your balance?

Student designs will vary, but they should mimic the action of a double-pan balance. Two holding devices may be attached to a lever that is balanced on a fulcrum, like a seesaw, or suspended from a fixed point, using string. For example, cans can be placed on the far ends of a ruler. The ruler must be positioned on a fulcrum at the ruler's midpoint. Or two pieces of identical cloth can be cupped to hold objects. These cloth holders can be suspended from a fixed hanger at an equal distance from the midpoint. Objects of known mass can be placed in one holding device, while small objects such as pennies or paper clips can be placed in the other device. When the two holders and their contents are level, both sides have equal mass. Specific suggestions for improvement may include using hanging devices with less friction or using holding devices that are equal in mass.

Developing a Classification System for Seeds

Key Concept: Classification is a tool used to organize and study living things.

Skills Focus: Observing, classifying, communicating

Time Required: 40 minutes

1

◆ Pre-Lab Discussion

Suppose you discovered a plant or an animal that no one had ever seen. What would you call it? Where would you even begin?

To simplify the identification and naming of organisms, scientists have developed a system of classification. The classification system groups similar animals, plants, and other organisms. There are seven major levels of classification. The broadest group is a kingdom. Kingdoms contain phyla (singular *phylum*), classes, orders, families, genera (singular *genus*), and species. Organisms of the same species have the most characteristics in common.

In this investigation, you will develop a system of classification for seeds.

1. Why do scientists classify organisms into groups?

Scientists classify organisms into groups so that they are easier to study and so that the

relationships among organisms can be better understood.

_____

2. How is evolution related to classification?

Species with similar evolutionary histories are grouped together in narrower classification levels.

_____

_____

◆ Problem

What characteristics can be used to classify seeds?

Advance Preparation: To prepare a mixture of seeds for each group, put eight of each of the following seeds in a small paper cup: pinto bean, kidney bean, lima bean, black-eyed pea, navy bean, and split pea.

◆ Materials *(per group)*

paper cup containing seeds
2 hand lenses
tray
metric ruler
scrap paper

Alternate Materials: Any available seeds or beans can be used. Pictures of flowers and other plants, pictures of different animals, or even common items such as miscellaneous buttons can be used in place of seeds.

Teaching Tips: Encourage students to use the hand lens for closer inspection of the seeds.

◆ Safety *Review the safety guidelines in the front of your lab book.*

Keep seeds in containers at all times to prevent accidents. Do not eat the seeds.

DEVELOPING A CLASSIFICATION SYSTEM FOR SEEDS *(continued)*

◆ Procedure

1. Get a cup containing seeds. Carefully pour the seeds onto the tray. **CAUTION:** *Immediately pick up any seeds that drop on the floor.* Use a hand lens to examine the seeds carefully. Answer question 1 in Observations.

2. Think about what characteristic you could use to divide all the seeds into two large groups. Remember, each group must contain seeds with similar characteristics.

3. Sort the seeds into two piles, based on the characteristic that you selected. On scrap paper, note the characteristics that you choose.

4. Working with one of the two large groups, divide the seeds in that group into two smaller groups based on another characteristic. Record the characteristic as in Step 3.

5. Continue to divide the seeds into smaller groups by choosing and recording new characteristics. Eventually, you should have only one seed left in each group.

6. Repeat steps 4 and 5 with the other large group.

7. In Observations, draw a diagram that shows how your classification system works.

8. Compare your classification system with those of other groups in your class. Answer questions 2–4 in Observations.

◆ Observations

Diagram of Seed Classification

Students need to keep clear records of the characteristics they use for classification. In addition to describing these characteristics, students could illustrate them for clarification.

The diagram students make might be a flowchart, a concept map, or a taxonomic key.

DEVELOPING A CLASSIFICATION SYSTEM FOR SEEDS *(continued)*

1. What are some of the characteristics of your seeds?

Answers may vary. Characteristics may include size, color, shape, and texture.

2. How many groups are in your classification system?

Answers may vary. If students are able to classify so specifically that they have only one seed in

each group, then they should have as many groups as there are seeds.

3. Compare the final classification system you have with those of other groups using different characteristics. Do they differ or are they the same? What different characteristics did they use?

Answers will vary. Classification systems will likely have similar divisions based on obvious

characteristics such as size and color. More subtle characteristics, such as texture, may not be

used by all groups.

◆ Analyze and Conclude

1. What characteristics did you find most useful for classifying the seeds?

Answers will vary. Students will probably mention specific physical traits such as color, shape,

and size.

2. Explain why your final classification groups differed or were the same as those of other groups.

Final groups may vary if different characteristics were used to differentiate the seeds.

3. How does a classification system help you understand organisms?

Grouping organisms that have similar physical traits lets you see possible relationships among

them. The more similar their traits, the closer their relationships are likely to be.

4. How is this investigation similar to the way in which scientists classify organisms?

Scientists place organisms with similar characteristics in the same group. On the basis of

differences among members of the group, scientists subdivide the organisms into subgroups and

so on.

DEVELOPING A CLASSIFICATION SYSTEM FOR SEEDS (*continued*)

◆ Critical Thinking and Applications

1. Could you have classified your seeds using another system? Give a reason for your answer.

Answers will vary. Students should be aware of the possibility of using other characteristics.

_____

2. Could you have classified each characteristic in groups of three or more types at each step? Do you think more groups would make choices harder or easier? Give a reason for your answer.

Answers will vary. Sample answer: Yes. But because of the complexity or similarity of some

organisms, a greater number of choices could lead to confusion. Even with two choices, it is

sometimes difficult to decide which characteristic best describes the organism.

_____

3. Suppose you wanted to classify all the birds that came to a particular area of a pond during a spring day. What are some of the characteristics that you would use to classify the birds?

Characteristics may include color and specific markings, body form, type of bill and feet, and

song.

4. When classifying organisms, do you think that it is better to go from general characteristics to specific characteristics or from specific characteristics to general characteristics? Give a reason for your answer.

Answers will vary. Sample answer: from specific to general. That way you base classifications on

specific characteristics, rather than trying to force characteristics to fit a broad category.

Alternative answer: from general to specific. That way it is easier to observe general patterns.

◆ More to Explore

Make a list of five or more household appliances. Combine your list with a class-mate's. Then separately devise classification systems for the combined list of appliances. What characteristics did you use to classify these items into groups? Did your classmate come up with the same classification system?

Have groups of students make different lists of five common items. Possible subjects could include video or movie titles, local vegetation, lab equipment, types of clothing, and so forth. Encourage the different groups to compare the characteristics used for classification.

A-2   LABORATORY INVESTIGATION

Key Concept: Eubacteria grow nearly everywhere.

Eubacteria That Dine on Vegetables

Skills Focus: Observing, predicting, designing experiments, controlling variables

Time Required: 40 minutes the first day plus 10 minutes of observations for each of 5 days

Members of the Eubacteria kingdom are among the most numerous organisms on Earth. If a microscopic bacterium is in the right temperature range and has enough moisture and food, it can reproduce rapidly. In 24 to 48 hours, it can multiply so often that its offspring form a visible colony.

In this investigation, you will witness this explosive growth as you grow eubacteria on common vegetables.

2

◆ Pre-Lab Discussion

1. How are the cells of eubacteria different from those of other organisms?

Eubacteria are prokaryotes. Their cells do not have nuclei that contain the cell's genetic material.

2. Name the two kingdoms of bacteria. Where do these different kingdoms live?

Bacteria are classified as Archaebacteria and Eubacteria. Archaebacteria live only in extreme

environments, while eubacteria live everywhere else.

◆ Problem

Advance Preparation: Bake potatoes and yams the day before the investigation.

What conditions do eubacteria need for growth?

◆ Materials *(per group)*

4 clear, resealable plastic bags
8 small pieces of masking tape
pen or pencil
2 slices of baked potato
spatula
2 cotton swabs
transparent tape
2 slices of baked yam

Alternate Materials: You could use other starchy vegetables, such as boiled carrots or cooked fresh beets.

Teaching Tips: You may want to wash and rinse the plastic bags yourself to prevent contamination problems.

Clean the knife thoroughly before cutting the vegetables. Do not cut the vegetables before class.

Have groups test different areas of the classroom for comparison purposes. Do not let students test areas where body fluids or potentially harmful bacteria or viruses could be present.

Disposal procedure: Cultures should be autoclaved or flooded with a disinfectant solution. Use a disinfectant such as Lysol or dilute chlorine bleach.

◆ Safety *Review the safety guidelines in the front of your lab book.*

Do not open the plastic bags after placing the vegetables inside. Wash your hands thoroughly after handling the vegetables and plastic bags. Have the teacher dispose of the specimens at the end of the experiment.

EUBACTERIA THAT DINE ON VEGETABLES *(continued)*

◆ Procedure

1. Thoroughly wash four plastic bags with soap and water and rinse them thoroughly.

2. Put a masking-tape label on the outside of each bag. Write the following words on the four different labels: "A-Potato," "A-Yam," "B-Potato," and "B-Yam."

3. Predict where eubacteria might be living in your classroom. Give a reason for your predictions. Record your predictions in Observations. Compare your predictions with those of your classmates, and choose an area of your classroom that you will test for eubacteria. Have the teacher approve your choice before you continue.

4. Get two slices of baked potato. Use the spatula to pick up the slices. Take care that each slice has one side that touches nothing but the knife that cut it.

5. Put a potato slice with its untouched side facing up in a bag labeled "A-Potato." Seal the bag securely and tape the sealed edge shut.

6. Put the other potato slice with its untouched side facing up in a plastic bag labeled "B-Potato."

7. Rub a cotton swab on the area in your classroom where you think eubacteria might live. Then rub the cotton swab on the untouched side of the potato in bag B.

8. Seal the bag securely and tape the sealed edge shut. Set both potato bags in a warm place. Do not open them again. Your teacher will tell you where to dispose of the used cotton swab.

9. Repeat steps 4–8, using two baked yam slices.

10. Wash your hands when you're finished with the lab.

11. Observe the potato and yam slices daily for 5 days. DO NOT OPEN THE BAGS. Each day, draw both slices of each vegetable in the appropriate spaces in Observations and record your observations in the Data Table.

12. At the end of the fifth day, ask the teacher to dispose of the plastic bags and their contents.

◆ Observations

1. Predict where eubacteria might be living in your classroom. Give a reason for your prediction.

   Answers will vary. Students may predict noticeably "dirty" areas such as the floor or desktops.

   _____

2. What area of your classroom will you test for eubacteria?

   Answers may vary. Encourage groups to pick different areas to test.

   _____

EUBACTERIA THAT DINE ON VEGETABLES *(continued)*

Vegetable 1: _____

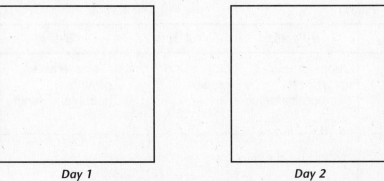

Day 1	*Day 2*	*Day 3*

Day 4	*Day 5*

Vegetable 2: _____

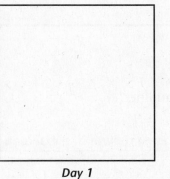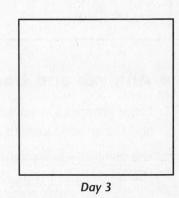

Day 1	*Day 2*	*Day 3*

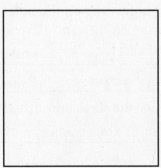

Day 4	*Day 5*

2

EUBACTERIA THAT DINE ON VEGETABLES *(continued)*

Data Table   Sample Data

Day	Date	Potato		Yam	
		A-Potato	**B-Potato**	**A-Yam**	**B-Yam**
1		Little to no growth	Considerable growth of bacterial colonies	Little to no growth	Considerable growth of bacterial colonies
2					
3					
4					
5					

◆ Analyze and Conclude

1. Large groups of eubacteria may look shiny or like mucus. Which container(s) had the greatest growth of eubacteria? The least growth?

The plastic bags labeled "B-Potato" and "B-Yam" usually have the greatest growth of eubacteria,

and the plastic bags labeled "A-Potato" and "A-Yam" have the least.

2. Do the organisms growing on the potato appear to be different from the organisms growing on the yam? Give a plausible reason for your results.

The organisms are likely to appear similar. Depending on the choice of vegetables, different types

of eubacteria may be observed.

3. Why did you leave the slices untouched in the plastic bags labeled "A"?

The untouched slices are a control for the experiment.

EUBACTERIA THAT DINE ON VEGETABLES *(continued)*

◆ Critical Thinking and Applications

1. Early biologists grew eubacteria on freshly cut slices of vegetables. They considered the inside of a vegetable to be sterile, or free of microorganisms. How did the eubacteria get on your vegetables?

In the plastic bags labeled "B," the cotton swab carried eubacteria from the test area to the

vegetables. Also, airborne eubacteria may have landed on the vegetables.

_____

2. Why was it important to thoroughly wash and rinse the plastic bags before placing the vegetable slices in them?

to prevent contamination of the vegetable slices by an unclean plastic bag

_____

_____

3. Why did you use a spatula instead of your hand to transfer the vegetable slices into the plastic bags?

to prevent contamination of the vegetable slices by your hand

_____

_____

4. Suppose you repeated this investigation, but this time you left the plastic bags labeled "A" open for a few minutes before sealing them. What do you think you might observe? Why?

The vegetable slices in the plastic bags labeled "A" would probably have nearly the same

amount of bacterial growth as the slices in the plastic bags labeled "B." This is because

eubacteria are in the air as well as in the areas tested by students.

_____

_____

5. What methods can you suggest for keeping vegetables unspoiled for a long time?

Suggestions should include refrigerating and covering the vegetables, to slow down bacterial

growth. Students may also suggest drying the food, so that the eubacteria do not have the

moisture they need to grow.

_____

_____

EUBACTERIA THAT DINE ON VEGETABLES *(continued)*

◆ More to Explore

Try this activity with other vegetables, such as boiled carrots or cooked fresh beets. Sample other areas of your classroom where you think eubacteria might be living. Have the teacher approve your procedure before you carry out the investigation. Do your results resemble results found in this lab?

All starchy vegetables are good substrates for bacterial growth. Students could compare the amount of bacterial growth found on these new vegetables to that on the potatoes and yams. Make sure that areas being tested for bacteria do not pose health risks to students. Follow the safety procedures used for the first part of this lab.

2

A-3   LABORATORY INVESTIGATION

Comparing Protists

Key Concept: Protists are a diverse group of eukaryotic organisms that live in moist environments.

Skills Focus: Observing, inferring, classifying, communicating

Time Required: 40 minutes

◆ Pre-Lab Discussion

Protists are organisms that have nuclei and live in wet environments, such as ponds, oceans, and the bodies of larger organisms. Other than that, protists don't have much in common. For example, some live independently as separate cells; others form colonies of many unattached cells. Plantlike protists are autotrophs—organisms that can make their own food. Animal-like protists and funguslike protists are heterotrophs—organisms that cannot make their own food.

In this investigation, you will observe and compare three common protists: amebas, euglenas, and paramecia.

1. Protists are eukaryotes. What does that mean?

It means that protists all have cells with nuclei.

2. Name three different protist structures that aid in movement.

The three structures that protists use in moving are pseudopods, cilia, and flagella.

3

◆ Problem

How are protists similar? How are they different?

◆ Materials *(per group)*

3 plastic droppers	microscope
ameba culture	piece of cotton
microscope slide	euglena culture
3 coverslips	paramecium culture
paper towel	

Advance Preparation: Cultures of organisms are available from biological supply companies.

Alternate Materials: Other protists may be used. Use prepared slides if living protists are not available.

Teaching Tips: Keep separate cultures for each protist. Make sure students use separate droppers for each culture.

Review how to make a wet-mount slide before students make theirs.

You may want to provide reference photos of protists for identification purposes.

◆ Safety *Review the safety guidelines in the front of your lab book.*

Do not use the same droppers for different cultures. Always use both hands to pick up or carry a microscope. Hold the microscope base with one hand and hold the microscope arm with your other hand. Handle glass slides carefully. Don't handle broken glass. Wash your hands thoroughly after the lab. Consider adding a drop of dilute methyl cellulose solution to slides to slow down protists' movements before students make sketches.

◆ Procedure

1. With a plastic dropper, place a drop of the ameba culture on the slide.

2. Make a wet-mount slide by gently laying the coverslip over the drop of ameba culture.

COMPARING PROTISTS *(continued)*

3. Touch a piece of paper towel to the edge of the coverslip to blot up any excess liquid. See Figure 1.

4. Place the slide on the stage of the microscope. Use the low-power objective to bring an ameba into focus. Have the teacher check to see that you have an ameba in focus.

5. Switch to the high-power objective. **CAUTION:** *When turning to the high-power objective, always look at the objective from the side of your microscope. Don't let the objective hit the slide.*

6. Use the fine-adjustment knob to bring the organism into sharper focus. **CAUTION:** *Never focus the high-power objective with the coarse-adjustment knob. The objective could break the slide.*

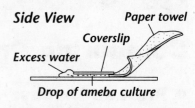

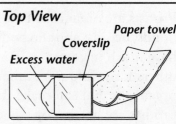

Figure 1

7. Observe an ameba and draw what you see in Plate 1 in Observations. Label the nucleus, cell membrane, cytoplasm, food vacuole, and pseudopods. Record the microscope magnification that you used below your sketch.

8. Carefully clean and dry the slide with a paper towel.

9. Separate a few strands of cotton and place them on the slide. The cotton strands will help slow down the euglena. Using a clean dropper, add a drop of the euglena culture to the strands of cotton.

10. Repeat steps 2–6 with the drop of euglena culture.

11. Observe a euglena and draw what you see in Plate 2 in Observations. Label the nucleus, cell membrane, cytoplasm, eyespot, flagellum, and chloroplasts. Record the microscope magnification you used below your sketch.

12. Carefully clean and dry the slide.

13. Separate a few strands of cotton and place them on the slide. Using a clean dropper, add a drop of the paramecium culture to the strands of cotton.

14. Repeat steps 2–6 with the drop of paramecium culture.

15. Observe a paramecium and draw what you see in Plate 3 in Observations. Label the cytoplasm, cell membrane, cilia, nucleus, contractile vacuole, food vacuoles, oral groove, and gullet. Record the microscope magnification you used below your sketch.

16. Clean and dry the slide once again. Return all the materials to the teacher. Wash your hands when you're finished with the lab.

◆ Observations

1. Describe the shape of the ameba.

   no definite shape

2. Describe the shape of the euglena.

   oval, with one pointed end and one round end

COMPARING PROTISTS *(continued)*

3. Describe the shape of the paramecium.

slipper shape

4. Describe how an ameba moves.

Streaming of the cytoplasm forms pseudopods.

5. Describe how a euglena moves.

whiplike motion of flagellum

6. Describe how a paramecium moves.

beating of cilia

7. What structures does the euglena have that the ameba and paramecium
do not have?

eyespot, flagellum, and chloroplasts

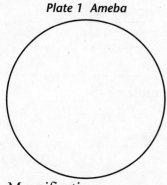

Plate 1 Ameba

Magnification _____

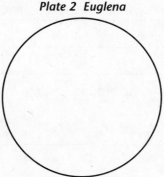

Plate 2 Euglena

Magnification _____

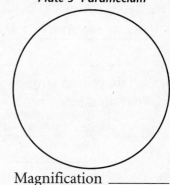

Plate 3 Paramecium

Magnification _____

◆ Analyze and Conclude

1. What structures do all protists have?

nucleus, cytoplasm, cell membrane, vacuoles

2. Which protist has structures that are characteristic of both autotrophs and
heterotrophs?

euglena

3. Classify the three protists that you observed as animal-like, funguslike, or
plantlike protists. Give a reason for your answers.

The ameba and paramecium are animal-like protists. Animal-like protists are heterotrophs and

move using pseudopods, cilia, or flagella. The euglena is a plantlike protist. Plantlike protists

are autotrophs.

COMPARING PROTISTS *(continued)*

4. Which is the slowest moving of the three protists?

ameba

5. Why are some protists able to move faster than others?

The ameba moves by extending its pseudopods, or parts of its cell. The euglena and

paramecium have specialized structures for movement that allow them to move faster.

◆ Critical Thinking and Applications

1. Why is the eyespot an important structure in the euglena?

Autotrophs need light to make their own food. The eyespot of the euglena helps it find areas that

are light.

2. The paramecium has two types of cilia. One type covers its entire surface. The other is at the entrance to the gullet. How does the paramecium use each type?

The paramecium uses the cilia covering its body to move and sense its environment. It uses the

other cilia to sweep food into the gullet.

3. Certain cells in your body, such as white blood cells, move by ameboid motion. What does this mean?

These cells can move slowly and surround smaller objects like amebas.

◆ More to Explore

A paramecium has thousands of cilia that project through the pellicle—the covering that gives the paramecium its shape. These cilia beat with a wavelike pattern that keeps a paramecium moving smoothly in one direction. Write a hypothesis for how a paramecium will respond when it runs into objects that are in its path. Write a procedure you would follow to test your hypothesis. Have the teacher approve your procedure before you carry out the investigation. Describe how the paramecium responds. Did your results support your hypothesis?

Objects such as cotton strands or toothbrush bristles could be added as obstacles to the paramecia. Alternatively, add boiled, crushed wheat seeds to a culture of paramecia and let the culture sit for several days. The seeds serve as obstacles. Students could then make a wet mount with a drop of the culture. They could search for a paramecium near a seed particle under low power. The paramecium will back up when it encounters an object, and then move forward in a new direction. To do this, the cilia briefly reverse the direction of their beating. The body of the paramecium may turn on its long axis, or it may bend.

Investigating Stomata

Key Concept: Stomata in leaves are in the best places for gas exchange.

Skills Focus: Observing, inferring, predicting

Time Required: 60 minutes

◆ Pre-Lab Discussion

For an organism to live and grow naturally in any place, it must be adapted to the conditions of that place. A land plant, for example, must have adaptations that prevent it from drying out. A thick, waxy layer of tissue, called the cuticle, is one adaptation that prevents water loss. However, the cuticle also prevents exchange of oxygen and carbon dioxide with the environment. Photosynthesis cannot take place without this exchange of gases. Small openings, called stomata (singular *stoma*), allow gases to move into and out of the plant. Each stoma is surrounded by two guard cells that control the size of the opening. When these guard cells absorb water, the stoma opens; when the guard cells lose water, the stoma closes.

In this investigation, you will observe stomata in a land plant and in a floating water plant.

1. Why is photosynthesis important for plants?

Plants use photosynthesis to make their own food.
_____

2. What adaptations make it possible for plants to live on land?

Plants have to absorb water and other materials from the soil, retain water, transport materials

throughout the plant, support their bodies, and reproduce with dry fertilization.
_____

4

◆ Problem

How do the number and position of stomata differ in plants from different environments?

◆ Materials *(per group)*

leaf from a land plant
leaf from a floating water plant
scissors
microscope
2 slides
dropper
2 coverslips

Advance Preparation: Have students bring in plants to examine. The land plants could be houseplants, garden, or outdoor plants near the school. Good plants to use include geraniums, *Coleus, Tradescantia,* fresh spinach, and lettuce. Water plants such as water lilies can be obtained from florists, or they can be ordered from a biological supply company. Check local ordinances before obtaining plants from the environment.

Alternative Materials: Students could use prepared slides instead of fresh plants.

Teaching Tips: Be sure students understand that the epidermis is the outermost layer of cells on the leaf—the leaf's "skin." Students may have a hard time removing the epidermis. You might want to provide some prepared epidermis or prepared slides.

Refer students to How to Use a Microscope on page 1 for a review of making wet mounts and using a microscope. You may want to compile a class data table on the board.

INVESTIGATING STOMATA *(continued)*

◆ Safety   *Review the safety guidelines in the front of your lab book.*

Use caution in handling sharp scissors. Handle glass slides carefully. Do not let the microscope lens touch the slide.

◆ Procedure

1. Predict where stomata are on the leaf of a land plant. Give a reason for your prediction.

Predictions will vary. Stomata are usually located only on the underside of the leaves to prevent

the plant from drying out when the stomata are open.

2. Select a land plant. With the lower epidermis (underside of the leaf) facing upward, bend and then tear the leaf at an angle as illustrated in Figure 1. This will reveal part of the thin, colorless, lower epidermis.

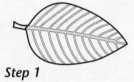
Step 1

Step 2

Step 3

Figure 1

4

3. With the scissors, cut off a strip of the colorless tissue and make a wet-mount slide. Place the slide on the microscope stage and focus under low power. Locate the stomata. Switch to high power. Draw the stomata, the guard cells, and a few of the lower epidermis cells in Observations. Count the stomata seen in the field of vision under high power. Record your data in the Data Table. (Identify and record the name of your lab group in the first column of the Data Table. Record data only in the row for your group.)

4. Repeat Step 3, using the upper epidermis of the same leaf. Draw your observations. Count the stomata seen in the field of vision under high power and record your data.

5. Predict where stomata are on the leaf of a floating water plant. Give a reason for your prediction.

Predictions will vary. Stomata are usually located only on the upper side of the leaves because

oxygen and carbon dioxide are more accessible there.

6. Repeat Step 3, using the lower epidermis of a leaf from a water plant. Draw what you see in Observations. Count the stomata in the field of vision and record this number in the Data Table.

7. Repeat Step 3, using the upper epidermis of a leaf from the water plant. Draw your observations and record your data.

8. Exchange and record data from other groups to complete your Data Table.

INVESTIGATING STOMATA *(continued)*

◆ Observations

Land Plant

Lower epidermis   Upper epidermis

◯   ◯

Water Plant

Lower epidermis   Upper epidermis

◯   ◯

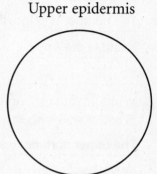

Data Table

| Group | Land Plant: _____ | | Floating Water Plant: _____ | |
	Lower Epidermis	Upper Epidermis	Lower Epidermis	Upper Epidermis
	Numbers will vary; several stomata should be seen.	Numbers will vary; usually there are no stomata on the upper epidermis.	Numbers will vary; very few, if any, stomata are on the lower surface.	Numbers will vary; several stomata should be visible.

◆ Analyze and Conclude

1. Is the class information more reliable than the information gathered by one group? Give a reason for your answer.

Yes, because more plants were studied.

2. Using data from the entire class, compare the number of stomata in the upper and lower epidermis of land plants.

The lower epidermis has more stomata.

3. Using data from the entire class, compare the number of stomata in the upper and lower epidermis of water plants.

The upper epidermis has more stomata.

INVESTIGATING STOMATA *(continued)*

◆ Critical Thinking and Applications

1. What advantage could the number of stomata and their location provide for land plants?

The number and location of stomata prevent the plant from drying out in the sun when the

stomata are open. The location prevents dirt that settles on the leaf from clogging up stomata.

2. What advantage could the number of stomata and their location provide for floating water plants?

The upper surface has better access to air; on the upper surface, stomata ensure adequate gas

exchange.

3. When do you think stomata are usually open—during the day or at night? Give a reason for your answer.

Stomata are open during the day, when photosynthesis takes place in sunlight. At night, they

close so that the plants do not lose too much water.

4. How could you change the procedure you followed to improve the accuracy of the data?

The actual area of the microscope field could be calculated to provide the number of stomata for

a specific area. Students could also take more data samples.

◆ More to Explore

New Problem Are stomata affected by a salt solution?

Possible Materials Consider which materials you can use from the previous part of the lab. What other materials might you need?

Procedure Develop a procedure to solve the problem. Keep in mind that, in osmosis, water moves from an area where it is concentrated to an area where it is less concentrated. Write your procedure on a separate sheet of paper. Have the teacher approve your procedure before you carry out the investigation.

Observations Keep records of your observations on a separate sheet of paper.

Analyze and Conclude Were more stomata open or closed in the salt solution? What might explain your results?

More stomata should be closed in the salt solution. The salt solution makes water leave the plant

through osmosis. The decrease in water pressure closes the stomata.

Students could make two wet-mount slides of the epidermis of a leaf, one with plain water and the other with a few drops of salt solution. Students compare the two slides by counting how many stomata are open and how many are closed.

A-5   **LABORATORY INVESTIGATION**

Investigating Hormones That Control Germination

Key Concept: Plant hormones control different plant functions.

Skills Focus: Observing, inferring, designing experiments, controlling variables

Time Required: 60 minutes and an observation period of 10 minutes a day for 8 days

◆ Pre-Lab Discussion

Tomato seeds usually germinate when exposed to moisture, oxygen, and a fairly warm temperature. Yet inside the tomato, where these conditions are met, seeds do not germinate. How do tomato seeds know when to develop and when not to develop?

Plants produce chemicals called hormones that control how the plants grow and develop. Only a small amount of hormone is needed to control plant processes such as the growth of the plant toward light.

In this investigation, you will explore the plant hormone that controls seed germination.

1. How can you tell if a seed is germinating?

Usually a root emerges from the seed.

_____

2. Besides germination, what other processes do plant hormones control?

Plant hormones control the formation of flowers, stems, and leaves; the shedding of leaves; and

the development and ripening of fruit.

_____

◆ Problem

Do tomatoes have a hormone that affects seed germination?

◆ Materials *(per group)*

wide, shallow bowl
metal or wooden spoon
tomatoes (2 or more varieties)
strainer
plastic cup
tap water
brush

funnel
beaker
glass-marking pencil
filter paper
4 plastic petri dishes
paper towel

Advance Preparation: Obtain several of each of two tomato varieties such as plum, cherry, and beefsteak. If time is limited, crush the tomatoes, wash the seeds, and strain the extract before class.

◆ Safety   *Review the safety guidelines in the front of your lab book.*

Handle glass objects carefully. If they break, tell the teacher. Do not pick up broken glass.

INVESTIGATING HORMONES THAT CONTROL GERMINATION *(continued)*

◆ Procedure

1. Use a spoon to crush a whole tomato (variety A) in a bowl. Strain the crushed tomato and collect the liquid extract in a beaker. With a glass-marking pencil, label the beaker "Extract A" and set it aside.

2. Empty the pulp from the strainer onto a paper towel and blot the pulp to remove some of the moisture. Separate 20 seeds from the pulp and rub them gently with a paper towel to remove the jelly-like capsule from the outside of the seeds.

3. Clean the strainer. (Use a brush, if necessary, to remove the pulp.) Place the 20 seeds in the strainer and rinse with water. Empty the seeds out on a fresh paper towel and blot them dry.

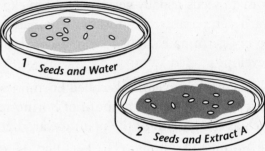

Figure 1

4. Label two petri dishes as shown in Figure 1. Line the petri dishes with filter paper. Place 10 seeds in each dish. Wet the filter paper in dish 1 with water; wet the paper in dish 2 with tomato extract. Cover the dishes.

5. Crush a different kind of tomato (variety B). Remove 20 seeds and wash them.

6. Line two more petri dishes with filter paper. Place 10 seeds in each petri dish.

7. Wet the filter paper in one dish with water. Label this dish 3. Wet the filter paper in the other dish with Extract A. Label it dish 4. Cover these two dishes.

8. Observe the seeds in the four dishes for several days, adding more water or tomato extract to keep the filter paper moist.

9. Each day record the total number of seeds that have germinated in each dish in the appropriate place in the Data Table.

◆ Observations

Data Table

Dish	Day 1	Day 2	Day 3	Day 4	Day 5	Day 6	Day 7	Day 8
1: Variety A with Water								
2: Variety A with Extract A								
3: Variety B with Water								
4: Variety B with Extract A								

Students' data should show the following trends: Dish 1: Most seeds germinate. Dish 2: Few or no seeds germinate. Dish 3: Most seeds germinate. Dish 4: Most seeds germinate.

INVESTIGATING HORMONES THAT CONTROL GERMINATION *(continued)*

◆ Analyze and Conclude

1. What is the purpose of dish 1?

Dish 1 is a control for the experiment. It provides a comparison for dish 2.

2. What conclusion can you draw after observing the results in dishes 1 and 2? Do tomatoes contain a hormone that inhibits germination? Give evidence to support your answer.

Yes, tomatoes contain a hormone that inhibits seed germination. No seeds, or very few,

germinated in the tomato extract. The extract must contain the hormone.

3. What conclusions can you draw after studying the results in dishes 3 and 4? Does the juice from variety A inhibit germination of seeds from variety B? Give evidence to support your answer.

Answers may vary depending on the varieties used. Most hormones that inhibit seed

germination are specific to the variety from which they are collected and may not inhibit

germination in other varieties.

◆ Critical Thinking and Applications

1. Explain why some of the seeds in dishes 1 and 3 may not have germinated, even though they had all the necessary conditions for growth.

Some seeds that were used in the experiment may have been dead.

2. Explain why many seeds that do not contain hormones that inhibit germination might begin to germinate outside during late spring.

During late spring, in many areas, the necessary conditions for seed germination—warmth and

moisture—become available.

3. What are three fruits and/or vegetables (besides tomatoes) that you think contain hormones that inhibit germination?

Answers will vary. Examples could include apples, oranges, watermelons, squash, cucumbers,

and so on.

5

INVESTIGATING HORMONES THAT CONTROL GERMINATION *(continued)*

◆ More to Explore

New Problem Is the hormone that inhibits the germination of tomato seeds a protein? (Hint: Proteins lose their effectiveness when boiled.)

Possible Materials Consider which materials you can use from the previous part of this lab. What else will you need?

Safety Be careful when boiling a liquid. Use a hot plate and pyrex beakers for heating. Use oven mitts to handle hot containers. Wear safety goggles and a lab apron.

Procedure Make a hypothesis that answers and explains the problem. Consider your data from the lab when developing your hypothesis. Make sure to keep a control to compare with the experimental dishes. Write your procedure on a separate sheet of paper. Have the teacher approve your procedure before carrying out the investigation.

Observations On a separate sheet of paper, make a data table to record your data.

Analyze and Conclude Is the hormone responsible for inhibiting seed germination a protein? Give a reason for your answer.

Results should show that the hormone inhibits seed germination of variety A even after it's

boiled, so it's not a protein. The hormone is abscisic acid.

5 Students could boil the extract from variety A tomato and then use it to see if it still inhibits seed germination.

B-1   **LABORATORY INVESTIGATION**

Observing Flatworms and Roundworms

Key Concept: Flatworms and roundworms have unique characteristics that allow them to live in different environments.

Skills Focus: Observing, inferring, communicating

Time Required: 40 minutes

◆ Pre-Lab Discussion

Flatworms have flat bodies and a body cavity with one opening. Most are parasites, living inside or on other organisms. Although most free-living flatworms live in the oceans, some live in fresh water or in soil.

Roundworms have long, cylindrical bodies that taper to a point at each end. There are more species of roundworms than any other kind of worm. They live in nearly every kind of moist environment, including forest soils, Antarctic sand, and pools of super-hot water. Like flatworms, some roundworms are parasitic and others are free-living.

In this investigation, you will observe some of the characteristics of parasitic and free-living flatworms and roundworms.

1. What are the three main groups of worms?

The three main groups of worms are flatworms, roundworms, and segmented worms.

2. Why are earthworms important to farmers and gardeners?

Earthworms improve growing conditions for crops by loosening and fertilizing the soil.

◆ Problem

Advance Preparation: Biological supply companies sell prepared slides. Get whole-mount slides of a planarian *(Dugesia)*, pork tapeworm *(Taenia)* with view of head and body segments, vinegar eel *(Turbatrix aceti)*, and trichina worm *(Trichinella)* inside a cyst in muscle.

What are some characteristics of flatworms and roundworms?

◆ Materials *(per group)*

To save time, set up microscopes with slides around the classroom before the lab. Label each microscope station with the name of the worm being observed.

microscope
planarian slide
pork-tapeworm slide
vinegar-eel slide
trichina-worm slide

More to Explore requires live planarians.

Alternate Materials: Preserved specimens and pictures of the worms may help students.

Teaching Tips: Review how to use a microscope before the lab.

Review the appearance of difficult-to-identify structures and the anatomical functions of structures with which students may be unfamiliar.

If students have trouble finding the different structures, show labeled transparencies of the worms for reference.

OBSERVING FLATWORMS AND ROUNDWORMS (continued)

◆ Safety 🔥 *Review the safety guidelines in the front of your lab book.*

Use both hands to carry a microscope. Hold the microscope base with one hand and the microscope arm with your other hand. Handle glass slides carefully.

◆ Procedure

Part A: Observing Flatworms

1. **CAUTION:** *Handle the slides carefully; they're breakable.* Use a microscope to look at a planarian slide under low magnification. Planarians are free-living, freshwater flatworms that have a definite head with a simple brain. Locate the two eyespots in the head region. They sense light. Find the mouth in the middle of the body on the ventral (belly) surface. Note a long tube, the pharynx, through which food moves from the mouth into the gastrovascular cavity. The gastrovascular cavity digests food and circulates it to the entire body. It also gets rid of waste.

2. Sketch a planarian under low power in the appropriate space in Observations. Label the eyespots, mouth, pharynx, and gastrovascular cavity. Record the magnification you used next to your sketch.

3. Tapeworms live as parasites inside the bodies of other animals. They attach themselves to the inner walls of their hosts and take in food through their skin. Examine a slide of a tapeworm under low magnification. Find the head. Note several suckers and the ring of hooks on the head. Behind the head is a narrow neck. The rest of the tapeworm's body is a string of nearly square sections that grow from the neck. The youngest sections are closest to the neck. These sections contain the male and female reproductive organs.

4. Sketch the tapeworm under low power in the appropriate space in Observations. Label the head, suckers, hooks, neck, young sections, and older sections. Record the magnification you used next to your sketch.

Part B: Observing Roundworms

1. A vinegar eel is a roundworm usually found in vinegar. Examine a slide of a vinegar eel under low magnification. Find the mouth at its anterior (head) end and the anus at its posterior (tail) end. Note the bulblike pharynx and long intestine. If the vinegar eel is female, eggs will be lined up in the uterus. If it is male, it will have a single testis.

2. Sketch the vinegar eel under low power in the appropriate space in Observations. Label the mouth, pharynx, intestine, anus, eggs (if female), and testis (if male). Record the magnification you used next to your sketch.

3. Examine a slide of a trichina worm. This worm is often found inside a hard capsule called a cyst. Such cysts are located inside the muscle tissue of the host.

4. Sketch what you see in the appropriate space in Observations. Label the trichina worm, cyst, and muscle tissue. Record the magnification you used next to your sketch.

OBSERVING FLATWORMS AND ROUNDWORMS *(continued)*

◆ Observations

Planarian

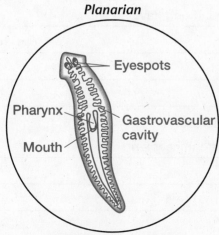

Magnification: __100×__

Tapeworm

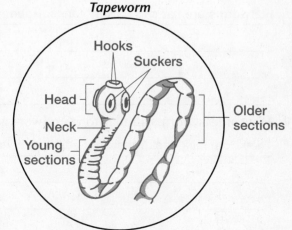

Magnification: __100×__

Vinegar eel (male)

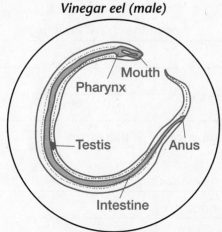

Magnification: __100×__

Vinegar eel (female)

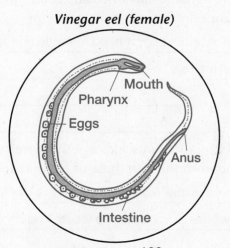

Magnification: __100×__

Trichina worm in muscle tissue

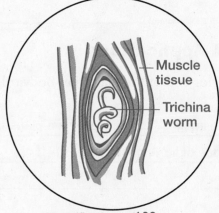

Magnification: __100×__

OBSERVING FLATWORMS AND ROUNDWORMS *(continued)*

◆ Analyze and Conclude

1. Identify two ways in which flatworms and roundworms differ in body structure.

   Flatworms are flat and have no anus. Roundworms are round and have an anus.

2. How are flatworms similar to roundworms in body structure?

   They both lack backbones, have bilateral symmetry, and are unsegmented.

3. How are parasitic flatworms and roundworms able to survive without structures for locomotion?

   Parasitic worms do not need to move around in search of food once they have attached

   themselves to a host.

4. Compare the nervous and digestive systems of the free-living forms of flatworms and roundworms with those of parasitic forms.

   The nervous and digestive systems of the free-living worms are more complex. Unlike parasites,

   these worms are adapted to locate and digest their own food.

◆ Critical Thinking and Applications

1. Why is the structure at the anterior end of the planarian body called an eyespot instead of an eye?

   Organisms with true eyes can see images. The eyespot on a planarian is only photosensitive.

   That is, it only detects the presence of light, not images.

OBSERVING FLATWORMS AND ROUNDWORMS *(continued)*

2. List two necessities that parasitic worms get from their hosts that free-living worms have to obtain for themselves.

Accept any two of the following: hosts supply parasites with oxygen, a constant temperature for growth, a well-protected moist environment, a steady supply of predigested food.

3. Why is it rare that an individual parasite kills its host?

If the parasite killed its host, it would also die unless it could quickly find another host. This effect is unlikely to promote the parasite's survival and reproduction.

4. You have a new job as a product inspector in a large meat-packing company. Your first assignment is to inspect pork for trichina worms. You've been warned that if humans eat undercooked or raw pork that has a large number of trichina worms in it, a serious infection can result. What should you look for?

Check the pork carefully for small cysts. These cysts might contain trichina-worm larvae.

◆ More to Explore

New Problem Do planarians prefer to live in a light environment or a dark one?

Possible Materials List materials that you will be using in this experiment.

Safety Keep planarians in pond water at all times, so they will not be harmed. Always treat animals with great care. Use both hands to carry a microscope. Hold the microscope base with one hand and the microscope arm with your other hand. Handle glass slides carefully. Wash your hands after completing the investigation.

Procedure Hypothesize whether planarians prefer to live in a light environment or a dark one. On a separate sheet of paper, write a procedure you would follow to test your hypothesis. Have the teacher approve your procedure before you carry out the investigation.

Observations Make appropriate data tables and drawings.

OBSERVING FLATWORMS AND ROUNDWORMS *(continued)*

Analyze and Conclude

1. Was your hypothesis supported by your data? Why or why not?

The hypothesis may or may not have been supported. If the planarians have been moved or kept in the classroom for a long period of time prior to the activity, they may not be healthy and may behave abnormally.

2. Based on your experiment, what can you infer about where planarians live in nature?

Students should find that planarians generally prefer a darker environment. Students might correctly infer that, in nature, planarians live under rocks in ponds and streams, which is a darker environment.

The following procedure is one way to demonstrate whether planarians prefer light or dark conditions. Fill a clear glass petri dish with pond water. Use a microscope to check the water for the presence of planarians. Cover half of the petri dish with cardboard, so that it will be dark. After 15 minutes, check to see which side of the petri dish the planarians are in. The planarians will move away from the light and into the dark half of the petri dish.

B-2   **LABORATORY INVESTIGATION**

Characteristics of Sea Stars

Key Concept: The anatomy of a sea star is adapted to life in a marine environment.

Skills Focus: Observing, inferring, developing hypotheses

Time Required: 40 minutes

◆ Pre-Lab Discussion

The sea star, or starfish, is a spiny-skinned sea invertebrate in the echinoderm phylum. Echinoderms are animals whose bodies are usually covered with hundreds of small spines. Brittle stars, basket stars, sand dollars, sea cucumbers, and sea urchins are also echinoderms.

Sea stars live in coastal waters and on rocky seashores. They are predators that eat oysters, clams, snails, barnacles, and worms. Sea stars usually have 5 arms branching out from a central disk. Sun stars have 7 to 14 arms, however, and some sea stars have 15 to 24 arms. If an arm breaks off, the sea star can regenerate a new one.

In this investigation, you will examine the external structures of a sea star.

1. What does *echinoderm* mean, and why is it a good name for this phylum?

Echinoderm means "spiny skinned." The skin of most of these animals is supported by a spiny

endoskeleton.

2. What characteristics are typical of echinoderms?

Echinoderms typically have spiny skin, radial symmetry, and a water vascular system.

◆ Problem

How is the anatomy of a sea star adapted to sea life?

◆ Materials *(per group)*

wet paper towels
preserved sea star
dissecting tray
2 hand lenses

Advance Preparation: Biological supply houses sell preserved sea stars. Make sure that water is available to moisten the paper towels. You may want to give students gloves for turning over the specimens.

Alternate Materials: Photos or models of a sea star may be used instead of preserved specimens.

Teaching Tips: If you don't give students gloves, you might want to handle the sea stars yourself.

Use overhead transparencies of the lab diagrams to help students find the different structures.

◆ Safety   *Review the safety guidelines in the front of your lab book.*

To prevent skin irritation, wear aprons and goggles during this investigation.

CHARACTERISTICS OF SEA STARS (continued)

Procedure

1. Put on safety goggles and a lab apron. **CAUTION:** *The preservative used on the sea star can irritate your skin. Don't touch your eyes or mouth while working with the preserved sea star. Keep a piece of wet paper towel handy to wipe your fingers after touching the star.* Rinse the sea star thoroughly with water to remove any extra preservative. Put the sea star, top surface up, in the dissecting tray. Notice that the sea star's body has 5 arms radiating from a central disk.

2. Using a hand lens, examine the skin on the top surface. Notice the many coarse spines that cover the entire top surface. The skin is spiny and irregular because parts of the endoskeleton protrude through the skin. Around the base of the spines are jawlike structures. They capture small animals and keep the skin free of foreign objects.

3. Use a hand lens to locate a spine and the jawlike structures around it. See Figure 1. Answer Observations question 1.

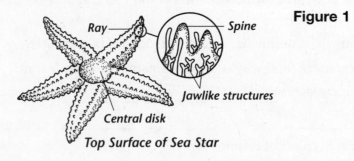

Figure 1

Ray — Spine

Jawlike structures

Central disk

Top Surface of Sea Star

4. Study the top surface of the central disk. Answer Observations question 2.

5. Locate a small red or yellow buttonlike structure on the top side of the central disk. This structure contains many tiny pores through which water enters the water vascular system. The water vascular system has water-filled canals that function primarily in movement and feeding.

6. Try to find the anus on the top surface of the central disk. The anus, which opens out from the intestine, lets solid wastes escape from the body.

7. In Observations, label the following structures on the top side of the sea star: central disk, arms, spines, and anus.

8. Turn the sea star over so that its bottom surface is visible. With the hand lens, examine the mouth, an opening in the middle of the central disk. Notice the small spines that surround the mouth. Many types of sea stars feed by pushing part of the stomach through the mouth. The stomach secretes enzymes that digest prey.

9. Find the groove that begins at the mouth and extends down the center of each arm. Find the small tube feet that line the groove. The tube feet are part of the water vascular system. A tube foot is a hollow, thin-walled cylinder with a bulb-like structure at one end and a sucker at the tip. Answer Observations question 3.

CHARACTERISTICS OF SEA STARS *(continued)*

10. In Observations, label the following structures on the bottom side of the sea star: groove, mouth, and tube feet.

11. When you have finished examining the specimen, follow the teacher's instructions for storing the sea star for further use. **CAUTION:** *Wash your hands thoroughly at the end of the lab.*

◆ Observations

Top Side of Sea Star

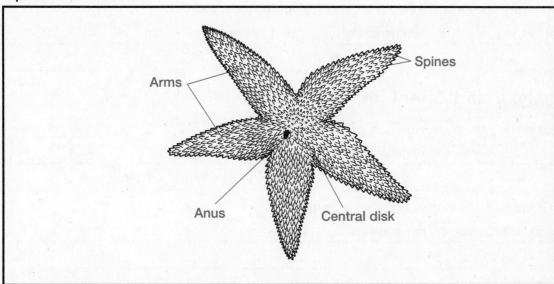

Bottom Side of Sea Star

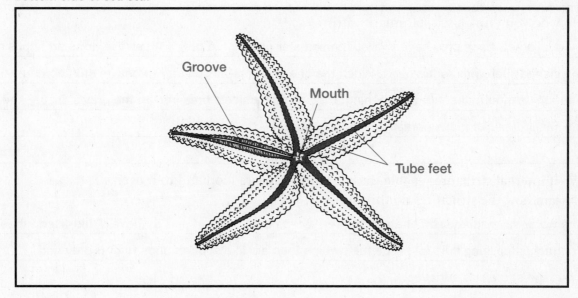

CHARACTERISTICS OF SEA STARS *(continued)*

1. Describe the appearance of a sea star's spines.

The spines are rough, bumpy, and hard.

2. How does the number of spines in the central disk compare to the number of spines in the arm?

Answers will depend on the specimens used. Many species of sea stars have fewer spines in the central disk than in the rays.

3. How many rows of tube feet does your sea star have?

Answers will vary. Sea stars generally have 2 or 4 rows per arm.

◆ Analyze and Conclude

1. What do you think the function of a sea star's spines might be?

The sea star's spines support the body and protect it from predators.

2. What kind of symmetry does a sea star have?

A sea star has five-part radial symmetry.

3. What do you think the tube feet might be used for?

The tube feet are used as suction cups to grip the surface below the sea star. They are also used for movement and feeding.

4. How do you think a sea star might eat?

Most of a sea star's prey have shells. The sea star grasps the prey with all five arms and pulls on the closed shell with its tube feet. When the shell opens, the sea star forces its stomach out through its mouth and into the opening. Digestive chemicals break down the prey's tissue, and the sea star sucks in the partially digested body.

5. What internal structures enable the sea star to capture food and to move? Explain how the structures do this.

The water vascular system enables the sea star to capture food and to move. Fluid-filled tubes contract, squeezing fluid into tube feet, which then act like suction cups to grip prey and move the star along surfaces.

CHARACTERISTICS OF SEA STARS *(continued)*

◆ Critical Thinking and Applications

1. Sea stars produce large numbers of eggs and sperm. Why is this production an adaptive advantage?

Large numbers of sperm and eggs increase a sea star's chances of producing young in a marine

environment.

_____

2. When a sea star pries open the shell of a clam or an oyster, the mollusk resists. Even if the shell opens only slightly, the sea star will get its meal. How does this happen?

The sea star pushes its thin, membranous stomach out through its mouth and into the slightly

opened shell of the mollusk. Digestive enzymes in the sea star's stomach turn the mollusk into a

soupy mixture that the sea star can easily take in.

_____

_____

3. Because sea stars eat many clams and oysters, divers were hired to catch sea stars and chop them into pieces. After this, fishers found even more empty clam and oyster shells than before. Why did their plan backfire?

A sea star can regenerate an entire body from a small part of the central disk and a single arm.

Each sea-star piece regenerated a new body, resulting in an increase of the population.

_____

_____

4. Can a sea star move equally well in any direction? Why or why not?

Its five radial arms allow the sea star to move in any direction. The sea star does not have an

anterior or a posterior end.

_____

_____

5. Many echinoderms, which are bottom dwellers as adults, have free-swimming larvae. What advantage do free-swimming larvae give to echinoderms?

Free-living larvae allow the new organisms to move away from the parent organisms. They can

find new places to live, which provide new sources of food.

_____

_____

2

CHARACTERISTICS OF SEA STARS *(continued)*

◆ More to Explore

New Problem Why do sand dollars, sea urchins, sea lilies, sea cucumbers, and brittle stars belong to the same phylum as sea stars?

Possible Materials List and gather the materials you will need. Decide which materials you could use from the previous lab.

Safety Wear aprons and goggles if working with specimens.

Procedure Write a hypothesis that includes those features that you think each of these organisms share. Write a procedure you would follow to test your hypothesis. Have the teacher approve your procedure before you carry out the investigation.

Observations Make drawings and record other observations on a separate sheet of paper.

Analyze and Conclude What characteristics do your observed animals share that place them in the same phylum as sea stars?

Without dissecting the animals, students can observe that all echinoderms share some

characteristics: a spiny endoskeleton, radial symmetry, and an internal water-vascular system.

Students could gather specimens of other echinoderms to observe. If live or preserved specimens are not available, make this a research project using printed and electronic information.

Adaptations of Fish

Key Concept: The structures of fishes are adapted to life in water.

Skills Focus: Observing, inferring, communicating

Time Required: 40 minutes

◆ Pre-Lab Discussion

Fishes are vertebrate members of the phylum Chordata. The largest group of fishes has skeletons made of bones. The perch and the goldfish are bony fishes. Bony fishes exhibit many adaptations for life in water. All fishes are ectotherms. They live in water and have fins. Fins are fanlike structures used for steering, balancing, and moving. Most fishes obtain oxygen through gills and have scales. Scales are thin, hard, overlapping plates that cover the skin of fish.

In this investigation, you will observe the movement and behavior of a live goldfish. You will also identify the external parts of a perch.

1. Explain how a fish breathes.

Oxygen moves from the water into the fish's blood, while carbon dioxide, a waste product,

moves out of the blood and into the water.

2. What are the three major groups of fishes? Describe their characteristics.

The three major groups of fishes are jawless fishes (skeleton of cartilage; no pairs of fins; no

teeth or scales), cartilaginous fishes (skeleton of cartilage; have jaws and pairs of fins; have

scales), and bony fishes (skeletons of bones; have scales and gills).

◆ Problem

How are the structures of fish adapted for life in water?

◆ Materials *(per group)*

large glass jar or beaker
water from an aquarium (to fill beaker)
fishnet
goldfish
paper towels
preserved perch
dissecting tray
probe
forceps
hand lens
microscope slide
medicine dropper
coverslip

Advance Preparation: Goldfish are available from pet stores. Biological supply houses sell preserved perch.

Make sure that water is available to moisten the paper towels. You may want to give students gloves for turning over the specimens.

Alternate Materials: Photos or models of a bony fish may be used instead of preserved specimens.

Teaching Tips: You can omit steps 1, 2, and 5 in Part A if the fish are already in separate containers.

If you don't give students gloves, you might want to handle the perch yourself.

Review the location of fins and other structures orally before students begin the lab.

Use an overhead transparency of the lab diagram to help students find the different structures.

ADAPTATIONS OF FISH *(continued)*

◆ Safety 🔲 🔲 🔲 🔲 🔲 🔲 🔲

Review the safety guidelines in the front of your lab book.

Always treat living things with great care. Keep the goldfish in the aquarium water as much as possible. Do not use tap water directly from the tap. Tap water must be left at room temperature for at least 24 hours before placing fish in it. To prevent slips or falls, immediately wipe up any water spilled on the floor. To prevent skin irritation, wear aprons and goggles during Part B. Handle glass items carefully. Tell your teacher about any broken glass.

◆ Procedure

Part A: Observing the Behavior of a Live Fish

1. Fill a large glass or beaker three-quarters full with water from an aquarium.

2. **CAUTION:** *Keep the goldfish in the water as much as possible.* With a fishnet, carefully remove one goldfish from the aquarium. Immediately transfer the fish to the jar of water.

3. Observe the goldfish. Find the gills. Carefully watch the movements of the body, fins, and tail as the goldfish swims. Answer Observations question 1.

4. Use the labeled diagram of the perch on page 48 to find the goldfish's dorsal, caudal, pectoral, pelvic, and anal fins. Answer Observations question 2. Observe the function of each fin as the fish swims. Complete the Data Table on fins.

5. With a fishnet, carefully return the goldfish to the aquarium.

Part B: Examining the External Anatomy of a Fish

1. Put on safety goggles and a lab apron. **CAUTION:** *The preservative used on the perch can irritate your skin. Don't touch your eyes or mouth while working with the fish. Keep a piece of wet paper towel handy to wipe your fingers after touching the fish.* Rinse the perch thoroughly with water to remove any extra preservative. Dry the fish with paper towels. Position the fish in a dissecting tray with the head of the fish pointing left.

2. Observe the dorsal (back) and ventral (belly) surfaces. Answer Observations question 3.

3. Find the three regions of the fish's body: the head, the trunk, and the tail.

4. Find the nostril—one of two openings between the eye and the mouth.

5. Insert a probe into the mouth and carefully pry it open. Observe the teeth. **CAUTION:** *Do not touch the fish's teeth; they are very sharp.* Answer Observations question 4.

6. With a probe, carefully lift the protective bony cover away from the gills lying underneath. Observe the flat, scalelike bones that support the gill cover.

ADAPTATIONS OF FISH *(continued)*

7. With forceps, carefully remove a single scale. Observe the scale with a hand lens. Notice the growth rings. As a fish grows, its scales grow. Each growth ring on the scale represents 1 year's growth. Answer Observations question 5. In Observations, draw a scale as seen under the hand lens. Label the growth rings on your drawing.

8. On the diagram in Observations, label the following parts of the external anatomy of a perch: head, trunk, tail, eye, nostril, mouth, upper jaw, lower jaw, gills, and scales.

9. When you have finished examining the fish, follow your teacher's instructions for storing the perch for further use. **CAUTION:** *Wash your hands thoroughly at the end of the lab.*

◆ Observations

See the information that came with the specimens for instructions of how to store the specimens. Specimens in vacuum-packed bags can be resealed and refrigerated. You can also place specimens in a pail along with a preservative solution made from a preservative concentrate such as Bio-Perm.®

3

Data Table

Fin	Function *Choose from among the following:* • *Helps fish steer and stop* • *Propels fish through water* • *Keeps fish from rolling over* • *No apparent function*
Anterior dorsal (on back near head)	Keeps fish from rolling over
Posterior dorsal (on back near tail)	Keeps fish from rolling over
Anal	Keeps fish from rolling over
Caudal	Propels fish through water
Pectoral	Helps fish steer and stop
Pelvic	Helps fish steer and stop

Perch Scale

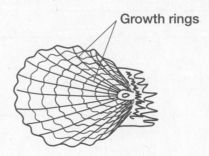

Growth rings

ADAPTATIONS OF FISH *(continued)*

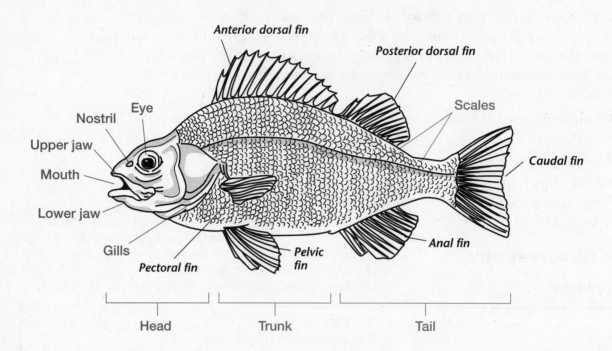

1. Describe the motion of the fish as it swims.

   Answers should include that the body bends from side to side as the fish swims.

   _____

2. How many fins does the goldfish have? Which fins occur in pairs?

   A goldfish has seven fins. The pectoral fins and the pelvic fins occur in pairs.

   _____

3. Compare the color of the dorsal and ventral surfaces of the fish.

   The dorsal surface is darker than the ventral surface.

   _____

   _____

4. Describe the perch's teeth. Where are they in the mouth?

   The teeth are sharp and slant backward/inward. They are on both jaws.

   _____

5. How old is your fish?

   Answers will vary. Students must count growth rings on a scale. Each growth ring represents

   1 year's growth.

   _____

ADAPTATIONS OF FISH (*continued*)

◆ Analyze and Conclude

1. What is the shape of the fish's body? Why do you think this body shape is suited to living in water?

The thin, streamlined body permits easy, fast movement through water.

2. The fish has different colors on its back and belly. How do these different colors protect the fish from its enemies, both the birds in the sky above it and the sea organisms that live below it?

The dark dorsal surface blends in with the dark bottom of a pond, when seen from above. The

light ventral surface blends in with the light sky, when seen from below.

3. How are the perch's teeth adapted to their function?

The perch is carnivorous, so its teeth are adapted to catch and hold its prey.

4. What structures on the perch make it adapted for life in water?

Answers may include gills and fins. Internal structures such as the air bladder may also be

mentioned.

◆ Critical Thinking and Applications

1. While many invertebrates have an exoskeleton, or hard shell covering, vertebrates such as fish have an endoskeleton. How does the endoskeleton help the fish?

An endoskeleton can support a larger body than an exoskeleton can and provides for greater

flexibility. Also, the endoskeleton grows as the organism grows, eliminating the need for molting.

2. The perch possesses a gas-filled internal structure called a swim bladder. What is the function of the swim bladder?

The swim bladder helps stabilize the fish at different levels in the water. The swim bladder lets a

fish adjust its buoyancy as it moves in the water. This allows the fish to float at different depths

without using a lot of energy.

ADAPTATIONS OF FISH *(continued)*

3. Certain species of fish that live deep in the ocean have chemicals in their skin that make them glow in the dark. How does this characteristic help these fishes survive in their environment?

   Answers will vary but may include the idea that this light enables fishes to find a mate or

   attract prey.

4. The perch fertilizes its eggs externally and leaves them exposed on underwater rocks. The guppy fertilizes its eggs internally and gives birth to live young. Which fish probably produces fewer eggs? Which species is likely to have a higher survival rate for its young?

   Because perch eggs are exposed, it is reasonable to assume that their eggs are more vulnerable

   to being eaten or destroyed. To compensate for this loss, the perch probably produces many

   eggs. The young of guppies are fully developed at birth, so guppies probably produce fewer

   young. Guppies probably have the higher survival rate of the two fishes.

◆ More to Explore

What does a fish skeleton look like? Obtain a fish from a grocery store. Boil the fish so that the flesh peels off easily. Or, if you prefer, cook the fish for dinner and carefully remove the meat so that the skeleton remains intact. Sketch and label the fish's skeleton.

Students could boil a fish from the grocery store in water until the flesh is soft, remove the flesh, and reassemble the skeleton. Students will need a reference to label their drawings. If a bony fish isn't available, use reference materials and/or models instead.

B-4   **LABORATORY INVESTIGATION**

Adaptations of Birds

Key Concept: Bills and feet of birds are adapted to different environments.

Skills Focus: Modeling, observing, inferring, predicting, classifying

Time Required: Part A: 40 minutes; Part B and Part C: 40 minutes

◆ Pre-Lab Discussion

Whether you are in an open meadow, a city park, or your own backyard, you are likely to hear the sounds of birds. There are many different bird species, and each has special adaptations to its environment. For example, birds can have different types of feathers. These feathers, which are actually modified scales, provide insulation and balance. Birds also have bills or beaks of various shapes and sizes. The shapes of bills are adaptations to the different kind of foods found in the birds' environment.

The feet of birds are also adapted to specific environments. In addition to walking and running, birds' feet are used for gripping and tearing food, climbing, and swimming. The shape and size of the feet determine how well a bird can perform these tasks within its specific environment.

In this investigation, you will examine how birds' bills and feet help them survive in their environment.

1. What are some types of food that birds eat?

Birds eat seeds, fruit, plants, worms, small animals and fish, nectar, insects, and so forth.

2. In addition to eating, what are other functions of birds' bills?

Bills are also used for protection, building nests, and preening feathers.

◆ Problem

How have birds adapted to living in different environments?

◆ Materials *(per class)*

30 petri dishes
4 bags of different seeds or seedlike materials, such as sunflower seeds, popcorn, lima beans, or couscous
6 different hand tools
clock or watch with a second hand

Advance Preparation: Have students bring in tools for modeling bills. Tools could include a variety of pliers, spring-type clothespins, cable clips, handheld vises, wire clips, tweezers, kitchen tongs, chopsticks, spoons, and craft sticks.

Alternate Materials: Use jar lids instead of petri dishes.

◆ Safety   *Review the safety guidelines in the front of your lab book.*

Use caution in handling pointed or sharp tools. Keep seeds in containers at all times to prevent spills and accidents. Do not eat seeds. Wash hands after handling seeds.

Name _____ Date _____ Class _____

ADAPTATIONS OF BIRDS (continued)

◆ Procedure

Part A: Modeling Bills

Teaching Tips: [Part A; Step 1] Set up and number 6 stations in the classroom, with a different tool at each station. Each station should have 5 dishes: 4 dishes, each of which contains 25 seeds of one type; the fifth dish is empty.

1. **CAUTION:** *Handle pointed or sharp tools carefully.* There are several stations around your classroom. At each station you will find the following: a tool; four petri dishes, each filled with a different type of seed; and an empty petri dish. The tools will be used to model the effectiveness of different bill shapes in picking up seeds. Each station has a different tool-bill. Visit each station briefly and examine the different tool-bills and seeds.

2. Predict which tool-bill will work best to pick up each type of seed. Give a reason for your prediction.

   Seed 1 __Answers will vary. Reasons for predictions may include the tool-bill being easy to__

   Seed 2 __manipulate; broad tool-bills that come to a point may make picking up__

   Seed 3 __individual seeds easier; and serrated edges aid in holding on to the seeds.__

   Seed 4 _____

   Predict which tool-bill will be the worst at picking up each type of seed. Give a reason for your prediction.

   Seed 1 __Answers will vary. Reasons for predictions may include the tool-bill being awkward to__

   Seed 2 __manipulate; broad, blunt tool-bills may not be able to pick up individual seeds effectively;__

   Seed 3 __and narrow, pointed, smooth tool-bills may lead to dropping the seeds.__

   Seed 4 _____

3. Go to one station and practice using the tool-bill to pick up the different seeds. Pick up one seed at a time. Each petri dish contains only one type of seed. Be sure not to mix the seeds in the petri dishes. Use either one or both hands to hold the tool-bill. Everyone in the group should practice using the tool-bill.

   Remind students to control variables by using the same physical procedures each time, for example, always using the dominant hand.

4. While a classmate times you, use the tool-bill to pick up as many seeds from the Seed 1 dish as you can within 30 seconds. Pick up only one seed at a time and place it into the empty petri dish. Count how many seeds you pick up within 30 seconds and record this number in Data Table 1 on the next page. When your time is up, return the seeds to the Seed 1 dish. Everyone in the group should take a turn at picking up as many seeds as possible from the Seed 1 dish.

5. Repeat Step 4 for the other three types of seeds at the station. Calculate the average number of seeds picked up by your group within 30 seconds for each type of seed. Record the averages in your data table.

6. Repeat steps 3–5 at each station. Record your data in Date Table 1.

[Part A; Step 3] Students could time each other or you could have all students pick up as many seeds with their tool-bills as they can during 30 seconds, while you time them.

Name _____ Date _____ Class _____

ADAPTATIONS OF BIRDS *(continued)*

◆ Observations

Part A

Data Table 1: Number of Seeds Picked up in 30 Seconds

Station Number _____   Tool _____

Student Name	Seed 1	Seed 2	Seed 3	Seed 4
1.				
2.				
3.				
4.				
Average Number of Seeds				

Station Number _____   Tool _____

Student Name	Seed 1	Seed 2	Seed 3	Seed 4
1.				
2.				
3.				
4.				
Average Number of Seeds				

Station Number _____   Tool _____

Student Name	Seed 1	Seed 2	Seed 3	Seed 4
1.				
2.				
3.				
4.				
Average Number of Seeds				

ADAPTATIONS OF BIRDS *(continued)*

Station Number _____   Tool _____

Student Name	Seed 1	Seed 2	Seed 3	Seed 4
1.				
2.				
3.				
4.				
Average Number of Seeds				

Station Number _____   Tool _____

Student Name	Seed 1	Seed 2	Seed 3	Seed 4
1.				
2.				
3.				
4.				
Average Number of Seeds				

Station Number _____   Tool _____

Student Name	Seed 1	Seed 2	Seed 3	Seed 4
1.				
2.				
3.				
4.				
Average Number of Seeds				

ADAPTATIONS OF BIRDS (continued)

1. List the tool-bills in order of effectiveness at picking up each type of seed. Begin with the most effective tool and end with the least effective.

Seed 1 _Answers may vary. Accept all reasonable answers. Tools that were compact enough to_

Seed 2 _easily handle and in which the tips come together to a point may seem to be the_

Seed 3 _best at picking up individual seeds._

Seed 4 _____

2. Were some tool-bills more effective at picking up a certain type of seed than other tool-bills? Name the tool-bills and which seeds they picked up more effectively.

Answers may vary, depending on the tools and seeds chosen. If seeds vary significantly in size

and shape, students will notice a greater difference in the effectiveness of certain tools among

the types of seeds. Accept all reasonable answers.

3. Were some tool-bills effective at picking up a variety of seeds? If so, name them.

Some tool-bills will probably be effective at picking up a variety of seeds; others will be more

specialized.

Part B: Examining Bird Beaks and Feet

To reduce class time, assign either Part B or Part C for homework.

4

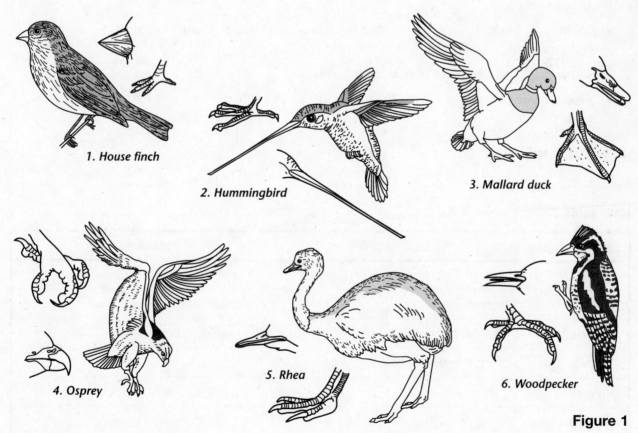

1. House finch

2. Hummingbird

3. Mallard duck

4. Osprey

5. Rhea

6. Woodpecker

Figure 1

ADAPTATIONS OF BIRDS (continued)

◆ Procedure

Part B: Examining Bird Beaks and Feet

1. Examine and compare the shape and size of each bird's bill in Figure 1. Use the following list to infer the likely structure and function of the bill for each bird. Record this information in Data Table 2.

   - *Straight and pointed:* used as a chisel to drill trees
   - *Flat and broad:* used to strain algae and small organisms from water
   - *Massive and hooked:* used to tear flesh
   - *Short and stout:* multipurpose; used to eat insects, seeds, and small crustaceans
   - *Long, fine, pipelike tube:* used to obtain nectar from flowers

2. Examine and compare the feet of the birds in Figure 1. Use the following list to determine the number and position (front or back of the foot) of the toes and to infer the function of the feet for each bird. Record this information in Data Table 3 on the following page.

   - *Climbing foot:* four toes; two toes in front and two toes in back for support when climbing upward to prevent falling backward
   - *Grasping foot:* four toes; two in front and two in back; large, sharp curved claws
   - *Perching foot:* four toes; three front toes and one back toe that can hold onto a perch tightly
   - *Running foot:* two to three toes rather than four
   - *Swimming foot:* four toes; three in front and one in back; webbed feet that act as paddles

◆ Observations

Part B

Data Table 2

Bird	Structure of Bill	Function of Bill
1. House finch	short and stout	multipurpose
2. Hummingbird	fine, pipelike	obtain nectar from flowers
3. Mallard duck	flat and broad	strain food from water
4. Osprey	massive and hooked	tear flesh
5. Rhea	short and stout	multipurpose
6. Woodpecker	long, straight, and pointed	chisel trees

ADAPTATIONS OF BIRDS *(continued)*

Data Table 3

Bird	Number of Toes	Toe Positions	Function
1. House finch	4	3 in front; 1 in back	perching
2. Hummingbird	4	3 in front; 1 in back	perching
3. Mallard duck	4 webbed	3 in front; 1 in back	swimming
4. Osprey	4	3 in front; 1 in back	grasping
5. Rhea	3	3 in front	running
6. Woodpecker	4	2 in front; 2 in back	climbing

◆ Analyze and Conclude

1. How do your results for the tool-bills compare with your predictions? Give possible reasons for differences.

   Accept all reasonable answers. Students may be surprised that a bill that easily picked up one

   type of seed was ineffective with other seed types.

2. Based on the information you have gathered, describe what a bill that can effectively pick up and crack small seeds might look like.

   Answers should reflect the data collected in Part A. The bill might come to a point and be

   broad. It would most likely be compact to increase control.

3. If a bird has grasping feet and a large hooked bill, what might the bird eat? Explain your answer.

   This bird would probably eat animals, such as fish, small rodents, snakes, and small mammals.

   The feet are adapted to holding prey, and the bill is adapted to tearing flesh.

◆ Critical Thinking and Applications

1. Why would a woodpecker probably be unsuccessful at depending on small mammals for food?

   The relatively thin toes of the woodpecker might make it difficult to hold and kill its prey. The

   straight, narrow beak would not be very useful for tearing the prey's flesh.

2. What advantage might a bird that is able to eat a variety of seeds have over a bird that can eat only one type of seed?

   During times when seeds are scarce, the bird that can eat a variety of seeds can switch to

   alternatives while the other bird may not be able to obtain enough food to survive.

4

ADAPTATIONS OF BIRDS (continued)

3. A bird has been sighted in a mountainous area, where it lives at high altitudes and low temperatures. There are few, if any, trees and food sources are limited. Only sagebrush and some grass grow up through the mostly snow-covered land. Most likely, the bird would spend a lot of time on the ground, as does the ptarmigan, with three toes in front and a large toe in back for balance. What might a bird in this environment eat? What might its beak and feet look like? Explain your answer.

A bird in a mountainous area would most likely have a multipurpose bill, which is short and

stout for eating anything that is available, such as insects, seeds, and young vegetation growing

out of the snow-covered ground. The bird might also have feathers on its feet for insulation from

the cold.

◆ More to Explore

Using the information below and the previous activity, draw the beaks and feet of the following birds in the spaces provided. If you like, use your imagination to draw the whole bird as well. To the left of each illustration, explain your drawing.

4

Bird A lives in a South American tropical forest and eats nuts, seeds, and fruit. This bird makes nests in holes in trees and has been seen gathering on a cliff of salty clay to lick minerals.

Bird A describes a macaw, the largest of the parrots. Based on the information given, students should have drawn a bird with a short, stout beak. The top beak over-hangs the lower beak somewhat. The feet are used for climbing—both trees and cliffs. This bird has four toes—two toes in front and two toes in back for support when climbing. Students may have also given this bird colorful plumage because many tropical birds are colorful. Macaws are brilliant red, blue, yellow, or green.

Bird B is a songbird that sits in the trees of India and Malaysia. This bird eats flower nectar as well as insects. Sometimes it hovers before tube-shaped flowers and reaches into them with its long tongue. But when it feeds from large blooms, it pierces the petals to reach the nectar at the base.

Bird B describes a yellow-backed sunbird. It has a long, pipelike, curved beak for reaching into flowers. The bill is pointed at the end for piercing hibiscus and other large blooms. Sunbirds have four toes—three in front and one in back—for perching on tree branches. Once again, this bird is colorful. The male is green, yellow, and red.

LABORATORY INVESTIGATION

Family Life of Bettas

Key Concepts: Instinctive behaviors enable betta pairs to breed.

Skills Focus: Observing, classifying, inferring, posing questions

Time Required: two 40-minute periods for setting up the fish containers; 10–15 minutes for observation each day for up to 2 weeks

◆ Pre-Lab Discussion

Betta fish, also known as Siamese fighting fish, live in fresh water and originally came from Southeast Asia. These beautiful aquarium fish are usually red, blue, or turquoise. The males' colors become brighter when the fish are courting or get excited. Bettas do not get all their oxygen from water; they rise to the surface from time to time for air. They can live in containers without special pumps or filters.

In this investigation, you will select a male and a female betta fish, set them up in a container, and observe them to see if they will produce a batch of eggs that will hatch into tiny fish, called fry. During your investigation, remember that fish, like all other living organisms, must be handled with care. The containers that you will be using must be filled with tap water that has been sitting for at least 24 hours. The water should be changed once a week. Floating aquatic plants must be present when both male and female bettas are in the same container. The fish prefer low light, and the water should be kept between 21°C and 29°C (70°F and 84°F). Betta fish should be fed a pinch of food twice a day. Male bettas are extremely territorial and MUST be kept out of sight of one another.

1. What type of behavior is courtship—instinctive or learned? Explain your answer.

Courtship is an example of instinctive behavior. An instinct is an inborn behavior pattern that the

animal performs correctly the first time.

2. Betta males are very aggressive toward one another. What is aggressive behavior?

Aggressive behavior is threatening behavior that one animal uses to influence the behavior of

another.

◆ Problem

What behaviors enable betta fish to reproduce?

Advance Preparation: To augment the information in this lab, consult the book, *Bettas—A Complete Introduction* by Walt Maurus (T.F.H. Publications, Inc. 1987).

The recommended total number of breeding pairs for an entire class is six.

Male bettas are extremely territorial and must be kept in separate containers before being paired with a female.

Betta food can be purchased at a pet store. One container will be enough for the entire class.

Make plans for continuing care of the fish after the lab. Most pet stores will buy betta fry from you if students do not want to take them home.

FAMILY LIFE OF BETTAS *(continued)*

◆ Possible Materials *(per group)*

colored pencils
2 clean 2-liter soda bottles filled
    with aged water
1-gallon or larger container filled
    with aged water
aquarium gravel
floating clump of aquatic plants
betta food
male and female betta fish
hand lens

Alternate Materials: Many different containers can be used in this activity, including large glass jars, 2-liter plastic bottles, and gallon milk containers. If bettas are not available, use gouramis instead. Test members of any other species for willingness to breed before using them in the lab.

Teaching Tips:

Keep males out of each other's sight and away from reflecting surfaces. To compensate for possible pH, hardness, and temperature extremes in local tap water, the water should sit for at least 24 hours before putting fish in it. Fresh tap water also contains chemicals that can kill the fish.

◆ Safety *Review the safety guidelines in the front of your lab book.*

Wash your hands after handling the fish.

If eggs are not laid by three days after the fish are introduced, new partners should be tried.

◆ Procedure

1. Read the entire lab before continuing your investigation.

2. Brainstorm with other students on how to use the materials to set up a container for your fish to live in. Have the teacher approve your plans before you set up these containers with your fish.

3. Place your male and female bettas in separate containers for one or two days. Sketch the fish in Observations and record their behaviors in the Data Table. Observations may include periods of inactivity, gill movements, how the fish swims, and which fins it uses in different maneuvers. Note differences in the sexes, gill movements, and fin and tail formation.

4. After one or two days, introduce both fish into a larger breeding container. Observe your fish for 10 minutes every day, for up to two weeks. Watch for the events listed below. You may not see every event take place. Compare your observations with those of your classmates. Record all of the fish's behaviors each day and answer the questions in Observations.
   • initial reaction of the male and female bettas after being introduced into the same container
   • initial courtship behaviors
   • male building nest (between 24 hours and 5 days after introduction to female)
   • female approaching male and laying eggs
   • care of eggs
   • hatching of eggs into fry (Eggs hatch within 24 to 28 hours of being laid.) Use a hand lens to check the eggs in the water. Fry are very small and may be difficult to see without magnification.
   • care of fry by adults

FAMILY LIFE OF BETTAS (*continued*)

5. When your observations are complete, plan with the teacher how to continue to care for the fish.

◆ Observations

Sketch of Male and Female Fish

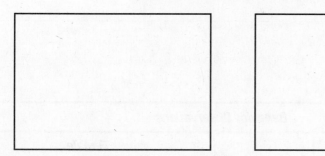

Male betta   *Female betta*

1. After placing the male and female fish into the same container, what happens to the bodies of the male and female fish when they first notice each other?

   Fins and gills are spread wide and the fish's colors become brighter. The female body's horizontal bar pattern (if present) is replaced by one of vertical bars.

2. What types of courtship behaviors do the fish show?

   Initially the fish may swim side by side at different times. Then the male becomes more aggressive. He may slap or lunge at the female and attempt to bite her. The female dodges these lunges and is usually not harmed as she hides among the aquatic plants.

3. While the male betta is building the nest, how do the behaviors of the two fish change?

   The male stops attacking the female and attempts to lure her to the nest. He approaches the female from the side. His fins and gills spread and he wags his body back and forth in an "S" shape. He then approaches his nest. This may occur several times with the male nipping the female if she refuses to come to the nest with him.

4. What behavior occurs before the eggs are laid and while the eggs are being laid?

   The female approaches the male in a submissive way with her head pointed downward. The male spreads his gills and fins and becomes gentle. The two fish circle and touch each other's sides with their noses. The female is upside down and the male is on his side. His body is curved over hers. It may take several of these embraces before eggs begin to drop.

5

FAMILY LIFE OF BETTAS *(continued)*

5. How do the adult bettas take care of the nest, eggs, and fry?

The male generally takes over all of the caretaking duties. He pushes the eggs into the nest by

placing them in his mouth. He continues working on the nest, making any repairs or enlarging as

necessary. After hatching, the male corrals the fry into the nest area.

_____

Data Table

Day	Behavior Observations	
	Male	**Female**
1–2; fish in separate containers		
3; fish are put into one container		

5

FAMILY LIFE OF BETTAS *(continued)*

◆ Analyze and Conclude

1. Did your bettas successfully reproduce? If not, suggest some possible reasons the pair did not breed.

Betta breeding was successful if fry are in the tank. If breeding was not successful, perhaps the

tanks were not properly prepared and maintained for the bettas. However, animal behavior is not

entirely predictable—sometimes pairs are not attracted to each other.

2. Why are the courtship behaviors of the male and female bettas important?

The courting behaviors ensure that males and females of the same species recognize one

another, so that they can reproduce.

◆ Critical Thinking and Applications

1. Why are the floating plants important to the female betta?

The female betta often uses the plants to hide from the male betta's attacks. They also supply

oxygen.

2. What methods could be used to prevent the male from hurting the female?

Methods may include using a much larger container with several aquarium objects on the bottom

of the container. A glass or plastic partition could be used to separate the two fish or the female

could be placed in a smaller, transparent container such as a jar. This jar could be floated in the

container holding the male betta.

3. Based on this investigation, what other questions might you like to investigate?

Possible questions could include: Do male bettas prepare bubble nests when females are not

present? What happens when two females are in the breeding container? Do the females ever

participate in caring for the eggs and fry?

FAMILY LIFE OF BETTAS (continued)

◆ More to Explore

New Problem Choose the response that interests you most from question 3 of Critical Thinking an Applications. Plan to investigate this problem.

Possible Materials Consider which materials you can use from this lab. What other materials might you need?

Safety Wash your hands after handling fish.

Procedure Make a hypothesis based on the question you want to investigate. Upon what do you base your hypothesis? Write your procedure on a separate sheet of paper. Include a control with which to compare results. Have the teacher approve your procedure before carrying out the investigation.

Observations Make a data table similar to the one for this lab.

Analyze and Conclude

1. Did your results support your hypothesis? Explain your answer.

   Answers will vary depending upon the question being investigated. Accept all reasonable

   answers.

2. Evaluate your procedure. What worked well? If you were to repeat this experiment, what parts of the procedure would you change?

   Answers will vary. Areas to be changed may include the physical setup of the fish container, the

   physical condition of the fish used, lack of an adequate control, or improper lighting and water

   temperature.

Help students design experiments that have clearly defined variables and controls, so that they will get valid results. Students may have to compare the results of their investigations to their previous investigations or to the investigations of other class members. Remember to check students' procedures before allowing them to begin their investigations.

LABORATORY INVESTIGATION

Cell Membranes and Permeability

Key Concept: Cell membranes are semipermeable. Both concentration and time affect diffusion of substances across the cell membrane.

Skills Focus: Observing, inferring, making models, controlling variables

Time Required: 60 minutes to set up Part A and do Part B; next day, 10 minutes to observe the beakers set up in Part A

1

◆ Pre-Lab Discussion

Can all substances move in both directions through a cell membrane? Why do some substances enter the cell through the cell membrane, while others do not? Sometimes you can use a model to answer questions like these. Part of this investigation models a living cell, so that you can observe changes that the cell membrane controls.

The cell membrane determines what diffuses into a cell. This characteristic of a cell membrane is called permeability. Many cells are semipermeable, which means that not all substances can pass through the cell membrane. Also, the amount of a substance that diffuses through a membrane is influenced by concentration and time.

In this investigation, you will model a cell membrane, determine if the membrane is permeable to certain substances, and find out if the concentration of a substance affects its diffusion.

1. Where is the cell membrane of a cell?

In cells with cell walls, the cell membrane is just inside the cell wall. In other cells, the cell

membrane is the boundary that separates the cell from its environment.

2. What types of materials pass through the cell membrane?

Materials the cell needs to survive pass through the cell membrane into the cell, including

food and oxygen. Waste products pass out through the cell membrane.

◆ Problem

How does a cell membrane work?

Advance Preparation: Make the following starch and iodine solutions (enough for one class).

Starch solution: Mix 20 g starch with 50 mL cold water to form a paste. Add the paste to 1 L boiling water. Stir for 2 minutes. Cool the solution.

Iodine solution for Part A: Use distilled water to make one liter of iodine solution by diluting stock solution from a biological supplier to 1–2% strength, the concentration typically sold over the counter in pharmacies. Alternate Materials: Dissolve 0.75 g potassium iodine in 1 L of distilled water, then add 0.15 g of crushed iodine. Store in a brown bottle.

Iodine solution for Part B: Use the iodine solution from Part A as the 100% solution. Make the 50% solution by combining equal amounts of distilled water and the iodine solution from Part A. Make the 10% solution by adding 9 parts of distilled water to every 1 part of the solution from Part A.

You may prefer to cut the potatoes into cubes before the lab.

CELL MEMBRANES AND PERMEABILITY *(continued)*

◆ **Materials** *(per group)*

plastic lunch bag
twist tie
100-mL graduated cylinder
starch solution
one 200-mL beaker
glass-marking pencil
water
iodine solution, three strengths
3 test tubes
test-tube rack
3 plastic cups
potato cubes
clock or watch with second hand
forceps
metric ruler

Alternative Materials: Use resealable bags instead of twist ties and regular plastic lunch bags. Dialysis tubing may be used instead of plastic lunch bags, but it is more expensive.

Teaching Tips: Different brands of plastic bags will have different rates of diffusion. Color changes are more obvious after 24 hours.

The starch at the bottom of the "cell" will change color first.

[Part B, Step 3] Using a single-edged razor blade, cut three potato cubes measuring 1 cm on each side for each group of students.

[Part B, Step 4] Dry the razor blade and use it to slice the potato cubes in half. Always dry the razor blade between cuttings.

◆ **Safety**   *Review the safety guidelines in the front of your lab book.*

Iodine is poisonous. Keep it away from your face, and wash your hands thoroughly after using it. Iodine will stain your hands and clothing, so be careful not to spill it. Handle glass objects carefully. If they break, tell the teacher. Do not pick up broken glass.

◆ **Procedure**

Part A: Model of a Cell Membrane

1. Write your name on a beaker with a glass-marking pencil. Then label three test tubes as follows: (1) "Iodine BEFORE," (2) "Iodine AFTER," and (3) "Starch."

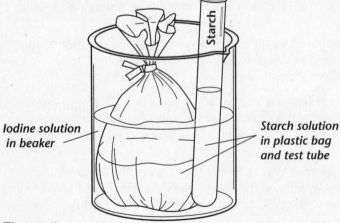

Iodine solution in beaker

Starch solution in plastic bag and test tube

Figure 1

CELL MEMBRANES AND PERMEABILITY *(continued)*

2. Fill the beaker with 40 mL of iodine solution. **CAUTION:** *Be careful with the iodine solution. If you spill any on yourself, immediately rinse the area with water and tell your teacher.* The iodine solution represents the environment outside the model cell.

3. Fill the test tube labeled "Iodine BEFORE" one-fourth full with iodine solution, and then set it aside in a test tube rack.

4. Fill a plastic lunch bag with 40 mL of starch solution, and seal the bag with a twist tie. Be careful not to spill starch onto the outside of the bag. Record the color of the solution in Data Table 1, and then place the bag into the solution in the beaker. The bag represents a cell.

5. Fill the "Starch" test tube about one-half full with starch solution, record the color of the solution, and then place the test tube in the beaker as shown in Figure 1. Let the beaker and its contents stand overnight.

6. The next day, remove the plastic bag and the test tube from the beaker. Record the colors of the solutions in the plastic bag and the test tube the "Color AFTER" column in Data Table 1.

7. Pour iodine solution from the beaker into the test tube labeled "Iodine AFTER" until the test tube has the same amount of solution as the test tube labeled "Iodine BEFORE."

8. Hold the two test tubes side by side, and look down through their openings. Record the colors of the solutions in the last line of Data Table 1.

Part B: Effect of Concentration on Diffusion

1. Label three plastic cups *100%*, *50%*, and *10%*.

2. Obtain about 30 mL of iodine solution at each strength, and pour that amount into the appropriate cup. Record these concentrations in Data Table 2.

3. Put a potato cube in each beaker. If necessary, add additional solution to cover the cube completely. Record the exact time the cubes were added to the solutions in Data Table 2.

4. After 30 minutes, use forceps to remove each potato cube from its solution. Keep track of which sample was in which beaker. The teacher will cut your potato cubes in half.

5. Use a metric ruler to determine the distance that the solution has diffused into each potato cube. See Figure 2. Read each distance to the closest 0.5 mm. In Data Table 2, record the distance that the solution diffused into each cube.
Tell students that the numbers given for the percents in Part B have been simplified.

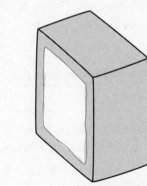

Figure 2

CELL MEMBRANES AND PERMEABILITY *(continued)*

◆ Observations

Data Table 1   Sample Data

Solution	Color Before	Color After
Starch in model cell	colorless or white	blue
Starch in test tube	colorless or white	colorless or white
Iodine in test tubes	dark rusty orange	light orange

Data Table 2   Sample Data

Potato Cube	Concentration of Substance	Time Cube Added to Solution	Distance of Diffusion (mm)
1	100%		2.0 mm
2	50%		1.0 mm
3	10%		less than 0.5 mm

◆ Analyze and Conclude

1. What part of the cell does the plastic bag represent?

The plastic bag represents the cell membrane.

2. What was the purpose of placing a test tube containing starch solution in the beaker of iodine?

The starch solution in the test tube was used as a control. It showed that starch left standing by itself for 24 hours did not change color.

3. When starch mixes with iodine, the mixture turns blue. What can you infer about the contents of the plastic bag?

The color change of the starch showed that iodine had mixed with the starch.

CELL MEMBRANES AND PERMEABILITY (*continued*)

4. a. Did starch move out of the bag? Give a reason for your answer.

No, the starch did not move out of the bag. The liquid outside the bag did not turn blue.

b. Did iodine move into the bag? Give a reason for your answer.

Yes, the iodine did move into the bag. When it mixed with the starch, it turned blue. Also, the iodine outside the bag was lighter after the experiment.

5. Based on your results, was the model cell membrane permeable or impermeable to iodine? To starch?

The model cell membrane is permeable to iodine and impermeable to starch.

6. In Part B, how did the concentration of iodine influence the amount of diffusion that took place?

Higher concentrations resulted in the iodine diffusing farther into the potato cubes.

◆ Critical Thinking and Applications

1. Cell membranes contain small holes, or pores. Pore size may determine why some chemicals can or cannot pass through a cell membrane. In your model, how might the size of the membrane pores compare to the size of the iodine molecules? Explain.

The membrane pores are larger than the iodine molecules. If they were not, the iodine molecules could not have moved into the model cell.

2. In your model, how might the size of the membrane pores compare to the size of the starch molecules? Explain.

The membrane pores are smaller than the starch molecules. If they were not, starch molecules would have moved into the iodine solution, and the mixture would have turned blue.

3. Based on what you learned from studying the diffusion of different concentrations, what might be one reason that sick or injured people wear oxygen masks? Explain.

Oxygen is needed for respiration. The oxygen from an oxygen mask is at a higher concentration than the concentration in air, so that oxygen will diffuse more rapidly into the blood cells that need it.

CELL MEMBRANES AND PERMEABILITY (continued)

◆ More to Explore

New Problem How does time affect the diffusion of substances across a cell membrane?

Possible Materials Consider which materials you can use from the previous part of the lab.

Safety Handle glass objects carefully. Ask your teacher to cut the potato cubes.

Procedure Develop a procedure to solve the problem. Predict what the results will show. Write your procedure on a separate sheet of paper. Have the teacher approve your procedure before you carry out the investigation.

Observations On a separate sheet of paper, make a data table like Data Table 2 in which to record your data and observations.

Analyze and Conclude Did your results support your prediction? Explain your reasoning.

Most students will correctly predict that, the longer the time, the farther the solution will diffuse into

the potato cube.

One possible procedure for this investigation would be to cut four 1-cm potato cubes. Keeping one as a control, put the remaining cubes in a beaker half-filled with iodine solution. Using forceps, remove one cube from the solution in the beaker every 10 minutes. Have the teacher slice open each cube. Measure the distance that the solution has diffused into each potato cube.

C-2   LABORATORY INVESTIGATION

Stomata Functions

Key Concept: Pairs of guard cells open and close tiny holes called stomata, which allow certain materials to pass into and out of the plant.

Skills Focus: Observing, inferring, measuring, calculating

Time Required: 60 minutes

◆ Pre-Lab Discussion

During photosynthesis, plants capture light energy and convert it into chemical energy that is stored in sugar molecules. The two raw materials needed for this process are water and carbon dioxide. Plants obtain water through their roots. They obtain carbon dioxide, a gas, through tiny openings, or pores, called stomata (singular *stoma*). Most of the stomata are located in the plant's leaves. The stomata must be open to allow carbon dioxide to pass into the leaf. The open stomata also allow water and oxygen to pass out of the leaf.

The opening and closing of the stomata is carried out by guard cells. When guard cells absorb water, they swell, and the stomata open, as shown in Figure 1. When guard cells lose water, the swelling is reduced, and the stomata close, as shown in Figure 2. Stomata are adaptations that help plants survive. When they are open, they allow carbon dioxide to enter. When they are closed, they help prevent the loss of water from the plant.

In this investigation, you will determine the number of stomata on different types of leaves.

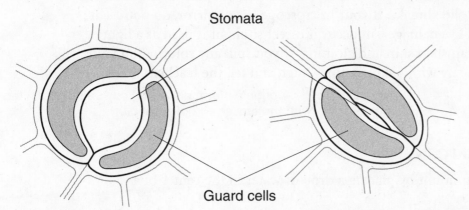

Stomata

Guard cells

Figure 1 *Stoma open*   **Figure 2** *Stoma closed*

1. Are the stomata usually open or closed during photosynthesis? Explain.

The stomata are open during photosynthesis. The open stomata enable plants to obtain a supply

of carbon dioxide, which they need for photosynthesis

2. Are stomata usually open or closed during dry periods? Explain.

The stomata are usually closed when it's dry. The closed stomata help the plant reduce the loss

of water.

STOMATA FUNCTIONS *(continued)*

◆ Problem

Approximately how many stomata are present on a typical leaf?

◆ Materials *(per group)*

microscope slide
coverslip
water
plastic dropper
lettuce leaf, fresh
forceps
iodine solution
compound microscope
paper towel
leaves from two different plants
metric ruler

The iodine solution should be about 1–2%, the strength usually sold over the counter in pharmacies.

Advance Preparation: For Part B, determine whether the types of leaves you are providing need to be blanched. The lower epidermis of some types of leaves—such as fresh lettuce and spinach, *Coleus, Tradescantia*, and *Peperomia*—usually peels off easily. Other leaves may need to be placed in boiling water for a few minutes before their epidermises become loose. Students can compare leaves from houseplants, garden plants, or wild-growing plants.

Alternate Materials: Ask students to bring in any plants they have.

Teaching Tips: You may wish to review how to focus the microscope. Discuss other precautions students should take to avoid damaging the microscopes or their slides.

IMPORTANT: The area of a leaf must be determined before it is blanched.

◆ Safety

Review the safety guidelines in the front of your lab book.

Wipe up spills immediately. Coverslips and slides break easily, so handle them carefully. Tell the teacher if a slide breaks. If your microscope has a mirror, do not use it to reflect direct sunlight. Eye damage can occur if direct sunlight is used as a light source. Iodine solution can stain skin and clothing. If you spill any solution on your skin, rinse it off immediately with cold running water, and tell the teacher.

Teaching Tip: If air bubbles form under the coverslip, gently tap the coverslip with the eraser end of a pencil.

◆ Procedure

Part A: Identifying Guard Cells

1. Prepare to make a wet mount by placing a drop of water in the center of a microscope slide.

2. Obtain a fresh lettuce leaf, and turn it over so that it curves downward. You are now looking at the lower epidermis, or bottom, of the lettuce leaf. Locate the large central rib in the leaf.

3. Bend the leaf backward against the curve until it breaks, as shown in Figure 3. Use forceps to carefully remove a small piece of the thin epidermal layer.

4. Spread out the epidermis specimen in the water drop on the slide. Be sure that no part of the epidermis is folded over.

STOMATA FUNCTIONS *(continued)*

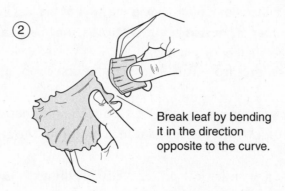

② Break leaf by bending it in the direction opposite to the curve.

③ Remove the thin layer (epidermis) from the bottom of the leaf.

④ Make a wet mount of the epidermis.

Figure 3

5. Add a drop of iodine to the water. **CAUTION:** *Iodine is poisonous, and it can cause stains. Handle it carefully.* Then hold a coverslip at the angle shown in Figure 3, and gently lower it over the specimen. Touch the edge of a paper towel to one side of the coverslip to remove excess water.

6. Observe the slide with a microscope under low power. **CAUTION:** *When using the microscope, follow safe procedures described on pages 1–5.* Look for different types of cells. Most of the cells you see will have an irregular shape. The rest of the cells, which are shaped like sausages, appear in pairs. The paired cells are the guard cells. Notice whether they are open or closed.

7. On the next page, make a labeled drawing of the epidermis under low power.

8. Examine a pair of guard cells under high power, and make a labeled drawing beside the one you drew in Step 7.

Part B: Comparing the Number of Stomata in Different Leaves

1. Obtain freshly cut leaves from two different kinds of plants. Record the types of plants you are using in the Data Table.

2. Use a metric ruler to determine the approximate length and width of the first leaf in millimeters. If the leaf has an irregular shape, estimate the length and width as closely as you can. Multiply the length times the width to find the area in square millimeters (mm^2). Record the area in the Data Table.

STOMATA FUNCTIONS *(continued)*

Teaching Tip: Another method for finding the area of the leaf involves tracing the leaf on graph paper, counting the number of squares in the leaf's area, then calculating the area of each square and multiplying by the number of squares.

3. Use the procedures from Part A to examine a section of the lower epidermis of the leaf.

4. Observe the slide under low power. Count the number of stomata in your field of view. Record this number in the appropriate column in the Data Table.

5. The field of view under low power is usually about 1.33 mm^2. To determine the total number of stomata in the leaf, use the equation below. Record the results in the Data Table.

$$\frac{\text{total area of the leaf in mm}^2}{1.33 \text{ mm}^2 \text{ in field of view}} \times \text{ number of stomata in field of view} = \underline{\quad} \text{ stomata}$$

6. Repeat Steps 2 through 5 for the second leaf. Wash your hands thoroughly when you are finished handling the materials.

◆ Observations

Epidermis	Guard Cells

STOMATA FUNCTIONS *(continued)*

Data Table

Type of Leaf	Area of Leaf (mm²)	Stomata in Lower Epidermis	
		In Field of View	In Total Leaf
Coleus	2,500	180	338,345
Pothos	2,900	500	1,090,225

◆ Analyze and Conclude

1. How do the number and shape of the guard cells compare with the number and shape of the cells around them?

The guard cells appear in pairs, and they have a sausagelike shape. The other cells, which have

irregular shapes, appear in much larger numbers.

2. How do guard cells control the stomata?

The guard cells open and close the stomata. When the guard cells are swollen because addi-

tional water has diffused into them, they are forced apart, and the stomata open. When the

excess water leaves the guard cells, they relax, and the stomata close.

3. How do the number of stomata compare for the two leaves you examined at low power?

Answers will vary. See the Data Table for samples. The field of view at low power is a little larger

than 1 square millimeter. Some leaves have as few as 40 stomata per square millimeter. Many

have more than 100 per square millimeter; some have more than 400 per square millimeter.

4. How did the number of stomata per leaf compare?

Answers will vary. See the sample answers in the Data Table.

◆ Critical Thinking and Applications

1. Can photosynthesis occur if the stomata are closed? Explain.

Little or no photosynthesis can take place when the stomata are closed because most of the

carbon dioxide needed as a raw material comes from the air. Carbon dioxide from the air cannot

enter the leaf when the stomata are closed.

2. The stomata tend to be closed during dry periods. How does that pattern aid the survival of the plant?

Plants give off water through open stomata, but they can conserve water when the stomata are

closed. Keeping the stomata closed may save the plant from drying out.

STOMATA FUNCTIONS (*continued*)

◆ More to Explore

Find a way to estimate the number of stomata on a specific plant. You could start with the number of stomata on a single leaf. You may be able to count or estimate the number of leaves on a plant directly.

However, if the plant is large and has a huge number of leaves, develop a method for estimating the number of leaves. For example, estimate the number of main branches of a tree; then estimate the number of smaller branches on the main branch; then estimate the number of leaves on a smaller branch; then multiply to find the total. (*Hint:* Use round numbers and any other math strategies you know to simplify your work.)

Be sure students understand that there are many acceptable ways to carry out these estimates. Urge them to explain why their chosen method is reasonable.

Sample for a coleus plant: About 300,000 stomata per leaf × 15 leaves = 4,500,000 stomata on the whole plant

Sample for a tree with 1 million stomata per leaf: About 10 main branches per tree × 10 smaller branches per main branch × 100 leaves per smaller branch = 10,000 leaves per tree; then 10,000 leaves per tree × 1 million stomata per leaf = 10 billion stomata per tree

If students have learned to use scientific notation, they can use that method of working with large numbers to carry out these calculations.

C-3   **LABORATORY INVESTIGATION**

Chromosomes and Inheritance

Key Concept: The traits of offspring are determined by the alleles of the parents.

Skills Focus: Observing, making models

Time Required: 40 minutes

◆ Pre-Lab Discussion

How are traits inherited? You can investigate this question by considering an imaginary animal called the unimonster. Suppose this animal has only one pair of chromosomes. Chromosomes carry genes, which control different genetic traits, such as hair color, height, and other physical characteristics. Different forms of a gene are called alleles. The presence of different alleles on the chromosomes of unimonsters determines whether they have one horn or two horns. During reproduction, parent unimonsters pass on alleles to their offspring.

In this investigation, you will determine the different allele combinations for the offspring of two unimonsters and figure out the number of horns the young unimonsters will have.

1. What are dominant and recessive alleles?

A dominant allele is one whose trait shows up in the organism when that allele is present. A

recessive allele is masked whenever the dominant allele is present.

2. Define *genotype* and *phenotype*.

An organism's genotype is its genetic makeup, meaning all the alleles on its chromosomes. An

organism's phenotype is its physical appearance.

3. What does it mean to say that an organism is homozygous for a trait? Heterozygous for a trait?

An organism is homozygous for a trait if it has two identical alleles for that trait; an organism is

heterozygous for a trait if it has two different alleles for a trait.

4. How do the numbers of chromosomes in cells compare with the number of chromosomes in sex cells? During reproduction, what fraction of chromosomes does each parent contribute to its offspring?

There are half as many chromosomes in a sex cell as in a body cell. Each parent contributes half

the normal number of chromosomes to its offspring.

◆ Problem

Advance Preparation: Get enough craft sticks so that you have 4 for each group of students (8 if students do the More to Explore).

How can you determine the traits of a unimonster's offspring?

Alternate Materials: If craft sticks are unavailable, strips of cardboard or acetate could be used. Using clear, colorless acetate strips for recessive alleles and colored strips for dominant alleles can be helpful.

CHROMOSOMES AND INHERITANCE *(continued)*

◆ **Materials** *(per group)*

marker
craft sticks

Teaching Tips:

[Step 2] Remind students that scientists generally represent a dominant allele with a capital letter, often the initial of the word that best describes the trait, and the recessive allele with the corresponding lowercase letter.

◆ **Procedure**

Figure 1

1. Figure 1 shows a mother and a father unimonster, each with different genetic traits. The allele for two horns is dominant over the allele for one horn. Look at the drawing and answer question 1 in Observations.

Mother Unimonster   *Father Unimonster*

2. The mother unimonster is heterozygous. This means that she has one allele for two horns and one allele for one horn. Each of her sex cells will have either a chromosome with the two-horn allele or a chromosome with the one-horn allele. Follow Figure 2 and steps 3 and 4 to make a model of the mother unimonster's sex chromosomes.

Figure 2

3. One of the mother unimonster's chromosomes will carry the two-horn allele. Write "M1" (for mother) at one end of a craft stick. At the other end of the stick, write *H* for the dominant two-horn allele.

4. The mother unimonster's other chromosome will carry the one-horn allele. Write "M2" at the end of a second stick. At the other end, write *h* for the recessive one-horn allele.

5. The father unimonster is homozygous (*hh*). Follow Figure 2 to make models of the father's chromosomes: F1 and F2.

6. During reproduction, the sex cells produced by the mother and father unimonsters combine to form a fertilized egg. The fertilized egg will grow into a young unimonster. Whether the young unimonster has one or two horns depends on the alleles on the chromosome contributed by each parent during reproduction. In Observations, use your chromosome models to answer questions 2–5. Remember that the allele for two horns is dominant. Anytime the dominant allele (*H*) is present, the unimonster will have two horns.

◆ **Observations**

1. Which unimonster parent has the dominant allele for number of horns? How do you know?

The mother unimonster has the dominant allele because she has two horns.

_____

_____

CHROMOSOMES AND INHERITANCE (continued)

2. During reproduction, the sex cells containing the chromosomes M1 and F1 combine to form a fertilized egg.

   a. Which alleles are on each of the chromosomes?

   H is on M1, and *h* is on F1.

   b. Will the young unimonster have one horn or two horns? Draw the appropriate number of horns on young unimonster 1 in Figure 3.

3. During reproduction, the sex cells containing the chromosomes M1 and F2 combine to form a fertilized egg.

   a. Which alleles are on each of the chromosomes?

   H is on M1, and *h* is on F2.

   b. Will the young unimonster have one horn or two horns? Draw the appropriate number of horns on young unimonster 2 in Figure 3.

4. During reproduction, the sex cells containing the chromosomes M2 and F1 combine to form a fertilized egg.

   a. Which alleles are on each of the chromosomes?

   h is on M2, and *h* is on F1.

   b. Will the young unimonster have one horn or two horns? Draw the appropriate number of horns on young unimonster 3 in Figure 3.

5. During reproduction, the sex cells containing the chromosomes M2 and F2 combine to form a fertilized egg.

   a. Which alleles are on each of the chromosomes?

   h is on M2, and *h* is on F2.

   b. Will the young unimonster have one horn or two horns? Draw the appropriate number of horns on young unimonster 4 in Figure 3.

Young Unimonster 1	Young Unimonster 2	Young Unimonster 3	Young Unimonster 4

Figure 3

◆ Analyze and Conclude

1. Which young unimonster(s) are homozygous and have one horn?

   Young unimonsters 3 and 4 are homozygous and have one horn.

CHROMOSOMES AND INHERITANCE *(continued)*

2. Which young unimonster(s) are heterozygous?

Young unimonsters 1 and 2 are heterozygous.

3. Are any young unimonster(s) homozygous with two horns? Explain.

No, because the only possible allele combination in which the alleles are identical would be *hh*,

which would produce only a one-horned unimonster.

◆ Critical Thinking and Applications

1. If a mother unimonster is homozygous and has two horns, and a father unimonster is homozygous and has one horn, what are the phenotypes and genotypes of the possible offspring? Remember that the two-horn allele is dominant.

All young unimonsters would have two horns, because all would be heterozygous (*Hh*).

_____

2. Predict the phenotypes and genotypes of the offspring of a mother unimonster and a father unimonster that are both heterozygous.

Based on the principles of probability, three fourths of the young unimonsters would have two

horns: one fourth would be homozygous (*HH*) and two fourths would be heterozygous (*Hh*).

The remaining fourth of the young unimonsters would have one horn, being homozygous (*hh*).

◆ More to Explore

Repeat the lab for the traits of curly hair versus straight hair. Assume that the curly-hair allele is dominant and the straight-hair allele is recessive. The mother is homozygous and has straight hair, while the father is heterozygous. Get four more craft sticks. Make all the combinations of different alleles. Determine all of the possible genotypes and the resulting phenotypes of the offspring. You may wish to use the Punnett square below to record the genotypes.

Father's Alleles for Curly Hair

	C	**c**
c	Cc	cc
c	Cc	cc

Mother's Alleles for Curly Hair

Remind students that Punnett square results show only probabilities. The traits of offspring from actual matings may not match the predictions.

Based on the principles of probability, two of four, or 50%, of the young unimonsters would have curly hair (Cc), and two of four, or 50%, of the young unimonsters would have straight hair (cc).

How Are Genes on Sex Chromosomes Inherited?

Key Concepts: Some genetic disorders, such as hemophilia and colorblindness, are sex-linked traits.

Skills Focus: inferring, making models, creating data tables

Time Required: 90 minutes

◆ Pre-Lab Discussion

Sex-linked genes are genes on the X and Y chromosomes. Traits controlled by these genes are called sex-linked traits. Two sex-linked traits include hemophilia and colorblindness. Hemophilia is a genetic disorder in which a person's blood clots slowly or not at all. If a person has the dominant allele X^H, he or she will have normal blood. If a person has only the recessive allele X^h, he or she will have hemophilia.

Red-green colorblindness is also a genetic disorder. In this disorder, the person does not see red and green properly. This person will see green as gray and red as yellow. If a person has at least one dominant allele X^C, he or she will not have colorblindness. If a person has only the recessive allele X^c, he or she will have colorblindness.

In this investigation, you will see how hemophilia and colorblindness are inherited.

1. How are the alleles for sex-linked genes passed from parent to child?

They are passed from parent to child on the sex chromosomes, which are in the egg and the

sperm along with the other chromosomes.

2. How many X and Y chromosomes do males have? How many of each do females have?

Males have one X chromosome and one Y chromosome. Females have two X chromosomes.

3. Define the carrier of a trait in terms of alleles.

A carrier is someone who has a recessive allele and a dominant allele for a specific trait.

◆ Problem

How are hemophilia and red-green colorblindness inherited?

◆ Materials *(per group)*

8 pennies
tape
pen
cloth to cover desktop

Teaching Tips: If students have a hard time understanding why sex-linked genes are distributed as they are, refer them to their answer to question 2 in the Pre-Lab Discussion.

HOW ARE GENES ON SEX CHROMOSOMES INHERITED? *(continued)*

◆ Procedure

Figure 1

Part A: Hemophilia

Use the following information and procedures for families 1 and 2 to model the inheritance of hemophilia. Keep in mind that only the X chromosome can carry the allele for hemophilia. A female can be $X^H X^H$, $X^H X^h$, or $X^h X^h$. A male can be $X^H Y$ or $X^h Y$.

Coin 1 Male
Front   Back

Family 1. Parents do not have hemophilia; mother is a carrier of hemophilia ($X^H X^h$).

Coin 2 Female
Front   Back

1. Place tape on two coins and mark them as shown in Figure 1. These coins represent the alleles of the parents. The coin with the Y chromosome on the back is the father. The coin with an X on each side is the mother.

Figure 2

2. Spread out a piece of cloth on your desk or tabletop. Shake the coins in your hands and drop them onto the cloth.

Coin 3 Male
Front   Back

3. Read the combination of letters that appears. This combination represents the result that might appear in a child of these parents.

Coin 4 Female
Front   Back

4. Use a tally mark in the correct row to record this combination of alleles in Data Table 1 in the column marked "Children Observed."

5. Repeat shaking, dropping, reading, and tallying the coins a total of 40 times. Record the totals of tally marks for each combination in Data Table 1.

Figure 3

Family 2. Father has hemophilia; mother is a carrier of hemophilia.

Coin 5 Male
Front   Back

6. Place tape on two coins and mark them as shown in Figure 2.

7. Repeat steps 2–5 and tally the combinations in Data Table 2.

Coin 6 Female
Front   Back

Part B: Colorblindness

The allele for red-green colorblindness is also located on the X chromosome. A female can be $X^C X^C$, $X^C X^c$, or $X^c X^c$. A male can be either $X^C Y$ or $X^c Y$.

Figure 4

Family 3. Father is colorblind; mother has two dominant alleles ($X^C X^C$).

Coin 7 Male
Front   Back

1. Place tape on two coins and mark them as shown in Figure 3.

2. Repeat steps 2–5 of Part A and tally the combinations in Data Table 3.

Family 4. Parents are not colorblind; mother is heterozygous.

Coin 8 Female
Front   Back

3. Place tape on two coins and mark them as shown in Figure 4.

4. Repeat steps 2–5 of Part A and tally the combinations in Data Table 4.

HOW ARE GENES ON SEX CHROMOSOMES INHERITED? *(continued)*

◆ Observations

Data from a single student's coin tosses may not match the probabilities that would be obtained from a Punnett square. You may want to combine all the students' results and then compare them with results from a Punnett square.

Data Table 1   Sample Data

Children of $X^H Y$ Father and $X^H X^h$ Mother		
Allele Combination	**Children Observed**	**Total**
$X^H X^H$	ЖЖ ‖‖‖	9
$X^H X^h$	ЖЖ ЖЖ ‖	12
$X^h X^h$		
$X^H Y$	ЖЖ ‖‖‖	8
$X^h Y$	ЖЖ ЖЖ ‖	11

Data Table 2   Sample Data

Children of $X^h Y$ Father and $X^H X^h$ Mother		
Allele Combination	**Children Observed**	**Total**
$X^H X^H$		
$X^H X^h$	ЖЖ ‖‖‖	8
$X^h X^h$	ЖЖ ЖЖ	10
$X^H Y$	ЖЖ ЖЖ ‖‖‖‖	14
$X^h Y$	ЖЖ ‖‖‖	8

Data Table 3   Sample Data

Children of $X^c Y$ Father and $X^c X^c$ Mother		
Allele Combination	**Children Observed**	**Total**
$X^C X^C$		
$X^C X^c$	ЖЖ ЖЖ ЖЖ ЖЖ ‖	22
$X^c X^c$		
$X^c Y$	ЖЖ ЖЖ ЖЖ ‖‖‖	18
$X^c Y$		

HOW ARE GENES ON SEX CHROMOSOMES INHERITED? *(continued)*

Data Table 4   Sample Data

Children of X^cY Father and X^cX^c Mother		
Allele Combination	**Children Observed**	**Total**
X^cX^c	~~IIII~~ III	8
X^cX^c	~~IIII~~ ~~IIII~~ I	11
X^cX^c		
X^cY	~~IIII~~ ~~IIII~~	10
X^cY	~~IIII~~ ~~IIII~~ I	11

◆ Analyze and Conclude

1. a. How many alleles for hemophilia do females have?

two

    b. How many alleles for red-green colorblindness do females have?

two

    c. How many alleles for hemophilia do males have?

one

    d. How many alleles for red-green colorblindness do males have?

one

2. Why is there a difference in the number of alleles for hemophilia and red-green colorblindness between males and females?

The male has a Y chromosome, and there are no genes for hemophilia and red-green

colorblindness on the Y chromosome.

3. Why are only females carriers for hemophilia? For red-green colorblindness?

Only females can be carriers for both because they carry two alleles for the traits.

4. Which of the parents can pass the allele for hemophilia to a son? Explain.

Only a mother can pass the allele to a son because a father gives a son only a Y chromosome,

which does not include the allele.

HOW ARE GENES ON SEX CHROMOSOMES INHERITED? *(continued)*

5. Which of the parents can pass the allele for hemophilia to a daughter? Explain.

Both a mother and father can pass an allele for hemophilia to a daughter because both parents

give an X chromosome, which does include the allele.

6. In Family 3, why are there no colorblind children even though one of the parents is colorblind?

The mother has 2 dominant alleles for normal vision. Any child who inherits the recessive allele

for colorblindness will also inherit a dominant allele for normal color vision. The dominant allele

will mask the recessive allele.

◆ Critical Thinking and Applications

1. The brother of a woman's father has hemophilia. Her father does not have hemophilia, but she is concerned that her son might. Could she have passed the allele for hemophilia to her son? Explain.

If the woman's father had the allele on his X chromosome, he would have had hemophilia, but he

does not. Thus, the X chromosome she received from him does not have the allele. It is possible

that she received from her mother an X chromosome that carries the allele. In that case, she

could pass the allele to her son.

2. A woman's father is colorblind. She marries a colorblind man. Might their son be colorblind? Might their daughter be colorblind? Explain.

The son and the daughter could be colorblind. The woman has at least one allele for

colorblindness. The father also has the allele.

3. What is the probability that a carrier and a person who has a sex-linked genetic disorder will have a son with the disorder? A daughter? Use your data and a Punnett square to answer these questions.

The probability is approximately 50 percent for both sons and daughters.

4. What is the probability that a carrier and a person who does not have a sex-linked genetic disorder will have a son with the disorder? A daughter?

There is an approximately 50-percent probability of having a son with the disorder and no chance

of having a daughter with the disorder.

HOW ARE GENES ON SEX CHROMOSOMES INHERITED? *(continued)*

◆ More to Explore

Use the Punnett squares to solve the following problems.

1. Two parents have the following alleles for hemophilia: $X^H X^h$ and $X^H Y$. What is the probability that a son will have hemophilia? That a daughter will have hemophilia?

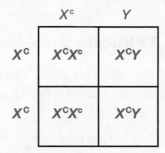

A son would have a 50-percent probability of having hemophilia. A daughter would have no

chance of having hemophilia.

2. Two parents have the following alleles for colorblindness: $X^C X^C$ and $X^c Y$. What is the probability that a son will be colorblind? A daughter?

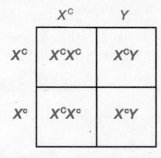

None of the children would have colorblindness. The probability is zero.

3. Two parents have the following alleles for colorblindness: $X^C X^c$ and $X^C Y$. What is the probability that a son will be colorblind? A daughter?

A son would have a 50-percent probability of having colorblindness. A daughter would have no

chance of being colorblind.

4. Do your data from the lab support the results from the Punnett squares above? Explain.

For the sons considered in questions 1 and 3, the data from Data Tables 1 and 4 will probably

be close to the 50-percent probabilities. For the daughters considered in these questions, the

data will show a probability of zero for hemophilia or colorblindness. The data from Data Table 3

should confirm that none of the children considered in question 2 would have colorblindness.

C-5   LABORATORY INVESTIGATION

Variation in a Population

Key Concepts: Variations occur in all species.

Skills Focus: Observing, inferring, measuring, graphing

Time Required: 40 minutes

◆ Pre-Lab Discussion

Are you and your friends all exactly alike? Of course not. Although you are all members of one species, you are different in many ways. These differences are called variations and exist in all species.

Some variations are inherited by the offspring of an organism. Most inherited variations are neutral, that is, they do not affect the organism's survival. Helpful inherited variations are called adaptations. Harmful inherited variations make the organism less well-suited to its environment. Better-adapted organisms are more likely to reproduce and pass beneficial traits to their offspring. This process is called natural selection.

In this investigation, you will observe variations in two types of plants and in your class population.

1. What does *variations* mean?

differences displayed by organisms of the same species

_____

2. What variations exist among members of your class?

Answers will vary but may include eye color, skin color, height, hair color and texture, nose

shape, and ear shape.

◆ Problem

How can you measure the variations in plant and animal populations?

◆ Materials *(per group)*

10 large lima beans
10 leaves of the same species
metric ruler
graph paper
3 colored pencils

Advance Preparation: Have students collect leaves before the experiment.

Alternative Materials: Other large seeds, such as kidney beans, pumpkin seeds, and pinto beans, may be used instead of the lima beans. Leaves can be from a variety of trees or house plants.

◆ Safety 🖐   *Review the safety guidelines in the front of your lab book.*

Do not eat the lima beans.

VARIATION IN A POPULATION (continued)

◆ Procedure

Part A: Variation in Plant Species

1. Obtain 10 large lima beans and 10 leaves of the same species of tree.

2. Measure the length of each lima bean and leaf blade in millimeters. See Figure 1. Record your measurements, rounded to the nearest millimeter, in Data Table 1.

3. Notice in Figure 1 the petiole of the leaf. Measure the length of the petiole of each leaf. Record your measurements, rounded to the nearest millimeter, in Data Table 1.

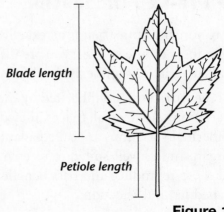

Blade length

Petiole length

Figure 1

4. Record on the chalkboard your measurements for each of the plants so that all groups' data can be seen.

5. Using data from the entire class, record the range in lengths for the lima beans, leaf blades, and petioles. Record the class findings in Data Tables 2, 3, and 4. Fill in the first row of each table with the lengths, from shortest to longest, using increments of one millimeter. Add more columns to the data tables if necessary.

6. Record the class's total number of each size of lima bean, leaf blade, and petiole in the second row of Data Tables 2, 3, and 4.

7. Using the data in Data Table 2, construct a line graph for the lima-bean lengths on a sheet of graph paper. Label the *x*-axis "Lima bean length (mm)" and the *y*-axis "Number of beans."

8. Using the data in Data Tables 3 and 4, construct line graphs for the leaf-blade lengths and the petiole lengths on your graph paper. Label the *x*-axis "Leaf blade and petiole length (mm)" and the *y*-axis "Number of leaves." Use a different colored pencil to graph each set of data and include a key for each graph.

Part B: Variation in Hand Spans

1. Measure your hand span. The measurement should be made from the top of the thumb to the tip of the little finger, as shown in Figure 2. Round off the measurement to the nearest centimeter. Record your hand span in a class chart on the chalkboard.

Hand span

Figure 2

2. After all your classmates have recorded their hand spans in the class chart, transfer the results to Data Table 5. Your results will show the total number of hands having the same hand span.

3. Construct a line graph of the results on a sheet of graph paper. Label the *x*-axis "Hand-span length (cm)" and the *y*-axis "Number of students."

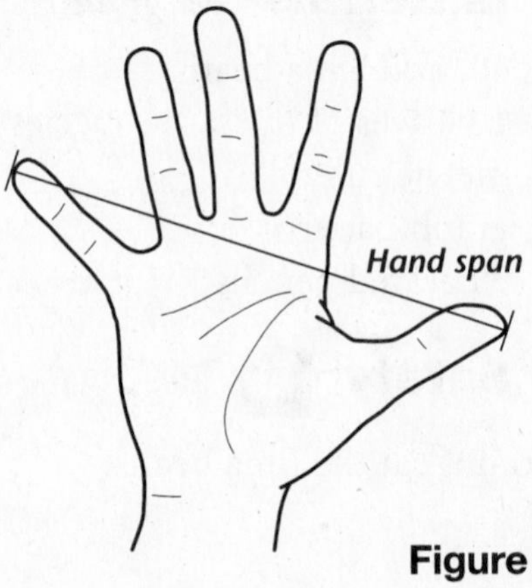

Name _____ Date _____ Class _____

◆ Observations

Data Table 1   Sample Data

Length (mm) (Group Data)										
	1	**2**	**3**	**4**	**5**	**6**	**7**	**8**	**9**	**10**
Lima beans	21	20	20	21	22	23	16	22	18	19
Leaf blades	90	85	90	86	91	87	94	88	92	88
Petioles	78	64	71	80	66	74	95	68	74	71

Data Table 2

Class Data for Lima Bean Lengths											
Length of lima bean (mm)	15	16	17	18	19	20	21	22	23	24	25
Total number of beans of this size											

Data Table 3

Class Data for Leaf Blade Lengths											
Length of leaf blade (mm)	84	85	86	87	88	89	90	91	92	93	94
Total number of leaf blades of this size											

Data Table 4

Class Data for Petiole Lengths											
Length of petiole (mm)	64	66	68	71	74	78	80	85	89	92	95
Total number of petioles of this size											

Data Table 5

Class Data for Hand-Span Lengths														
Length of hand span (cm)	15	16	17	18	19	20	21	22	23	24	25	26	27	28
Total number of hand spans of this size	1	0	1	1	2	4	8	6	5	3	2	1	0	0

◆ Analyze and Conclude

1. In what length range are most of the lima beans? Most of the leaf blades? Most of the petioles?

Most samples should fall close to the middle of the length range.

VARIATION IN A POPULATION *(continued)*

2. In what length range are the fewest beans? The fewest blades? The fewest petioles?

The fewest samples should be at the extremes of the length range.

3. What is the general shape of the graphs of the lengths of the lima beans, leaf blades, and petioles? What does the shape of the graphs indicate about these lengths?

Each graph should be shaped like a bell or an upside-down U. Most of the lengths are near the average, with fewer lengths at both extremes.

4. Which hand-span length occurs most often? Least often?

Answers will vary but should be based on Data Table 5 and the class graph.

5. What is the general shape of the graph of hand spans? What does the shape of the graph indicate about the hand spans of students in your class?

The shape of the graph should look like the graphs for beans and leaves, indicating that most measurements are near the average, with fewer measurements at both extremes.

◆ Critical Thinking and Applications

1. List two ways in which a large hand span might be a useful human adaptation.

Answers will vary but might include prehistoric needs to grasp large tools and weapons such as big sticks, carry large loads, and fight off predators with bare hands.

2. Do you think having many seeds in a pod would be a more useful adaptation for a bean plant than having only a few seeds? Give a reason for your answer.

Answers may vary. In general, the more seeds a pod has, the better is the chance that some of them will land in suitable growing places.

3. Why might having large leaves be a harmful characteristic for a desert plant?

Answers may vary. Desert plants need to conserve water, and leaf surfaces lose a lot of water in very hot conditions.

◆ More to Explore

Students with severe allergies to peanuts should not participate in this activity.

Investigate variations that occur in the lengths of peanut shells. Make your measurements and graph the results as you did in the previous part of this lab. Do you think that all organisms of the same species show variation in all of their traits? Give a reason for your answer. **CAUTION:** *Do not eat the peanuts.*

The results for peanuts should be similar to the variations found in the lima bean, leaf, and hand studies. Sample size will influence results. All organisms of the same species show variations in different traits. Heredity and environment both affect how traits vary.

D-1   **LABORATORY INVESTIGATION**

Exploring Body Tissue and Body Systems

Key Concepts: The human body is made up of many tissues and organ systems working together.

Skills Focus: Observing, inferring, predicting, classifying

Time Required: 40 minutes

1

◆ Pre-Lab Discussion

Your body has four levels of organization. The smallest unit of life is the cell. Some organisms consist of only one cell, and all the organism's life activities take place in that cell. Most organisms have many cells, however, and their cells are specialized to perform specific functions. In many-celled organisms, like yourself, cells that work together to perform a function form a tissue. An organ, in turn, consists of different kinds of tissue that work together to perform a function. Your heart, lungs, and skin are organs. Groups of organs that work together to perform a specific function form an organ system.

In this investigation, you will look at several kinds of tissue. You will also explore which body systems work during a common activity.

1. What are the four basic types of human tissue?

The four basic types of human tissue are muscle, nerve, connective, and epithelial tissues.

_____

2. Name the eleven organ systems in the human body.

The eleven organ systems are the muscular, skin, digestive, circulatory, respiratory, excretory,

immune, nervous, skeletal, endocrine, and reproductive systems.

_____

_____

◆ Problem

What do different human tissues look like? What organ systems work together to perform a simple activity?

◆ Possible Materials (per group)

microscope
prepared slides of skeletal muscle, surface skin cells, cartilage, and brain tissue
notebook

Advance Preparation: Biological supply houses sell prepared slides of human tissues.

Teaching Tip: Refer students to page 1 of their lab manual for a review of how to use a microscope.

EXPLORING BODY TISSUE AND BODY SYSTEMS *(continued)*

1

◆ **Safety** *Review the safety guidelines in the front of your lab book.*

Always use both hands to pick up or carry a microscope. Hold the microscope base with one hand, and hold the microscope with your other hand. Handle glass slides carefully.

◆ **Procedure**

1. Using the microscope, first on low power and then on high power, observe a prepared slide of skeletal muscle.

2. Under Observations, draw the muscle tissue that you observe. Note the magnification you use to view it.

3. Using the microscope, first on low power and then on high power, observe a prepared slide of surface skin cells.

4. Under Observations, draw the skin cells that you observe. Note the magnification you use to view them.

5. Using the microscope, first on low power and then on high power, observe a prepared slide of cartilage.

6. Under Observations, draw the cartilage that you observe. Note the magnification you use to view it.

7. Using the microscope, first on low power and then on high power, observe a prepared slide of brain tissue.

8. Under Observations, draw the brain tissue that you observe. Note the magnification you use to view it.

9. Slide a notebook across the lab counter to one of your partners. What does your body have to do to move the notebook? What does your partner's body have to do to catch the notebook before it falls off the counter?

   The person sliding the notebook must use his or her nervous system to determine how far it

   must travel to the person receiving it and decide how much force should be applied. The slider

   then uses his or her muscles to move the bones of the hand, arm, and back, making a motion

   that slides the notebook. Similarly, the receiver must use his or her nervous, skeletal, and

   muscular systems to perceive when the

   notebook is approaching and to catch it.

EXPLORING BODY TISSUE AND BODY SYSTEMS *(continued)*

◆ Observations

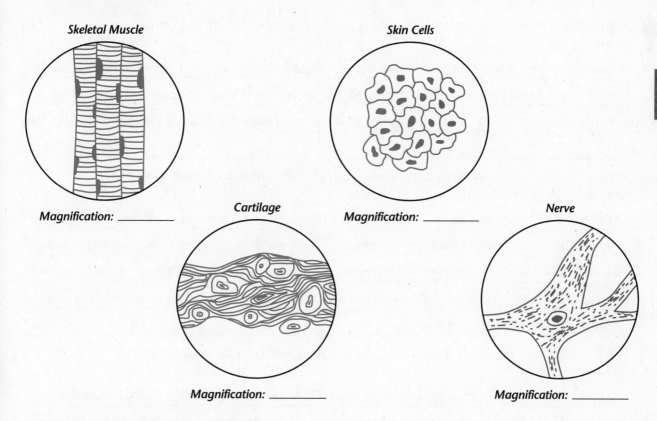

Skeletal Muscle

Magnification: _____

Skin Cells

Magnification: _____

Cartilage

Magnification: _____

Nerve

Magnification: _____

◆ Analyze and Conclude

1. What type of tissue is cartilage? Surface skin? Brain tissue?

connective tissue; epithelial tissue; nerve tissue

2. Choose two of the slides you observed. Compare and contrast the two tissues in the slides.

Answers will vary. A similarity for all tissues is that they are made of cells. A difference is that the

cells are grouped in different ways.

3. What organ systems must work together for a person to successfully slide a notebook across a table? Give reasons for your answer.

Sliding and stopping a notebook require coordination of muscular, skeletal, and nervous

systems. The brain of the nervous system must interpret and coordinate information from the

environment to determine how hard to push. Then the muscles and bones work together to

actually slide and stop the object.

EXPLORING BODY TISSUE AND BODY SYSTEMS *(continued)*

◆ Critical Thinking and Applications

1. Your hand contains all four basic tissue types. Describe one function of each tissue type in your hand.

Answers will vary. Sample answer: Nerve tissue carries information about what the hand touches.

Muscle tissue helps the hand grasp things. Skin is an epithelial tissue that protects the nerves

and muscles. Cartilage is connective tissue that cushions the ends of the finger bones at the

joints.

2. Predict whether other animals have tissues that look like human tissues. Give a reason for your prediction.

Answers will vary. Animal tissues should reflect similarities or differences in the animals'

functioning. For example, if students compare invertebrate animals to humans, they might say

they don't have similar connective tissue because body support is very different. If they compare

vertebrate animals to humans, they might say that the connective tissues would be quite similar

because the body functions are alike.

3. What organ systems are working while you are sleeping? Give reasons for your answer.

Answers may vary. All involuntary organ systems would be working, such as skin, circulatory,

respiratory, immune, nervous, and endocrine systems. The digestive system could be working on

food. Muscles often twitch while dreaming, which would also move the skeletal system. The

excretory system is filtering wastes and forming urine. The reproductive system could also be

active, such as during menstruation.

◆ More to Explore

Design a physical activity that uses a specific organ system, such as the muscle system or the respiratory system. Write your procedure on a separate sheet of paper. Have the teacher approve your procedure before you carry out the investigation. What other systems are also involved? Can you think of specific events that could trigger other organ systems to work hard?

Activities that could target the respiratory and circulatory systems (and muscular and skeletal systems) could include any type of physical activity. Intense physical activity can result in heavy breathing and sweating (involving skin) and require additional oxygen. Cuts and other skin invasions could trigger the immune system to work harder. A heavy meal may tax the digestive system and make the endocrine system produce more insulin.

Examining Bones, Muscles, and Skin

Key Concepts: Each part of the human body has specific functions. The structure of the part is often related to its functions.

Skills Focus: Observing, inferring, communicating, controlling variables

Time Required: 40 minutes; Parts A and B are not dependent on each other. If time is a factor, the parts can be done separately, with appropriate questions chosen for each part. More to Explore should be done with Part B.

◆ Pre-Lab Discussion

Have you ever seen a picture of a jellyfish? The body of the animal has no rigid shape because it has no bones. Think of what your body would be like without bones. Bones provide the structure needed for you to stand upright and to hold this paper. Bones work closely with muscles to allow your body to move. Muscles also keep important parts of your body, such as your heart, working. In Part A of the following investigation, you will examine bone and muscle cells to see how their structure relates to what they do.

Of course, you can't see your bones and muscles. They are covered by the largest organ in your body—your skin. What does skin do? One of its many purposes is to protect the inside of your body against injury and disease. It also contains sense receptors that give you your sense of touch. In Part B of this investigation, you will examine one important function of the sense of touch—the ability to distinguish different temperatures.

1. What are the three types of muscles? Explain how they differ.

Skeletal muscles are striated muscles that are voluntary and move bones. Smooth muscles are

not striated and are involuntary. Cardiac muscles are in the heart, are striated, and involuntary.

2. Name three functions of bones and three functions of skin.

Bones protect internal organs, produce blood cells, and store certain minerals until the body

needs them. Skin regulates body temperature, eliminates wastes, and produces Vitamin D.

◆ Problem

How are the three types of muscle cells and bone cells alike, and how do they differ? How does your body sense differences in temperature?

Alternative Materials: Any identical containers can be used for Part B and More to Explore.

◆ Materials *(per group)*

prepared slides of
    smooth muscle
    skeletal muscle
    cardiac muscle
    cross-section of compact human bone
microscope

3 transparent plastic cups
cold water
room-temperature water
paper towel
clock or watch with a second hand

EXAMINING BONES, MUSCLES, AND SKIN *(continued)*

◆ **Safety** *Review the safety guidelines in the front of your lab book.*

Use caution when handling the microscope slides. If they break, tell the teacher. Do not pick up broken glass.

Advance Preparation: Review with students the proper use and care of a microscope. Set out large containers of water several hours before class so that they can reach a consistent room temperature. If materials are limited, you may want to set up stations, one each for Part A, Part B (cold water), and, perhaps, More to Explore (warm water) so that different students can be working on different parts of the investigation at the same time. Test the water before the lab starts to be sure temperatures aren't too cold or hot.

◆ **Procedure**

Part A: Observing Bone and Muscle

1. Using the microscope, first on low power and then on high power, examine a prepared slide of skeletal muscle. Look for nuclei in the cells.

2. In Part A of Observations, sketch the skeletal muscle tissue that you see. Note the magnification you use to view it. Label details of the cells such as striations (stripes) and nuclei.

3. Using the microscope, first on low power and then on high power, examine a prepared slide of cardiac muscle. Look for nuclei in the cells.

4. In Observations, sketch the cardiac muscle tissue that you see. Note the magnification you use to view it. Label details of the cells.

5. Using the microscope, first on low power and then on high power, examine a prepared slide of smooth muscle. Look for nuclei in the cells.

6. In Observations, sketch the smooth muscle tissue that you see. Note the magnification you use to view it. Label details of the cells.

7. Using the microscope, first on low power and then on high power, examine a prepared slide of compact bone. Look for cells and structural features.

8. In Observations, sketch the bone tissue that you see. Note the magnification you use to view it. Label details of the structures.

Part B: Examining the Sense of Touch

1. Place a cup of cold water and a cup of room-temperature water on two or three paper towels in front of you. Put your index finger in the cold water for about 5 seconds.

2. Remove your finger from the cold water, and put it in the room-temperature water. Immediately tell your partner how the water feels. For this step and each of the following steps, have your partner record all your observations in the Data Table.

3. Leave your finger in the room-temperature water. Describe how the water feels after a few minutes.

4. While one finger is still in the water, put your index finger from your other hand in the same cup.

5. Remove both fingers from the water. Put your original finger into the cold water and leave it there for about 20 seconds. Then move it into the room-temperature water. Leave your finger in the cup for a few minutes.

EXAMINING BONES, MUSCLES, AND SKIN *(continued)*

6. Put your other index finger into the room-temperature water. Compare how the water feels now to how it felt in Step 3.

7. Remove both fingers from the water.

◆ Observations

Part A

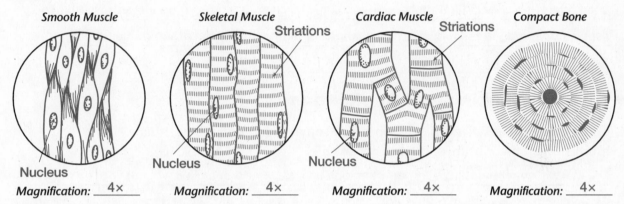

Smooth Muscle

Nucleus

Magnification: ___4×___

Skeletal Muscle — Striations

Nucleus

Magnification: ___4×___

Cardiac Muscle — Striations

Nucleus

Magnification: ___4×___

Compact Bone

Magnification: ___4×___

Part B
Data Table   Sample Data

Step	What to Observe	Observations
2	How did the water feel when you first put your finger in the room-temperature water?	It felt as if it were warm water.
3	How did the water feel when you left your finger in the room-temperature water?	The water felt less warm as time passed.
4	How did the water feel to your other finger when you put it in the room-temperature water?	The water felt cooler to this finger than to the other finger.
5	How did the water feel when you first put your finger in the room-temperature water this second time?	It felt as if it were warm water.
6	How did the water feel when you left your finger in the room-temperature water this second time?	It took longer for the water to feel room-temperature rather than warm.
7	How does the water feel now compared to how it felt in Step 5?	There was a greater difference in perceived temperature than in Step 5.

◆ Analyze and Conclude

1. What structure can you clearly see in the muscle cells that you cannot see in the bone? Describe this structure.

Students should see nuclei—rounded or elliptical structures generally in the middle of the cells.

Answers might also note that the bone slide is a cross-section.

EXAMINING BONES, MUSCLES, AND SKIN (continued)

2. What is the main structural difference between cardiac and skeletal muscle?

The cardiac fibers have side branches. Because the fibers are more strongly held together, the

muscles are stronger and exhibit less fatigue.

3. Did the sensors in your fingers respond in the same manner to the room-temperature water? Explain your answer.

The fingers' sensors did not respond in the same manner to the room-temperature water. The

sensors appeared to respond more to changes in temperature rather than to the actual

temperature of the water.

2

◆ Critical Thinking and Applications

1. Can you infer that striations, or stripes, have anything to do with whether a muscle is voluntary or involuntary? Explain.

No, there is no relationship between striations and whether a muscle is voluntary or involuntary.

For example, both cardiac and skeletal muscles are striated, but skeletal muscle is controlled by

your will and cardiac muscle is not.

2. You looked at a cross-section of a bone. Describe how you could model the interior structure of an entire bone.

Answers may vary but should indicate that the bone in the cross-section could be modeled with

concentric tubes.

3. Suppose one person has been outdoors on a hot day and another person has been in an air-conditioned room. They both go into a room of average temperature. Use your results from Part B to explain the temperature sensed by both people in the room of average temperature.

The person who had been outside would sense the room as cool, and the person who had been

in the air-conditioned room would sense the room as warm.

◆ More to Explore

Repeat Part B of this experiment, using warm water in place of cold water.
CAUTION: *Do not use water that is hot enough to burn you or cause discomfort.*
Record all of your observations in a table similar to the one used in Part B.

After placing their fingers in the warm water for 5 seconds, students' observations should be the opposite of those in the Data Table for Part B; that is, for steps in which the water felt warmer in Part B, the water should feel cooler in More to Explore. Where the water felt cooler, it should now feel warmer.

D-3   **LABORATORY INVESTIGATION**

Nutrient Identification

Key Concepts: Nutrients in food can be identified using simple tests.

Skills Focus: Observing, predicting, classifying, posing questions

Time Required: 40 minutes

◆ Pre-Lab Discussion

Do you know what foods have a lot of protein? Plenty of carbohydrates? Carbohydrates, fats, proteins, vitamins, minerals, and water are all nutrients in your food. You can detect the presence of some of these nutrients by taste. For example, all foods that taste sweet contain some form of sugar unless they are artificially sweetened. On the other hand, some foods, such as milk and onions, contain sugar but do not taste sweet. Therefore, scientists do not rely on taste or appearance to determine what nutrients a food contains. They use other tests to identify nutrients.

In this investigation, you will perform tests to detect starches, sugars, and proteins in foods.

3

1. What are the two groups of carbohydrates? What are their common names?

   Simple carbohydrates are called sugars, and complex carbohydrates are called starches.

   _____

2. What functions do proteins perform in your body?

   Proteins repair cells and permit cell growth in the body. They also provide energy.

   _____

◆ Problem

Advance Preparation: Encourage students to bring in food samples to be tested for the presence of starches, sugars, and proteins. Mix one part honey with about five parts water before the lab.

How can you determine what nutrients are in various kinds of food?

Alternative Materials: Obtain indophenol if students will be doing More to Explore.

◆ Materials *(per group)*

samples of various foods, including flour, honey, and gelatin

paper towels
3 medicine droppers
iodine solution
hot plate
beaker, 400-mL
water
2 test tubes
Benedict's solution
test-tube holder
Biuret solution

Teaching Tips: Anyone who gets Benedict's or Biuret solution on himself or herself should flush the area with plenty of water. Clothes that receive a spill should be washed before being worn again. Be sure students wear aprons and goggles.

Make class data tables on the board or on an overhead to record the test results.

Remind students not to shake test tubes too vigorously and never to point a test tube at anyone.

Holding the test tubes up against a piece of white paper may make the color changes easier to see. The different colors for Benedict's solution correspond to different concentrations of sugar: green shows a low concentration, orange or red a high concentration, and yellow a moderate concentration.

◆ Safety   *Review the safety guidelines in the front of your lab book.*

Iodine solution and Biuret solution can stain skin and clothing. Benedict's solution can burn skin. If you spill any of these solutions on your skin, rinse it off immediately with cold running water and tell the teacher. Use a test-tube holder when handling hot test tubes.

◆ Procedure

If foods are semiliquid, have students add water to make the foods more liquid before testing them.

Part A: Test for Starches

1. Place a small amount of flour on a paper towel.

2. Use a medicine dropper to put 1 or 2 drops of iodine solution on the flour. **CAUTION:** *Keep iodine solution off your skin because it will leave a stain.*

3. Notice that the iodine solution turns purplish blue or blue-black. This color change indicates that flour contains starch. If the iodine remains yellow-brown, starch is not present.

4. Choose two to five other foods to test. Predict whether each food contains starch. Give a reason for your prediction.

Predictions will depend on foods chosen. Predictions may be based on experiences where foods

have been described as starchy.

_____

5. Test these additional foods for the presence of starch and record your results in Data Table 1.

Part B: Test for Sugars

1. Set up a hot-water bath by placing a beaker half full of water on a hot plate and starting to heat the water.

2. Use a medicine dropper to put 30 drops of honey-and-water solution in a test tube.

3. Use another medicine dropper to add Benedict's solution until the test tube is about one-third full. **CAUTION:** *Keep Benedict's solution away from your skin because it can burn you. If you spill some on you, rinse it off immediately with cold running water and inform the teacher.*

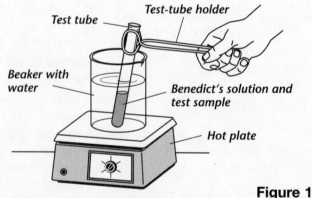

Test-tube holder
Test tube
Beaker with water
Benedict's solution and test sample
Hot plate

Figure 1

NUTRIENT IDENTIFICATION *(continued)*

4. Wait until the water in the water bath is boiling. **CAUTION:** *Be careful when using the water bath. Adjust the heat so that the water does not boil too vigorously. Take care not to point the opening of the test tube toward anyone. Remember to wear your safety goggles.* Use a test-tube holder to hold the test tube upright in the water bath. See Figure 1. Gently boil the mixture for 2 to 5 minutes.

5. Remove the test tube from the water bath. The solution should have turned green, yellow, orange, or orange-red. Any of these colors indicates that sugar is present. If the Benedict's solution remains blue, sugar is not present. Note: Benedict's solution indicates the presence of simple sugars such as glucose and fructose, which are found in most fruits. It does not detect the presence of complex sugars such as lactose (milk sugar).

6. Choose two to five additional foods to test. If you use solid foods, crush the material to be tested, put it in a test tube, and add 30 drops of water. If you use liquids, test 30 drops.

7. Predict whether each of these foods contains sugar. Give a reason for your prediction.

Predictions will depend on foods chosen. Predictions may be based on experiences where foods

have been called sweet.

_____

8. Test these additional foods for sugar and record your results in Data Table 2.

Test C: Test for Proteins

1. Use a medicine dropper to fill a test tube about one-third full of gelatin solution.

2. Add 10 drops of Biuret solution. **CAUTION:** *Biuret solution will burn skin and clothing. If you spill any solution on yourself, rinse it off immediately with cold running water and inform your teacher.*

3. Hold the tube against a white background. Notice that the mixture has turned violet. This color change indicates the presence of protein. If there is no color change, protein is not present.

4. Choose two to five other foods to test. Predict whether each contains protein. Give a reason for your prediction.

Predictions will depend on foods chosen. Predictions may be based on personal experience with

reading food labels.

_____

5. Test these additional foods for protein and record your results in Data Table 3.

NUTRIENT IDENTIFICATION *(continued)*

◆ Observations

Data Table 1   Sample Data

Food Tested	Color with Iodine Solution	Is Starch Present?
Flour	*Purplish-black or blue-black*	*Yes*
Diet clear soda	Yellow-brown	No
Regular clear soda	Yellow-brown	No
Milk	Yellow-brown	No
Apple	Yellow-brown	No
Bread	Purplish-black or blue-black	Yes

Data Table 2

Food Tested	Color with Benedict's Solution	Is Simple Sugar Present?
Honey and water	*Green, yellow, orange, or orange-red*	*Yes*
Diet clear soda	Blue	No
Regular clear soda	Green, yellow, orange, or orange-red	Yes
Milk	Blue	No
Apple	Green, yellow, orange, or orange-red	Yes
Bread	Green, yellow, orange, or orange-red	Yes

Data Table 3

Food Tested	Color with Biuret Solution	Is Protein Present?
Gelatin solution	*Violet*	*Yes*
Diet clear soda	No color change	No
Regular clear soda	No color change	No
Milk	Violet	Yes
Apple	No color change	No
Bread	Violet	Yes

NUTRIENT IDENTIFICATION *(continued)*

◆ Analyze and Conclude

1. Of the foods you tested, which contain starch? How do you know? Were your predictions correct?

Answers will vary. For the sample data, flour and bread contain starches. Food containing starch turns iodine blue-black.

2. Of the foods you tested, which contain sugar? How do you know? Were your predictions correct?

Answers will vary. For the sample data, honey, regular soda, apples, and bread contain simple sugars. Foods containing simple sugars will turn Benedict's solution green, yellow, orange, or orange-red.

3. Of the foods you tested, which contain protein? How do you know? Were your predictions correct?

Answers will vary. For the sample data, gelatin, milk, and bread contain protein. Foods containing protein will turn Biuret solution violet.

◆ Critical Thinking and Applications

1. If a food does not turn Biuret solution violet, do you know what nutrients the food contains? Give a reason for your answer.

No, Biuret solution is used to test for proteins only. It does not indicate whether fats, starches, or sugars are present. The tests for these nutrients must be done individually.

2. Why is it important to include starches, sugars, and proteins in your diet?

By eating foods from the different food groups, you will maintain a balanced diet and get the nutrients necessary for good health.

3. Write at least two new questions about other nutrients (such as minerals, vitamins, and so forth) that might be in the foods you tested.

Answers will vary. Sample questions: Does a food contain saturated or unsaturated fats? Are there tests to detect certain vitamins and minerals?

NUTRIENT IDENTIFICATION *(continued)*

4. Briefly, how would you go about answering your questions above? (**CAUTION:** *Do not perform any experiment unless the teacher approves your written plan.*)

Answers will vary. Sample answer: Find out what chemicals test for saturated fats, unsaturated

fats, certain vitamins, and minerals.

_____

_____

_____

◆ More to Explore

Chemical tests can detect different vitamins in foods. Indophenol is a chemical that tests for vitamin C. To conduct this test, wear safety goggles and a lab apron. Pour indophenol into a test tube to a depth of 2 cm. Add the substance to be tested, one drop at a time. Keep track of the number of drops added and shake the test tube after each drop is added. Continue until the blue color disappears. The more drops of test substance required to eliminate the blue color, the less vitamin C the substance contains. Compare the vitamin C content of various fruit juices, such as orange, apple, grapefruit, or lemon, or various brands of one kind of juice.

Amounts will vary. The content of vitamin C is influenced by the following factors: whether vitamin C has been added; whether water has been added; and whether the juice is fresh, frozen, or canned.

Direction of Blood Flow

Key Concepts: Veins have valves that keep blood flowing in one direction.

Skills Focus: Observing, inferring, communicating

Time Required: 40 minutes

◆ Pre-Lab Discussion

If you're healthy, you probably don't think much about your circulatory system. It just pumps along, keeping you alive. But think about this: liquids flow downhill. How can blood travel up to your heart, against the flow of gravity, as well as down? Somehow the muscle that is your heart and the arteries, veins, and capillaries work together to keep blood flowing to every part of your body.

In this investigation, you will demonstrate a feature of your veins that helps keep blood flowing throughout your body.

1. Compare and contrast the structures of arteries and veins.

Artery walls have three layers and are muscular and thick. Walls of veins also have three layers,

but they are thinner and less muscular than artery walls. Large veins contain valves, which

arteries don't have. A valve is a flap of tissue that prevents blood from flowing backward.

2. Why is it essential that blood flow upward in the body?

Answers may vary. Sample answer: If blood couldn't flow uphill, it would go to your feet and stay

there and couldn't flow up to your brain.

◆ Problem

What prevents blood from flowing backward toward the lower part of the body?

◆ Materials *(per group)*

Teaching Tips: Be sensitive to students who may have physical difficulty with this activity. Some students, such as overweight students, might have trouble observing their veins or exercising (in More to Explore). These students can still be observers or recorders.

◆ Safety ⚠ *Review the safety guidelines in the front of your lab book.*

Be gentle when exerting pressure on veins.

Students should press gently on their veins. Demonstrate the procedure if students have trouble following the directions.

Step 6 may show no change in the vein, or the valves may let a little blood drop back.

DIRECTION OF BLOOD FLOW *(continued)*

◆ Procedure

1. Work with two partners. Decide which partner will observe, which one will be the subject, and which one will record observations.

2. Have the subject stand with both arms down at his or her sides until the veins on the back of the hands stand out.

3. The subject should keep both arms down. The observer should put one finger from each hand next to each other on one of the subject's raised veins. See Figure 1.

4. The observer leaves the finger closest to the ground where it is. He or she slides the other finger upward along the vein for about 4 cm, pressing firmly but gently.

5. The observer tells the recorder what happens to the vein. The recorder writes the observations in the Data Table.

6. The observer keeps the finger closest to the ground in place, then releases the upper finger. The observer tells the recorder what happens to the vein, and the recorder writes the observations in the Data Table.

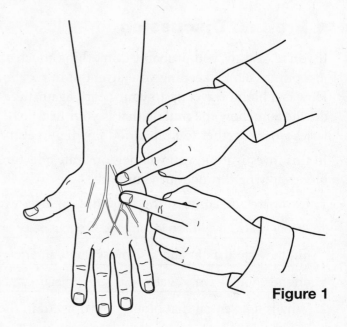

Figure 1

7. The observer releases the finger that is still in place and tells the recorder what happens to the vein. The recorder writes the observations in the Data Table.

8. Everyone switches roles and repeats steps 2–7.

◆ Observations

Data Table

	Effect on Vein	
Step	**Subject 1**	**Subject 2**
Observer moves fingers apart.	The vein seems to disappear.	The vein seems to disappear.
Observer releases upper finger.	The vein stays flat.	Blood comes a little way back into the vein.
Observer releases both fingers.	The vein fills up.	The vein fills up.

DIRECTION OF BLOOD FLOW (*continued*)

◆ Analyze and Conclude

1. How do veins and valves contribute to the effect you saw when the observer's fingers moved apart?

The blood was pushed out of the vein by the top finger, and the bottom finger prevented any

more blood from coming into the vein.

2. How do veins and valves contribute to the effect you saw when the observer released the upper finger?

A valve prevented blood from coming back into the vein.

3. How do veins and valves contribute to the effect you saw when the observer released both fingers?

The vein filled up after the pressure was removed. Valves enabled the blood to flow in the proper

direction.

4. Use your observations to summarize why blood doesn't flow backward in your body.

Valves in the veins allow blood to pass in one direction but not in the other direction. Thus, blood

cannot flow backward in the body.

4

◆ Critical Thinking and Applications

1. What would have happened if you had used an artery instead of a vein in this experiment?

Arteries do not contain valves. If an artery had been used, blood would have filled the artery

when the observer released the finger between the heart and the lower finger in Step 6.

2. In terms of circulation, why is it important to wear clothes that are not too tight? Include evidence from the lab in your answer.

Clothes that are too tight might prevent proper blood flow. If clothing presses on veins, it might

have the same effect as the fingers in the investigation did on blood flow.

DIRECTION OF BLOOD FLOW *(continued)*

3. Many buildings have plumbing in rooms that are below ground level, so the plumbing is lower than the building's drain pipe. Use what you learned in the investigation to explain how someone could design a bathtub drain in such a room. The drain water must not flow back into the bathtub.

The drain pipe would need to contain a valve that would allow the drain water to go out but not

come back in the other direction.

◆ More to Explore

New Problem When you exercise for cardiorespiratory fitness, you want your heart to beat at a target heart rate. What kind of exercise takes you closer to your target heart rate in 1 minute?

Possible Materials Use a stopwatch or other timer with a second hand.

Safety Do not exercise if you have health conditions, such as asthma, that might make exercise harmful.

Procedure Take your pulse while resting, and calculate the low end of the range of your target heart rate. See pages 112 and 259 in your textbook.

Develop a procedure to determine whether 1 minute of jumping rope or 1 minute of running in place gets you closer to your target heart rate. On a separate sheet of paper, list the steps of your procedure. Have the teacher approve your procedure before you carry out the investigation.

Observations On a separate sheet of paper, create a data table to record the resting heart rate, calculated target heart rate, and actual heart rate for both types of exercise.

Analyze and Conclude

1. Why do different exercises affect how long it takes you to reach your target heart rate?

Jumping rope uses arm muscles as well as leg muscles, so the whole body works and the heart

has to pump harder to supply blood to more muscle tissue.

2. Why do you think it is important for the heart rate to stay in the target range?

Answers will vary. Sample answer: The target rate exercises the heart without exhausting or

damaging heart muscle.

Procedures should have the subject take a resting pulse, exercise for 1 minute, and take a pulse immediately. The subject needs to rest until the pulse is normal resting pulse again; then the subject does the second exercise. Sample calculation: resting heart rate = 77 beats/min; maximum heart rate = 210 − 77 = 133 beats/min; lower limit of target rate = (133 × 0.6) + 77 = 157 beats/min.

D-5   LABORATORY INVESTIGATION

Measuring the Volume of Exhaled Air

Key Concept: During breathing, differences in air pressure inside and outside the human body force air into and out of the lungs. The volume of air involved in this process can be measured.

Skills Focus: Observing, inferring, making models, measuring, calculating, designing experiments, controlling variables

Time Required: 40 minutes

◆ Pre-Lab Discussion

If you have healthy lungs, you usually are not conscious of breathing. But have you ever felt like you were "out of breath"? Maybe you had to run to answer the phone or catch the school bus. Maybe you were ill, and your lungs were congested. Whatever the reason, you felt that the volume of air your lungs could hold was not enough for the amount of air you needed.

The amount of air that lungs can hold varies from person to person. It also varies in any one person from time to time. In this investigation, you will design and use a plan to measure and compare the volume of air you exhale when you exercise and the volume of air you exhale when you are not exercising.

1. How does the respiratory system work?

Air is taken into the lungs. Oxygen from the air is exchanged with waste products, mainly carbon

dioxide, which are carried in the blood. These wastes are then removed from the body as the

person exhales air from the lungs.

2. Explain the difference between *breathing* and *respiration*.

Breathing involves the movement of air into and out of the lungs. Respiration involves processes

that occur in cells.

◆ Problem

How can you measure the volume of exhaled air?

◆ Possible Materials *(per group)*

2-hole rubber stopper
2-L plastic bottle
glass tubing, long and short
rubber or flexible plastic tubing, 2 pieces
100-mL graduated cylinder
paper towels
cloth towel
glycerin
timer

Teaching Tips:

[Step 2] Either insert the glass tubing into the rubber stopper for the students or demonstrate how to safely do this procedure. Tubing may break and cause cuts. Wrap tubing securely in a cloth towel, covering the area you will hold. Use a lubricant, such as glycerin, on the tubing before carefully inserting it with a twisting motion into the stopper.

[Step 2] A few drops of food coloring in the water may make measurement easier.

[Step 2] In constructing the spirometer, be sure the glass tube through which the exhaled air enters is above the surface of the water and that the other glass tube is well below the surface of the water but does not touch the bottom of the bottle. Thus, the exhaled air increases the air pressure above the liquid. To equalize atmospheric pressure and the pressure in the bottle, a volume of liquid equal to the volume of air added is pushed out of the bottle.

[Teaching Tips continued on next page]

5

MEASURING THE VOLUME OF EXHALED AIR *(continued)*

◆ Safety   *Review the safety guidelines in the front of your lab book.*

When you blow through the tubing, first place a paper towel over the end of it and blow through the towel. Do not put your mouth directly on any of the tubing. If you insert glass tubing into the rubber stopper, use extreme caution and follow the teacher's instructions. Inform the teacher of any physical reasons you should not exercise. Your teacher must approve your plan before you can perform the experiment.

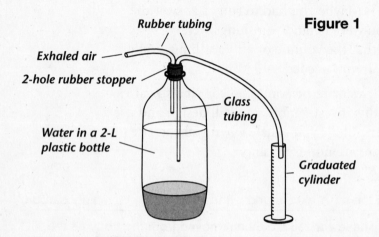

Figure 1

Rubber tubing
Exhaled air
2-hole rubber stopper
Glass tubing
Water in a 2-L plastic bottle
Graduated cylinder

This movement of liquid increases the volume the air can occupy and thereby reduces the air pressure. Be sure it is clear to students that the volume of air they exhale equals the volume of water that comes out of the bottle. Have students return the water to the bottle after each trial.

[Step 3] If some students exhale more than 100 mL of air, use a larger container to collect the water. The collected water can then be measured using the graduated cylinder.

[Step 6] Before students run in place, be sure they have no physical conditions, such as asthma, that could cause health problems. If such conditions exist, suggest that another student in the group perform the exercise.

◆ Procedure

5

1. Read through this entire lab before you perform any part of it.

2. Use the materials listed here or other materials to assemble a spirometer—an instrument that can be used to measure the volume of air that your lungs can exhale. A spirometer is shown in Figure 1.

3. Plan how you will use your instrument to measure your lung volume. Consider what unit you will use for this measurement. On another sheet of paper, write a step-by-step plan for using your spirometer to measure the volume of your exhaled air.

4. Use Data Table 1 in Observations to record your data. You will need to record data for at least three trials; you may want to do more. You will then calculate the average volume of water displaced for all of your trials.

5. After the teacher has approved your plan, carry out your investigation. Then answer questions 1 and 2 in Observations.

MEASURING THE VOLUME OF EXHALED AIR *(continued)*

6. After you have completed Data Table 1, run in place for two minutes.
   CAUTION: *Do not perform this part of the activity if you have any medical condition that makes the activity unsafe.* Repeat your experiment, using Data Table 2. Perform the same number of trials as before and average the trials. Then answer question 3 in Observations.

7. Rest for a few minutes until your breathing returns to normal. Then repeat the experiment using Data Table 3.

◆ Observations

1. How is the volume of water that is forced out of the bottle related to the volume of air you exhale?

   The volumes are equal.

2. In the spirometer in Figure 1, why is it important that one glass tube is above the surface of the water and one glass tube is beneath it?

   The glass tube above the surface of the water is the tubing through which the exhaled air enters

   the bottle. The increased air pressure in the bottle forces the water through the other glass tube.

   If this tube were not beneath the surface of the water, air—which could not be measured in the

   graduated cylinder—would be forced out the second tube.

3. How does your average volume of exhaled air when you have not been exercising compare to your average volume of exhaled air right after you exercise?

   Data should show that the average volume of air after exercising should be greater than the

   average volume measured when students are not exercising.

5

Data Table 1
(before exercising)   Sample Data

Trial	Volume of Water (mL)
1	75
2	79
3	77
Average	77

Data Table 2
(after exercising)

Trial	Volume of Water (mL)
1	97
2	102
3	99
Average	99

Data Table 3 (when
breathing returns to normal)

Trial	Volume of Water (mL)
1	80
2	79
3	80
Average	80

MEASURING THE VOLUME OF EXHALED AIR *(continued)*

◆ Analyze and Conclude

1. Why is it important to perform several trials for each part of the investigation?

One trial might be affected by different variables even if you try to control for them. An average

of several trials should provide a valid volume.

2. Choose one of your data tables. Were the volumes the same for each trial? What could you change about your plan to assure that your data are more consistent?

Volumes were likely similar but not exactly the same. Students could allow several minutes of

time between each trial or make a special effort to exhale normally and not use a breath that is

deeper than usual.

3. Infer why the volume of air you exhaled after exercise differed from the volume you exhaled before exercising.

Oxygen is needed for cellular respiration. Respiration proceeds at a faster rate when a person

exercises, so the person needs more oxygen then. Larger breaths—larger volumes of air—

provide more oxygen.

◆ Critical Thinking and Applications

1. What might cause differences in lung volume among students in the class?

Answers might include that students involved in activities requiring a lot of lung capacity, such as

athletics or some music activities, would exhale more air. Also, larger students might have larger

lung capacities.

2. Denver, Colorado, is located at a high altitude. Miami, Florida, is located at sea level. Predict how the average Data Table 1 results for students who live in Denver compare to those of students who live in Miami. Explain your reasoning.

Students will probably predict that the volumes in Denver would be larger. At a high altitude, the

air is thinner. You would have to take a deeper breath to get the same amount of oxygen you can

get in a smaller breath in Miami.

◆ More to Explore

How could you determine the total volume of air someone can exhale in one minute? Write a procedure that you would follow to answer this question. Have the teacher approve your procedure before you carry out the investigation.

Procedures may include using several spirometers. One can be used for each exhaled breath, giving other students time to measure and record the volume of the liquid forced out and to return the liquid to the bottle before that particular spirometer is used again.

5

D-6   **LABORATORY INVESTIGATION**

Do Mouthwashes Work?

Key Concepts: Antiseptic mouthwashes prevent the growth of disease-causing microorganisms.

Skills Focus: Observing, inferring, predicting, controlling variables

Time Required: 40 minutes initially; 10 minutes on each of three subsequent consecutive days for observations

◆ Pre-Lab Discussion

What do you use to take care of your teeth: toothbrush, toothpaste, dental floss, mouthwash? Mouthwashes are supposed to kill microorganisms that contribute to tooth decay, gum disease, and bad breath. They contain antiseptics, chemicals that kill or prevent growth of disease organisms on living tissues. How well do these mouthwashes work? Do they really kill microorganisms?

In this investigation, you will compare the effects of two mouthwashes.

1. Name four groups of organisms that cause diseases.

bacteria, viruses, fungi, protists

2. From where do disease-causing microorganisms come?

Sources include another person, a contaminated object, an animal bite, and the environment.

◆ Problem

How well do mouthwashes control the growth of bacteria?

◆ Materials *(per group)*

3 petri dishes with sterile nutrient agar
pen
masking tape
2 types of mouthwash
2 small jars
filter paper
scissors
metric ruler
forceps
transparent tape

Advance Preparation: Have students bring in different brands of mouthwashes. Obtain nutrient agar plates, three for each group.

Teaching Tips: Caution students to handle forceps carefully.

Cultures should be autoclaved or flooded with a strong household disinfectant solution. Use a disinfectant such as Lysol or dilute chlorine bleach. Be sure to follow state and local guidelines for disposal.

6

◆ Safety   *Review the safety guidelines in the front of your lab book.*

Do not drink the mouthwashes. Have the teacher dispose of the sealed petri dishes at the end of the activity.

DO MOUTHWASHES WORK? *(continued)*

◆ Procedure

1. Obtain three petri dishes containing sterile agar. Do *not* open the dishes. Using a pen and pieces of masking tape, label the bottoms of the petri dishes *A, B,* and *C.* Also put your initials on each dish.

2. Wash your hands thoroughly with soap, then run a fingertip across the surface of your worktable. Your partner should hold open the cover of petri dish A, while you run your fingertip gently across the agar in a zigzag motion. Close the dish immediately.

3. Repeat Step 2 for dishes B and C.

4. Obtain a small sample of each mouthwash in separate containers. Use a pen and masking tape to label the containers.

5. Cut two 2-cm squares of filter paper. Soak a square in each mouthwash.

6. Using forceps, remove one square from a container. Open the cover of dish A just long enough to put the filter paper in the center of the agar. Close the cover immediately. Record the name of the mouthwash in the Data Table.

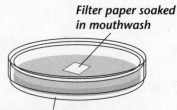

Filter paper soaked in mouthwash

Petri dish with sterile agar

Figure 1

7. Repeat Step 6 for dish B, using the filter paper soaked in the second mouthwash.

8. Do not add anything to dish C.

9. Tape the covers of all three petri dishes so that they will remain tightly closed. Let the three dishes sit upright on your work surface for at least 5 minutes before moving them. **CAUTION:** *Do not open the petri dishes again.* Wash your hands with soap and water.

10. As directed by the teacher, store the petri dishes in a warm, dark place where they can remain for at least three days. You will remove them only for a brief examination each day.

11. Predict what you will observe over the next three days in the three petri dishes.

    Possible predictions are that the mouthwashes will be equally effective in preventing

    microorganism growth or that one mouthwash will be more effective. Predictions may reflect

    personal experience or advertising effectiveness.

12. After one day, observe the contents of each dish without removing the cover. Estimate the percentage of the agar surface that shows any changes. Record your observations in the Data Table. Return the dishes to their storage place and wash your hands with soap and water.

13. Repeat Step 12 after a second day and after a third day.

14. After you and your partner have made your last observations, give the unopened petri dishes to the teacher.

6

DO MOUTHWASHES WORK? *(continued)*

◆ Observations

Less bacterial growth should occur in dishes A and B than in C.

Data Table

Bacterial growth should increase every day in the control, especially in the areas where students ran their finger across the agar.

Petri Dish	Mouthwash	Day 1	Day 2	Day 3
A				
B				
C				

◆ Analyze and Conclude

1. How did the appearance of dish C change during three days?

Dish C had more bacteria growing in it every day.

2. How did the appearance of dishes A and B compare with dish C? Explain any similarities or differences.

Dishes A and B should have less bacterial growth than dish C. The mouthwashes in dishes A and

B prevented some bacterial growth.

3. How did the appearance of dishes A and B compare with each other? How can you account for any differences?

Answers may vary. There may be different amounts of bacteria growing in dishes A and B.

Different mouthwashes may have different effectiveness.

4. Explain why it is important to set aside one petri dish that does not contain any mouthwash.

Dish C is a control for the experiment. Without it, students could not see how much bacteria

would have grown without any mouthwash. Therefore, they could not compare the effect of the

mouthwashes as completely as by using the control.

6

DO MOUTHWASHES WORK? *(continued)*

◆ Critical Thinking and Applications

1. Based on the results of this lab, what recommendation would you make to your family about mouthwashes?

Most students will recommend the mouthwash that prevented the most bacterial growth in its

dish. Other factors in their recommendation might include price, flavor, and odor of the

mouthwash.

2. What other products could you test using a procedure similar to this lab?

Answers may include antibacterial soaps and various kitchen and bathroom cleaners that claim

to kill bacteria.

◆ More to Explore

Test one of the products in your answer to question 2 above. For example, visit a store and look at antibacterial soaps. How do their ingredients differ from other soaps? How do their prices compare to regular soap?

Antibacterial soaps contain ethyl alcohol to kill bacteria. Usually antibacterial soap costs more than

regular soap.

New Problem How well do antibacterial soaps control the growth of bacteria?

Possible Materials Consider which materials you can use from the previous part of this lab. What else will you need?

Procedure Develop a procedure to solve the problem. Write your procedure on a separate sheet of paper. Have the teacher approve your procedure before you carry out the investigation.

Observations On a separate sheet of paper, make a data table like the one in the previous part of this lab in which to record your data.

Analyze and Conclude

What effects of antibacterial soap do your results show?

There should be less bacterial growth with the antibacterial soap than with other kinds of soap.

_____

_____

Experiments to test the effectiveness of these products will follow the steps of the previous part of this lab. Students could place a drop or two of liquid antibacterial soap or a mixture of antibacterial bar soap and water in the middle of the agar without using filter paper.

D-7   LABORATORY INVESTIGATION

Locating Touch Receptors

Key Concepts: The sense of touch depends on receptors in the skin, the largest sense organ. The number of receptors per area of skin differs for different areas of the body.

◆ Pre-Lab Discussion

Skills Focus: Observing, inferring, communicating, measuring, controlling variables

Have you ever wondered why your hand instantly pulls back when it touches a hot pan on the stove? Have you noticed that smooth fabrics feel better to your skin than rough fabrics do? Both of these reactions involve your sense of touch.

Time Required:
40 minutes

Touch receptors in your skin help you respond to your environment. Your body responds to different stimuli, including pain, temperature, and pressure. Not all parts of your body respond equally to these stimuli. Different parts of the body contain different numbers of receptors for a given amount of skin area.

In this investigation, you will test several areas of your skin and compare their sensitivity to touch.

1. How does the location of the sense of touch differ from the location of other senses?

The sense of touch is not in one specific place. It is in skin all over the body.

_____

2. Where in the skin are the receptors that would sense a light touch?

in the upper part of the dermis

◆ Problem

Where are the touch receptors located on the body?

◆ Materials *(per group)*

scissors
metric ruler
piece of cardboard, 6 cm × 10 cm
marker
9 toothpicks
blindfold

Teaching Tips: The exact size of the cardboard rectangle is not important. What is critical is the distance between the toothpicks.

Supervise all students when they are touching their partner with the toothpicks. Emphasize that they must not apply pressure and point out that they will have a turn as the subject.

7

◆ Safety   *Review the safety guidelines in the front of your lab book.*

Use caution in handling sharp scissors. Tie the blindfold loosely, using special care if the blindfolded student is wearing contact lenses. Students who wear eyeglasses should remove them before wearing a blindfold.

LOCATING TOUCH RECEPTORS (continued)

◆ Procedure

1. Using scissors, cut the piece of cardboard into five rectangles, each measuring 6 cm × 2 cm. Label the pieces A–E.

2. As shown in Figure 1, insert two toothpicks 5 mm apart into rectangle A. Insert two toothpicks 1 cm apart into rectangle B, two toothpicks 2 cm apart into rectangle C, and two toothpicks 3 cm apart into rectangle D. In the center of rectangle E, insert one toothpick.

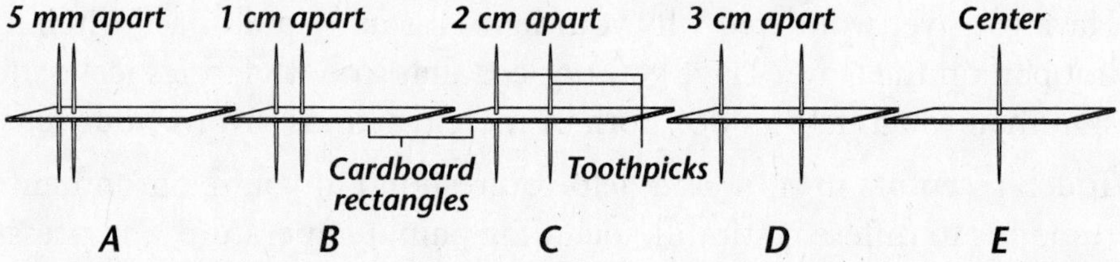

3. Carefully blindfold your partner.

Figure 1

4. Using one of the rectangles, carefully touch the palm side of your partner's fingertip with the ends of the toothpicks. **CAUTION:** *Only* touch *the toothpicks to the skin; do not press them against the skin.* Ask your partner how many points he or she feels.

5. In Data Table 1, record how many points your partner felt.

6. Repeat steps 4 and 5, touching the palm of the hand, back of the neck, back of the hand, and inside the lower arm.

7. Repeat steps 4–6 with the other cardboard rectangles. Select each rectangle randomly, not in alphabetical order.

8. Reverse roles with your partner and repeat the investigation using Data Table 2.

9. Answer question 1 in Observations.

◆ Observations

Sample Data: Results will vary. People will feel two points with the most sensitive part of their skin and one point with the least. Most people's sensitivity increases in this order, with the inside lower arm being least sensitive: inside lower arm, back of hand, back of neck, palm of hand, fingertip.

Data Table 1

Body Part	Number of Points Felt				
	A 5 mm apart	**B** 1 cm apart	**C** 2 cm apart	**D** 3 cm apart	**E** 1 point
Subject 1					
Fingertip					
Palm of hand					
Back of hand					
Back of neck					
Inside lower arm					

LOCATING TOUCH RECEPTORS *(continued)*

Data Table 2

Body Part	Number of Points Felt				
	A **5 mm apart**	**B** **1 cm apart**	**C** **2 cm apart**	**D** **3 cm apart**	**E** **1 point**
	Subject 2				
Fingertip					
Palm of hand					
Back of hand					
Back of neck					
Inside lower arm					

1. On which area of the skin were you best able to feel two separate points?

Answers will vary. The most sensitive areas are usually the fingertip and palm.

◆ Analyze and Conclude

1. Which area of the skin that you tested probably had the most touch receptors? The fewest? On what observations do you base this conclusion?

Answers will vary, but most students will feel the most sensation in the fingertips and the least in

the inside lower arm. Students can distinguish two points more often in the more sensitive areas.

2. Rank the tested skin areas in order from the most to the least sensitive.

Answers will vary, but most students will rank from most to least sensitive in the following order:

fingertip, palm of hand, back of neck, back of hand, inside lower arm.

3. In Step 7, why was it important to select each rectangle randomly instead of in alphabetical order?

If you apply the rectangles in order, your partner might remember that E was the only rectangle

with one point. This knowledge might bias the results.

7

LOCATING TOUCH RECEPTORS *(continued)*

4. Did you and your partner sense the same number of points in each test? If not, why do you think your results were different?

Answers will vary. Sample answer: No, some people have thinner dermis, which allows more

sensitive touch reception.

◆ Critical Thinking and Applications

1. Think about the test area that had the most touch receptors. How does having a lot of receptors in this area benefit you?

Fingertips are a primary means of touching to explore properties such as texture and

temperature. For safety, fingertips must quickly sense temperature to avoid burns or sense pain

to avoid injury.

2. Explain how a lack of touch receptors in the bottom of your feet would affect your ability to walk.

Walking depends on being able to feel when your feet are touching the ground. If you lacked

touch receptors in your feet, you might think your feet were on the ground when they weren't.

Also you might walk on hot or sharp objects unknowingly and harm yourself.

3. Why is it important to you that your body respond to pain?

Pain alerts the body to possible danger or the existence and extent of an injury.

◆ More to Explore

New Problem Can you identify similar objects by touch alone?

Possible Materials Consider which materials you can use from the previous part of the lab. What else will you need?

Procedure Develop a procedure to solve the problem. Write your procedure on a separate sheet of paper. Have the teacher approve your procedure before you carry out the investigation.

Observations On a separate sheet of paper, create a table to organize data for two subjects trying to identify three coins each.

Analyze and Conclude Do different people have different touch sensitivity? Support your answer with data from your experiment.

Answers may vary. Sample answer: Maybe. In our experiment, both subjects got the same results,

but we might have had different results with a more difficult test.

A possible method is to blindfold one partner, hand him or her a coin, and ask what coin it is. The
data table should track what coin was offered and what the subject thought it was.

D-8   **LABORATORY INVESTIGATION**

Model of a Negative Feedback Mechanism

Key Concept: The endocrine system uses negative feedback to maintain homeostasis.

Skills Focus: Observing, inferring, making models

Time Required: 40 minutes

◆ Pre-Lab Discussion

The endocrine system, along with the nervous system, controls your body's daily activities. It also controls how your body develops. Endocrine glands produce chemicals called hormones, which move directly into the bloodstream. Hormones affect specific cells called target cells. These target cells are often in another part of the body. To control the amount of hormone an endocrine gland produces, the endocrine system sends chemical information back and forth in a negative feedback system. Negative feedback is an important way that the body maintains homeostasis. In this investigation, you will model how a negative feedback system works.

1. How does the pancreas act as an endocrine gland?

The pancreas produces hormones that help control the level of glucose in the blood.

_____

2. Your blood carries hormones to every part of your body. Why doesn't a hormone affect all your cells the same way?

The hormone attaches to and affects only target cells that recognize its chemical structure.

_____

_____

◆ Problem

Teaching Tips: Have students review the section on homeostasis in the textbook.

How does the pancreas use negative feedback to help maintain glucose at a certain level in the blood?

◆ Materials *(per group)*

2-liter plastic soft-drink bottle
scissors
rubber ball, solid, 2.5–4.0 cm in diameter
2 screw eyes
string
fishing float
dowel, about 6 cm long
sink or bucket
water
large pitcher
marker

The model simplifies the insulin/glucose cycle. The pancreas uses *two* hormones to control blood glucose levels. When levels are high, it releases insulin, which makes cells take up glucose from the blood, and the liver stores glucose as glycogen. When levels are low, the pancreas releases glucagon, which makes the liver break down glycogen and release glucose to the blood. Both of these hormones are regulated by negative feedback loops.

Advance Preparation: Collect plastic bottles before the activity. Ask students to begin bringing them to class a week or two ahead of time. You may want to cut the plastic bottles before class. To save time, you may wish to construct the models yourself or have a small group of students construct them.

8

MODEL OF A NEGATIVE FEEDBACK MECHANISM *(continued)*

◆ **Safety** *Review the safety guidelines in the front of your lab book.*

Take care when cutting off the bottom of the soft-drink bottle. To prevent slips or falls, immediately wipe up any water spilled on the floor.

◆ Procedure

1. Carefully cut off the bottom half of the plastic bottle.

2. Insert a screw eye into a rubber ball. Cut a piece of string 20 cm long. Tie one end of the string to the screw eye and the other end to a fishing float.

3. Insert a second screw eye into the other side of the rubber ball, directly opposite the first screw eye. Cut a piece of string 10 cm long. Tie one end of the string to the screw eye and the other end to the middle of the dowel.

4. Hold the bottle upside down. Lower the float, the rubber ball, and the attached rod into the bottle. Carefully pass the rod through the neck of the bottle so that the rod hangs below the mouth, as shown in Figure 1.

Figure 1

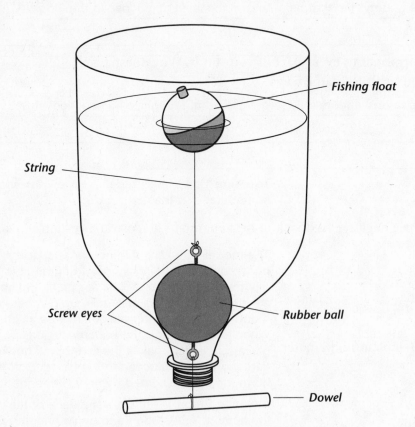

MODEL OF A NEGATIVE FEEDBACK MECHANISM *(continued)*

5. One of you should hold the bottle over a sink or bucket, while the other slowly pours water into the bottle until the string stretches to its full length. Do not lift the ball out of the bottle opening. Mark the level of the water on the outside of the bottle.

6. Slowly add more water to the bottle and observe what happens. Answer questions 1 and 2 in Observations.

7. Add about 100 mL of water rapidly to the model. Be careful not to overfill the bottle. Observe what happens and answer question 3 in Observations.

◆ Observations

1. What happens to the water level when you add more water after the string has stretched to its full length?

   The level of the water goes up a little and then the water begins to drain out. This brings the

   water back to its original level.

   _____

   _____

   _____

2. What happens to the float and ball whenever you add water slowly?

   The float moves up and pulls the string with it. The string draws the ball out of the neck of the

   bottle and water can escape. This makes the water drain out until it returns to its original level

   and the ball falls back into the neck.

   _____

   _____

3. How does the model act when you pour the water quickly, compared to when you pour it slowly?

   The faster the water flows into the model, the wider the opening at the bottom of the model

   becomes, and the faster the water drains out of the model.

   _____

   _____

   _____

8

MODEL OF A NEGATIVE FEEDBACK MECHANISM *(continued)*

◆ Analyze and Conclude

Figure 2 shows the role of the pancreas in a negative feedback loop that controls the amount of glucose in the blood. The pancreas makes the hormone insulin. Insulin enables body cells to take in glucose from the bloodstream. When the glucose level in the blood is high, the pancreas releases insulin, which enables body cells to take glucose from the blood. When the glucose level in the blood drops, the pancreas stops releasing insulin. Body cells stop removing glucose from the bloodstream. When blood glucose increases, the cycle starts again.

Figure 2

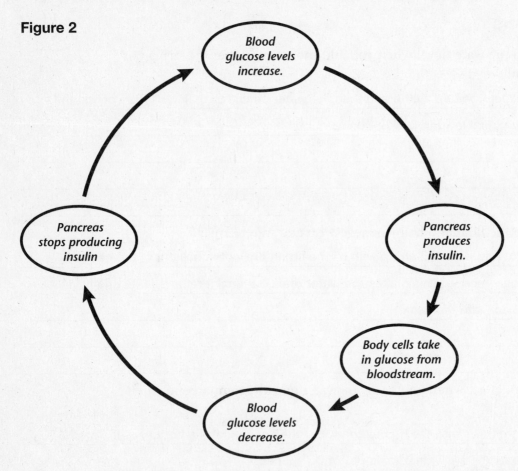

1. The water in the model represents blood glucose. Which part of your model represents the pancreas? (Drawing a cycle like the one in Figure 2 might help you find an answer.) Give a reason for your answer.

   The fishing float represents the pancreas because it detects and controls the amount of water

   (glucose) in the system.

8

MODEL OF A NEGATIVE FEEDBACK MECHANISM *(continued)*

2. Which part of your model represents the body cells? Give a reason for your answer.

The rubber ball represents the body cells. It reacts to the detection of too much water (glucose)

by removing the excess.

3. Which part of your model represents insulin? Give a reason for your answer.

The string represents insulin, as it sends a message from the float to the ball.

4. Explain how your model demonstrates the negative feedback mechanism used by the pancreas to control glucose levels in the blood.

In the model, the float responds to the increased water level. In the body, the pancreas responds

to an increase in the blood glucose level. The float responds by pulling the ball out of the bottle

neck. The pancreas responds by producing insulin. Once the ball is out of the way, water

escapes and its level drops. Once insulin is released into the bloodstream, the excess glucose in

the blood is taken up by the cells, causing the glucose level to drop.

◆ Critical Thinking and Applications

1. How would lengthening the string between the float and the ball affect the water level? How would shortening this string affect the water level?

A longer string would stabilize the water at a higher level, and a shorter string would

stabilize the water at a lower level.

2. Based on this model, explain how negative feedback works.

Negative feedback restores certain substances in the blood to "normal" levels. When a

substance is above or below this level, the negative feedback mechanism triggers a response

that restores the substance to its appropriate level.

8

MODEL OF A NEGATIVE FEEDBACK MECHANISM *(continued)*

3. What part of the negative feedback mechanism that keeps blood glucose at one level is not represented in the model? How could you improve the design of the model to make it more accurate?

This model represents the part of negative feedback where too much glucose is present in the

blood and the pancreas releases insulin until blood glucose levels drop to normal conditions. It

does not represent the opposite condition, low blood glucose level. The model could be

improved by adjusting it so that the water level (blood glucose level) could go lower than the

standard and the mechanism would restore the water level to normal.

◆ More to Explore

The body's regulation of glucose levels is more complicated than the model you made of it. Use the library to find out more about glucose regulation. Which part of the regulation process is missing from your model?

The missing pieces are storing glycogen in the liver and releasing it as glucose when blood glucose is low. The hormone glucagon controls this process.

8

Weather and Whooping Cranes

Key Concept: Many aspects of any organism's habitat are important in that organism's survival. When an organism is endangered, all that is possible must be done to study it and its habitat and protect that organism from extinction.

Skills Focus: Inferring, calculating, graphing

Time Required: 40 minutes

◆ Pre-Lab Discussion

The whooping crane is a tall white bird with red markings on its forehead and face. It is native to certain North American wetlands. In the twentieth century, the population of this magnificent bird has decreased almost to the point of disappearing. In 1941, only 14 cranes were living. Although about ten times as many cranes are now living, they are still at risk. About half of the cranes live in the wild. They breed in Wood Buffalo National Park in Canada and winter in Aransas National Wildlife Refuge in Texas.

Scientists, working to save the whooping cranes, investigated what abiotic factors affect the birds. In this investigation, you will analyze the data from one such study.

1. What do whooping cranes need to obtain from their habitat?

The habitat must provide food, water, shelter, and other things the whooping crane needs to live, grow, and reproduce.

2. What abiotic factors might limit the population of whooping cranes?

Answers may include destruction of habitat, pollution, and bad weather.

◆ Problem

How does precipitation affect the population of whooping cranes?

◆ Materials (per group)

ruler
calculator
pencil

Teaching Tips: [Step 1] Review with students how to label axes on a graph. Be sure that the intervals chosen are equal.

[Step 2] If students have trouble visualizing what Data Table 1 represents, have them create as a class a visual representation of some of the data. You might duplicate pictures of adult whooping cranes, eggs, and young birds. Students could use the pictures to model the number of birds at the end of a particular year and the number of birds from that year that died before migrating time the next year, for example.

[Step 3] If computers are available, students can use a spreadsheet to find the hatching success rate.

◆ Procedure

1. Using Figure 1 and the data in Data Table 1, plot a graph showing how the crane population changed from year 1 to year 16 of the study. The crane population in any given year is the total number of migrating adults and hatched eggs. Answer questions 1–3 in Observations.

2. Study the data in Data Table 1. Answer questions 4–6 in Observations.

Name _____ Date _____ Class _____

WEATHER AND WHOOPING CRANES *(continued)*

3. Using a calculator, determine the hatching success rate for each year.

$$\text{Hatching success rate} = \frac{\text{Number of eggs hatched}}{\text{Number of eggs laid}} \times 100\%$$

Write these values in the corresponding boxes in Data Table 2. Answer question 7 in Observations.

Data Table 1

One Study Relating Weather and Reproductive Rate of Whooping Cranes

Year	Migrating Adults	Number of Nests	Eggs Laid	Hatched Eggs	Rainfall (cm)	Snowfall (cm)
1	21	6	6	4	8.9	3.6
2	20	3	2	0	15.0	0.5
3	20	4	4	3	11.7	2.0
4	22	5	5	4	6.1	2.8
5	23	4	6	2	6.4	14.2
6	23	8	8	4	8.1	4.6
7	30	6	6	5	7.4	0.0
8	32	0	0	0	19.3	7.6
9	28	4	6	2	15.0	1.3
10	26	10	10	7	8.1	2.0
11	32	10	10	6	7.4	2.5
12	36	2	2	0	13.7	7.4
13	30	4	4	3	8.9	1.0
14	32	3	4	3	7.1	1.8
15	33	3	3	1	14.7	6.1
16	32	5	5	4	5.3	1.5

WEATHER AND WHOOPING CRANES *(continued)*

◆ Observations

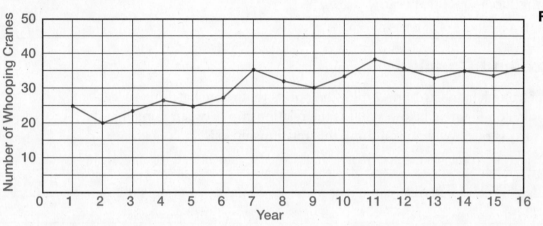

Figure 1

1. When was the crane population at its highest level? When was it at its lowest level?

year 11; year 2

2. During which year did the population increase the most?

year 7

3. In which year did the most adult cranes die?

year 13

4. Which four years were the poorest breeding years for the cranes? In which year were the most eggs laid and hatched successfully?

years 2, 8, 12, and 15; year 10

5. During which five summers was rainfall greatest?

years 2, 8, 9, 12, and 15

6. Was snowfall ever high the same year that rainfall was high? If so, in which year or years?

Answers will vary but should include years 5, 8, 12, and 15.

Data Table 2

Year	1	2	3	4	5	6	7	8	9	10	11	12	13	14	15	16
Hatching success rate (%)	67	0	75	80	33	50	83	0	33	70	60	0	75	75	33	80

WEATHER AND WHOOPING CRANES *(continued)*

7. In which year was total precipitation (rainfall plus snowfall) lowest? What was the hatching success rate that year?

year 16, with a total of 6.8 cm; 80%

◆ Analyze and Conclude

1. Using data from data tables 1 and 2, plot the points that relate hatching success rate to rainfall on Figure 2 below. What is the relationship between rainfall and hatching success rate? Why do you think this relationship exists?

In general, increased rainfall results in lower hatching success rate. Explanations may include

the flooding of nesting areas.

Figure 2

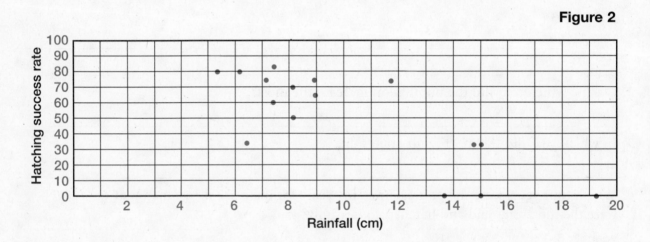

2. Suppose you want to find out how rainfall affects the whooping-crane population. Why would you use daily or weekly amounts of rainfall rather than seasonal amounts?

A few large rains would probably be more devastating to nesting areas than would more frequent

lighter rains. Whether or not the rain fell during the nesting season would also be a factor. These

specific amounts and times of rainfall would not show up in seasonal data.

3. Suppose that years 10 and 11 had high levels of precipitation. How would this have affected the population? Give a reason for your answer.

Answers might include that fewer eggs would have hatched and the population might have been

greatly altered. Although 13 hatched eggs is a small number, they represent an important

increase in a small population.

WEATHER AND WHOOPING CRANES *(continued)*

◆ Critical Thinking and Applications

1. What other factors besides weather might influence the population growth of whooping cranes? What do you think lowered the whooping-crane population to the endangered level?

Answers will vary but might include the number of predators and the effects of humans on the

habitat of the whooping crane. Factors lowering the number of whooping cranes might include

destruction and pollution of habitat, killing of the birds by predators and humans, and climate

change.

2. Once laws protecting the American alligator went into effect, the alligator population recovered quite rapidly. In contrast, the whooping-crane population has remained low in spite of protection. What factors might prevent a rapid increase in the number of cranes?

Answers might include few young produced per year, small habitat areas, and the fact that the

whooping cranes migrate and are thus affected by more environmental factors.

3. Why is international cooperation necessary to protect species that migrate, such as the whooping crane?

Most migrating species travel across more than one country. Such species need protection in all

countries involved.

4. Whooping cranes often lay two eggs. However, a pair can rarely raise two chicks. Therefore, wildlife biologists sometimes "steal" one of the two eggs in the nest and replace it with a fake one of plastic. What do you think the biologists do with the stolen eggs? Why?

Scientists attempt to increase the hatching success rate by hatching the eggs in captivity. The

birds are released when they are old enough, increasing the population.

WEATHER AND WHOOPING CRANES *(continued)*

◆ **More to Explore**

Find out the difference between an endangered species and a threatened species. Is the whooping crane endangered or threatened? List three species that are endangered and three species that are threatened. What is being done to protect each species?

1

An endangered species is the most seriously threatened with extinction. The species must be completely protected from human interference or it will die out. A threatened species may be numerous in some areas but its overall numbers are declining and it may become an endangered species.

Encourage students to use a wide variety of resources. The *World Almanac* provides an up-to-date list of endangered and threatened species. The Internet is another good source. Be sure students understand that they must evaluate information obtained from the Internet. Web sites for the National Wildlife Federation (www.nwf.org), Audubon Society (www.audubon.org), the Sierra Club (www.sierraclub.org), and universities are some reliable sources.

E-2   **LABORATORY INVESTIGATION**

Ecosystem Food Chains

Key Concept: All ecosystems have biotic and abiotic factors, which affect the way energy flows through the ecosystem.

Skills Focus: Observing, classifying, measuring, creating data tables, inferring

Time Required: two 40-minute classes

◆ Pre-Lab Discussion

Ecosystems are made up of both living (biotic) and nonliving (abiotic) things. Energy moves through ecosystems in the form of food. When an organism eats another organism, it obtains energy from the food. A food chain is a series of events in which one organism eats another and thereby obtains energy.

Do you know what makes up the ecosystems in your area? In this investigation, you will become an ecologist studying a local ecosystem. You will observe and collect data about the biotic and abiotic factors found at your site. You will also study the relationships among the different biotic and abiotic features you observe.

1. What is a consumer? What are the four classifications of consumers?

A consumer is an organism that eats another organism to get its energy. The four classifications

of consumers include herbivores, carnivores, omnivores, and scavengers.

2. What is the source of all the food in an ecosystem? What process is generally used to make this food?

Producers are the source of all the food in an ecosystem. Most producers make sugars using the

process of photosynthesis.

◆ Problem

What food chains can you observe in a local ecosystem?

◆ Possible Materials *(per group)*

meterstick	colored pencils
4 stakes	hand lens
string	
notebook	
pen	

Advance Preparation: Investigate different sites near the school where students could do the field study. You may wish to combine this lab with a field trip to a nature center or to another natural environment, which could provide students with a variety of ecosystems to study.

Find out if students have allergies that might be of special concern for this lab. Stress that students with allergies to certain plants observe their site without touching the plants.

◆ Safety   *Review the safety guidelines in the front of your lab book.*

Use care when working with stakes. Be careful when working around land and water sites so that you do not fall and injure yourself or others. Review the safety rules on pages v–vi in the front of this book for handling plants and animals.

ECOSYSTEM FOOD CHAINS *(continued)*

2

◆ Procedure

Part A: Class Preparation

1. As a class, discuss the different types of ecosystems found around your home and school. Determine which ecosystem you will examine. Be aware that the type of ecosystem you choose will influence the types of food chains you will find.

2. Use different colored pencils to represent the different types of organisms you expect to find within your chosen ecosystem. Make a key representing the different organisms in the Data Table under Observations. Types of organisms might include trees, bushes, flowers, grasses, mosses, fungi, insects, and other animals. You might also include evidence of animals, such as burrows, nests, and egg cases. Finally, consider including dead organic materials such as logs, dead trees, fallen leaves, and animal remains.

3. Make a list of the materials that you need to conduct your field study of the ecosystem. Develop a plan for gathering these materials. Decide who will gather what materials.

Part B: Field Study

1. At your study site, measure a 25-square-meter site with a meterstick (5 m × 5 m). Place one stake at each corner of the site. Loop string around one stake and continue to the next stake until you have formed the boundaries for the site. See Figure 1.

Figure 1

2. On a separate sheet of paper, draw a map of your site. Draw the abiotic features on your map, such as streams, sidewalks, trails, or boulders.

3. Draw colored circles on the map to represent the different organisms you find. Some of your circles will likely overlap. For example, if your site is mostly grass, you may have a colored circle around the entire map. Within this circle might be other colored circles representing trees.

4. Observe your site quietly for 30 minutes. On a separate sheet of paper, record any interactions between organisms that you observe. Such interactions may include getting food or just moving across the site.

5. When you have finished your observations, remove the string and stakes. Leave the site as you found it; do not take anything from it or damage it in any way.

Teaching Tips: You might want to suggest sites with a variety of abiotic features, for example, with both sloping and level ground and with both sunny and shady areas. Encourage different groups to study sites with different features. You may be more comfortable assigning sites rather than letting students choose. As students observe their field site, remind them to be as quiet and as still as possible to improve their chances of observing sensitive biotic factors.

ECOSYSTEM FOOD CHAINS (continued)

◆ Observations

Data Table   Sample Data

Color Key for Organisms			
Color	*Type of Organism*	*Color*	*Type of Organism*
Medium green	Trees	Brown	Evidence of dead animals
Red	Flowers	Blue	Animals
Light green	Bushes	Black	Dead materials
Yellow	Grass	Orange	Fungi

◆ Analyze and Conclude

1. What producers did you observe at your site? What characteristics do these organisms have in common?

   Producers may include a variety of trees, bushes, flowers, mosses, and grasses. All the

   producers at the site are plants and make sugars through photosynthesis.

2. Think about the consumers you observed at your site. Categorize them according to the four main types of consumers that you listed in Pre-Lab question 1.

   Answers will vary based on the animals students observe in their ecosystem. Common

   herbivores include certain insects, caterpillars, mice, squirrels, and rabbits; common carnivores

   include spiders, hawks, owls, and foxes; common omnivores include raccoons and most birds;

   common scavengers include vultures and crows.

3. What are the most important abiotic features of your site? Explain your answer.

   Answers will vary depending on the site. Students might discuss water sources, slope or

   drainage of the site, amount of sunshine the site receives, or presence of human-made features

   as important abiotic features.

ECOSYSTEM FOOD CHAINS (continued)

◆ Critical Thinking and Applications

1. Draw two food chains you observed in your site that contain a producer, a primary consumer, and a secondary consumer. Include appropriate organisms in your drawings even if you did not observe the actual consumption of food.

Answers will vary. Food chains generally include: producer→herbivore→carnivore→top carnivore→decomposer. Sample food chains include: (a) grass→grasshopper→bird→fungi; (b) tree→insect→spider→bird→fungi; (c) tree→beetle→fungi; (d) tree→insect→spider→frog→fungi; (e) plant→rabbit→fox→bacteria; and (f) phytoplankton→snail→bluegill fish→bass→fungi.

2. How do the abiotic factors in your ecosystem affect how the living things in the ecosystem are distributed?

Answers will vary. For example, fewer plants may be found on sloping land where the soil has

eroded, or more plants may be found near a stream where water is abundant.

3. What would happen to the producers and consumers at your site if there were no decomposers?

Raw materials, such as water and minerals, would not be returned to the environment for use by

other organisms. Also, wastes and dead organisms would pile up and overwhelm the

environment.

4. Predict how the biotic and abiotic features might change at your site during different seasons.

Answers will vary but might refer to changes in sunlight, temperature, and precipitation; changes

in animal populations due to migration and hibernation; and changes in the process of

photosynthesis depending on whether trees have leaves.

◆ More to Explore

Compare your site to other sites nearby. Consider both biotic and abiotic features. Also describe any evidence of human influence on your site.

Sites in proximity to one another generally have similar biotic and abiotic features unless there is a distinct change in terrain, such as a body of water or a severe change in topography. Evidence of human influences may include litter and other signs of pollution, sidewalks and other products of construction, and landscaping. If students' sites are at a park, the trees in the park were likely planted by people.

E-3   **LABORATORY INVESTIGATION**

Managing Fisheries

Key Concepts: Living resources must be managed wisely to keep the populations at a level that will provide adequate supplies for future generations.

Skills Focus: Observing, inferring, making models, communicating, forming operational definitions

◆ Pre-Lab Discussion

Time Required: 40 minutes

When explorers first came to the shores of North America, they were amazed at the abundance of resources—towering forests, clear streams, vast grasslands, and a large variety of wildlife. As they began to use these resources, they also began to affect them. Throughout the years, populations of plants and animals have increased and decreased as a result of both natural events and human actions.

One example of a population that has changed over the years is fish. The waters off the shores of North America have supplied large quantities and varieties of fish. Overfishing and other abuses of the fishing areas have caused the populations to greatly decrease. But people are also taking action to protect the fish. In this investigation, you will model a population of cod fish off the Grand Banks—a famous fishing area off the coast of Newfoundland, Canada. You will determine the effect of different events on that fish population.

1. Is a fishery a renewable resource or a nonrenewable resource? Explain your answer.

   It is a renewable resource because the fish population may replenish itself within a short period

   of time.

2. Aquaculture is the farming of water organisms. How might increased aquaculture of fish in an area help the local fisheries? How might it harm them?

   Answers might include the following. The variety of local fish might increase and depletion of

   fisheries would be less likely. It may replace natural habitats, can cause pollution, and can spread

   disease.

◆ Problem

How does a fish population change over time?

◆ Materials *(per group)*

notebook paper, 1 sheet
colored construction paper, 8 sheets of one color
scissors
pencil or pen
set of event cards

Advance Preparation: Use colored construction paper to prepare one set of event cards for each student group. These cards must be a different color than the fish cards. Write "Event" on one side of each card. Write one of the events listed on page 140 of this book on each card. You can use other events if you prefer.

Alternative Materials: Colored index cards can be used instead of sheets of colored paper for the fish cards and event cards.

MANAGING FISHERIES *(continued)*

◆ Safety ✂ *Review the safety guidelines in the front of your lab book.*

Use caution when cutting with scissors.

◆ Procedure

1. As a group, make 8 "fish cards" from each sheet of colored paper, for a total of 64 cards. Write "Fish" on one side of each card. These fish cards represent the population of cod in fisheries off the Grand Banks. Each card represents many fish.

2. Divide a sheet of notebook paper in half. Label one half "Live Fish" and the other half "Dead Fish."

3. Obtain a set of event cards from your teacher. These cards represent events that can affect a fish population.

4. Shuffle and spread out the event cards, facedown. Count off 25 fish cards and place them by the notebook paper, as shown in Figure 1. Set the remaining 39 fish cards aside.

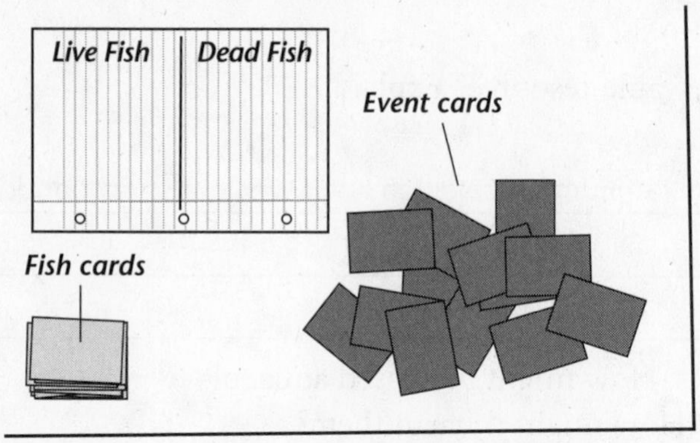

Figure 1

Teaching Tips
- Groups of three students each work well for this activity. Be sure each student participates.
- Be sure students justify their decisions as to why an event will likely increase or decrease the fish population.
- Discuss with students why it is important to replace the event card after each turn. (Similar events can reoccur.)

5. Pick up an event card. As a group, discuss and decide if the event you have chosen will likely increase or decrease the fish population.

6. If the event will increase the population, place a fish card from the stack of 25 on the Live Fish area of the notebook paper. If it will decrease the population, place a fish card on the Dead Fish area of the paper.

7. Replace the event card and mix up the event cards again.

8. Repeat this procedure until all 25 of the fish cards have been placed on either live or dead fish piles on the paper.

9. Count the number of live fish cards on the paper. Add half that number of fish cards from the remaining 39 cards to the live fish stack to represent additional fish added by reproduction. Remove the dead fish cards and set them aside with the remaining fish cards. Complete the Data Table in the Observations section for Generation 1.

MANAGING FISHERIES *(continued)*

10. The stack of live fish cards now represents the beginning of the second generation of fish. Repeat steps 5–9 to find out what happens to the second generation of fish.

11. Repeat steps 5–9 to find out what happens to the third generation of fish.

◆ Observations

Data Table   Sample Data

Starting number of fish cards: 25		
Generation	**Number of Live Fish Cards at End of Generation Before Reproduction**	**Number of Fish Cards After Reproduction**
1	15	23
2	12	18
3	13	20

3

◆ Analyze and Conclude

1. How did your fish population change over time?

Answers will vary but should compare the 25 fish at the beginning of the activity with the ending

number for generation 3 and mention any trends in population change.

2. Compare the number of fish at the end of each generation. Explain your results.

Answers will vary but should reflect the data from the Data Table.

3. What are some ways this investigation models natural selection?

This investigation is like natural selection because it reflects changes in fish population based on

natural environmental factors.

4. What are some ways in which natural selection differs from this model?

This investigation is unlike natural selection because human factors affect the fish population

also.

MANAGING FISHERIES *(continued)*

◆ Critical Thinking and Applications

1. How would fishing crews using a net with a large mesh affect the fish population compared to fishing crews using a net with a small mesh?

Large mesh allows small fish to escape. Large fish are captured, leaving the small fish to grow and reproduce, thus allowing the fish population to remain steady or grow. Small mesh would capture a greater variety of sizes of fish. This would decrease the fish population because fewer young fish would be left to reproduce.

2. List two other factors not listed in the questions or on the event cards that would affect the fish population.

Answers will vary but might include climate and salinity changes.

3. Think about the effect that an increase in the predator population has on the fish population. Does this effect apply to all animal populations? Explain your answer.

Populations of all animal species decrease when the population of predators increases because there is more competition among the predators for resources such as food and habitat.

◆ More to Explore

Choose a different species to investigate. Make your own set of event cards and a data table. Be sure some events will likely increase the population and some will likely decrease it. Repeat the activity, using your event cards and data table. Write a paragraph explaining your results.

Students can work individually or in groups. Be sure students choose events applicable to their chosen species. Some events can be the same as those used for the fish, but some should vary. One strategy is to have students choose different species and compare and contrast how their populations are affected by the same events.

Events for event cards:

Fishing areas are overfished.
Organizations of fishers place limits on the number of fish that can be caught.
Laws state that young, small fish can now be caught.
Laws state that fish smaller than a certain size must be released back into the water.
Water of fishing areas becomes polluted.
Water pollution in fishing areas is cleaned up.
Predator population increases.
Predator population decreases.
Another species is introduced that competes for the same food source as fish.
The population of a species that eats the same food decreases.
Only licensed fishers can catch fish.
Unlicensed fishers illegally catch fish.
Aquaculture cuts down on the number of cod caught.
Aquaculture introduces disease into the fish population.
Laws are enacted to protect the fish population.
Laws to protect the fish are broken.

E-4 | **LABORATORY INVESTIGATION**

Choosing Packing Materials

Key Concepts: Biodegradable packing materials break down when exposed to environmental factors such as water or bacteria. These materials protect package contents as effectively as nonbiodegradable packing materials and reduce the amount of solid waste in landfills.

Skills Focus: Observing, inferring, predicting, posing questions, designing experiments, controlling variables

Time Required: 40 minutes; longer if you discuss results for each part after it is completed

◆ Pre-Lab Discussion

You've just opened a box containing the new CD player you bought. You pull out packing material, more packing material, and more packing material. It's obvious why the shippers used all that packing material—dropping the box could damage your CD player. It has to be cushioned against a jolt.

Packing materials are certainly helpful, but there are some problems with them, too. They are among the many materials dumped daily in landfills. If the packing materials do not break down, they accumulate in the landfill. Biodegradable packing materials are becoming more and more important in reducing the amount of material in landfills. In this investigation, you will compare biodegradable and nonbiodegradable packing materials.

1. What makes a material biodegradable?

A biodegradable material breaks down when exposed to certain environmental factors.

2. How do biodegradable materials break down in a landfill?

They are acted upon by bacteria or by other factors such as water.

◆ Problem

How do biodegradable packing materials compare to nonbiodegradable packing materials?

Advance Preparation: Obtain nonbiodegradable (polystyrene) packing "peanuts" from shipping departments. Biodegradable packing material can be obtained from Clean Green, 720 Florida Avenue, Golden Valley, MN 55426, (612) 545-5400. Hard boil eggs for students to use in Part C.

Teaching Tips: To minimize the materials needed, set up four stations, one for each part, and have students rotate through the stations.

Students may see more air pockets if they break or cut the materials before observing them in Part A.

CHOOSING PACKING MATERIALS *(continued)*

◆ **Possible Materials** *(per group)*

biodegradable packing material,
   about 1 L

nonbiodegradable packing material,
   about 1 L

2 hard-boiled eggs

2 reclosable plastic bags, 1-L size

2 transparent plastic cups

water

hand lens

metric ruler

several heavy books

balance

graduated cylinder

2 stirring rods

Teaching Tips (continued): A compression experiment for Part B might include measuring the thickness of each type of material before and after compression. The amount of force should be held constant, such as stacking the same books on the materials for the same amount of time.

An effectiveness experiment for Part C might include packing a hard-boiled egg in a reclosable bag and dropping it from a certain height. All factors other than the type of packing material should be constant. Avoid using raw eggs because of potential health problems. Students must wash their hands thoroughly after handling eggs.

An experiment for Part D might include putting equal masses of packing materials in equal volumes of water and stirring them.

Explain to students that the biodegradable material is made of starch, and the nonbiodegradable material is made of a plastic called polystyrene.

◆ **Safety**   *Review the safety guidelines in the front of your lab book.*

Do not eat or taste any materials in the lab. Wash your hands after the lab.

4 ◆ **Procedure**

Part A: Appearance

1. Do biodegradable and nonbiodegradable packing materials differ in what they look like when viewed through a hand lens? Predict whether their structures will look the same or different. Explain your prediction.

   Students may predict the structures are different because the overall shape, color, or visible

   appearance of the two materials are different.

2. Look at both types of packing materials through a hand lens. Record what you observe in the Data Table in the row for Part A.

Part B: Change in Shape

1. To be effective, a packing material must not change much in size or shape while it is being used. Predict which material, if either, will change less in size or shape. Explain your prediction.

   Predictions may be based on how flexible and resilient the material looks.

2. Design an experiment that compares how well the packing materials withstand forces of compression. Write your procedure on a separate sheet of paper.

3. Have the teacher approve your procedure before you carry out the experiment. Record your results in the Data Table in the row for Part B.

CHOOSING PACKING MATERIALS *(continued)*

Part C: Effectiveness

1. Is one type of packing material more effective than the other type? Predict which type will better protect a fragile object. Explain your prediction.

Predictions should be based, at least partly, on students' observations in Part A and Part B.

_____

2. On a separate sheet of paper, design an experiment that compares how well both types of packing materials protect a fragile object such as an egg.

3. Have the teacher approve your procedure before you carry out the experiment. Record your results in the Data Table in the row for Part C.

Part D: Biodegradability

1. What do you think will happen to each type of packing material when you put it into water? Explain your prediction.

Students may infer that the biodegradeable material will dissolve in water. They may indicate that

it will dissolve slowly or quickly.

2. Design an experiment that compares what happens to each type of packing material in water. Write your procedure on a separate sheet of paper.

3. Have the teacher approve your procedure before you carry out the experiment. Record your results in the Data Table in the row for Part D.

◆ Observations

Data Table

Part	Observations
A	Materials look similar. Both contain air pockets that vary in size and are visible using a hand lens.
B	Both materials change size and shape about equally under compression.
C	The materials are about equally effective. When the eggs were surrounded by the packing material, they didn't break.
D	The biodegradeable material dissolved. The other material didn't.

◆ Analyze and Conclude

1. How do your predictions compare with your observations? For each prediction that differs from the observations, explain why it differs.

Answers will vary. Predictions may reflect the belief that, to get a benefit (biodegradability), you

have to sacrifice some usefulness.

_____

CHOOSING PACKING MATERIALS *(continued)*

2. How do air pockets make a packing material useful?

The air pockets compress enough to cushion an impact and then return to their original size and

shape. Air pockets also make the packing material lightweight, so the material does not add

much weight to the package.

3. What factors did you keep constant in Part B?

Student answers might include the force applied, the amount of material used, and the method

used to measure the differences in thickness.

◆ Critical Thinking and Applications

1. Do you think that breaking apart in water is a good way for a packing material to degrade? Give a reason for your answer.

Answers will vary, but may include that it is good because water is plentiful, found in nature, and

will cause the material to break down in a landfill; or that it is not good because packages have

to be protected from any exposure to water.

2. What other uses can you think of for a material that breaks down in water?

Answers might include pills that can be time-released as their outer coating dissolves, or foods

released from packaging when placed in water.

3. What are some disadvantages of using biodegradable materials as packing materials?

If the package gets wet, the water may seep into the packaging material and begin dissolving it.

Even if the package dried, the packing material would lose its effectiveness and become messy.

4. If you were shipping a fragile gift to a friend, which of the two packing materials from this lab would you use? Why?

If both materials were equally effective at protecting the contents of a package, students might

choose the biodegradable material because it will break down quickly in a landfill.

◆ More to Explore

Think about other materials that would make good packing materials and are biodegradable. Examine several of these materials. For each, explain why it would or would not be a practical packing material. Predict its effectiveness at protecting a package's contents. On a separate sheet of paper, write a procedure you could use to test your predictions. Have the teacher approve your procedure before you carry out your investigation.

Have some potential packing materials on hand for students to explore. These might include popcorn, shredded paper, peanut shells, and sawdust. Students might base suitability on whether the material attracts water or insects, settles too much, or is expensive.

Pollution Prevention With Rocks

Key Concepts: Environmental pollution by acids harms organisms in streams and lakes and on land. Limestone can neutralize acidity.

Skills Focus: Observing, making models, communicating, measuring

Time Required: 40 minutes

◆ Pre-Lab Discussion

Pollution that increases the acidity of lakes and streams is not a new problem. For millions of years, natural sources of air pollution, such as volcanoes, have released materials that react with rainwater to produce acids. However, the problem has increased as more pollutants enter the air from industry and motor vehicles. Acid rain pollutes land and water, harming the life found there. Because wind can carry these pollutants a long way, the problem is not limited to areas with extensive industry and lots of traffic.

Another source of acid pollution is water that drains from coal-mining sites. Acids form when water flows through the coal layers and rocks. The polluted water then flows into nearby streams.

To monitor acid content in a stream or lake, scientists test the pH of water. pH indicates how acidic or basic the water is. The pH scale ranges from 0 to 14. Pure water is neutral and has a pH of 7. A solution with a pH less than 7 is an acid, and one with a pH greater than 7 is a base.

In this investigation, you will see how rocks can be used naturally to help solve the problem of acidic lakes and streams.

5

1. What are two sources of acid pollution?

Sources of acid pollution include motor vehicles and power plants and factories that burn coal

and oil.

2. If acid pollution killed most of the plants in a pond, what would happen to the fish population? Give a reason for your answer.

The fish population would decrease because the food and oxygen supply for the fish has

decreased.

◆ Problem

How can acid pollution from mines be prevented?

Advance Preparation: Cut an appropriate number of pieces of gutter and blocks of wood. Scrap wood may be available from a local lumberyard or an industrial arts class.

Alternative Materials: Use graduated cylinders or metric measuring cups instead of beakers. Any nonmetallic container that fits under the lower end of the gutter can be used instead of the plastic bowl. In place of the gutter, you can use folded oak tag or cardboard lined with plastic wrap. Any noncarbonate rock can be used instead of granite. Any objects that provide a stable, gradual slope for the gutter can replace the wood blocks; provide objects that will not be damaged by spilled vinegar. If you use books, be sure they are covered.

POLLUTION PREVENTION WITH ROCKS *(continued)*

◆ **Materials** *(per group)*

granite chips
limestone chips
vinyl rain gutter, 30–40 cm long
block of wood, about 7 cm high
block of wood, about 10 cm high
plastic bowl or cup
white vinegar, 100 mL
beaker, 250-mL
pH test paper and chart

Teaching Tips: If the gutters do not seem stable, set up other blocks of wood to support the sides.

Do not use any acid with noticeable color, such as cider vinegar, as this may affect the color observed on the pH paper. The amount of vinegar poured into the gutter is not critical. However, the same amount should be used for each trial.

If the vinegar has little difference in pH after traveling through the limestone, decrease the slope of the gutter. A lower slope will increase the time that the vinegar is in contact with the rocks.

The rocks can be reused. Rinse and dry them before storing.

◆ **Safety**   *Review the safety guidelines in the front of your lab book. Be careful not to spill any of the materials.*

◆ **Procedure**

1. Use granite chips to line the bottom of a piece of rain gutter.

2. Set each end of the gutter on a block of wood so that the gutter has a gentle slope. The slope should be gentle enough so that the rocks do not slide.

3. Place a plastic bowl under the lower end of the gutter to catch any liquid that drains through.

4. Pour about 50 mL of vinegar into the beaker.

5. Dip the end of a strip of pH test paper into the vinegar. Match the color of the pH paper to the number on the pH indicator chart. Record the pH in the Data Table.

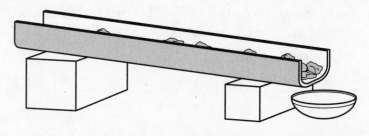

Figure 1

6. Slowly pour the vinegar into the upper end of the gutter, allowing it to flow through the granite to the lower end. Observe what, if anything, happens as the vinegar touches the rocks.

7. Dip the end of a strip of pH test paper into the vinegar that has flowed through the granite and collected in the bowl. Match the color to the chart and record the pH in the Data Table.

8. Remove the rocks from the gutter. Rinse the rocks and the gutter with water.

9. Repeat the experiment, using limestone chips instead of granite.

10. Answer question 1 in Observations.

POLLUTION PREVENTION WITH ROCKS *(continued)*

◆ Observations

Data Table   Sample Data

Type of Rock	pH of Vinegar Before Flowing Through Rocks	pH of Vinegar After Flowing Through Rocks
Granite	3	3
Limestone	3	6

1. What did you observe as you watched the vinegar flow through the rocks in the two trials?

The vinegar and limestone produced bubbles, indicating a reaction. No bubbles appeared with

the granite and the vinegar.

◆ Analyze and Conclude

1. Is vinegar an acid, a base, or neither? Give a reason for your answer.

Vinegar is an acid because its pH is less than 7.

2. Compare the acidity of vinegar before and after it flowed through the granite and before and after it flowed through the limestone.

The pH of vinegar was the same after flowing through the granite and higher after flowing

through the limestone.

3. Use your observations and data to state which rock could be used to help prevent pollution from acid mine drainage. Explain your answer.

Limestone chips could be used because they will react with the acid, reducing the acidity of any

water passing through them.

◆ Critical Thinking and Applications

1. Some streams flow over limestone. How do you think the limestone affects the pH of the stream?

The limestone keeps the pH neutral if it was initially neutral, raises the pH of acidic water

(because the limestone reacts with the acid), and has no effect on water that is basic.

POLLUTION PREVENTION WITH ROCKS (continued)

2. Ditches that are lined with limestone are often seen in coal-mining areas. Would these ditches help prevent pollution of groundwater? Give a reason for your answer.

Yes, acidic drainage water passing through these ditches would become less acidic as the acid reacts with the limestone.

3. Farmers often spread lime, made from powdered limestone, on their fields. Why do you think they use lime?

Some soils are naturally acidic or become acidic from acid rain. Some crops require neutral or basic soil. The lime lessens acidity of the soil so the crops can grow.

4. Powdered limestone is often dumped into lakes that have become highly acidic. Why do you think powdered limestone is used instead of limestone chips?

Limestone chips would produce the same effect but would take longer because the surface area of limestone chips is much less than that of powdered limestone. The powdered limestone reduces the acidity much more quickly.

5. Why wouldn't powered limestone be used in a stream or drainage ditch?

Limestone chips stay in place. Powdered limestone would wash away and not be available to neutralize additional acid that flows downstream.

More to Explore

New Problem What other materials could help prevent acid pollution from mines?

Possible Materials Consider which materials you can use from the previous part of this lab. Consider what materials you would like to test.

Safety Wear lab aprons and safety goggles.

Procedure Develop a procedure to solve the problem. Write your procedure on a separate sheet of paper. Have the teacher approve your procedure before you carry out the investigation.

Observations On a separate sheet of paper, make a data table in which to record your data.

Students may choose to test other rocks including roadside gravel. Limestone and dolomite are common rocks that will react with acids. Sandstone, shale, and granite will not. Another material that will react with acids is chalk. When approving student plans, be sure they include necessary precautions for using acids.

5

E-6   **LABORATORY INVESTIGATION**

Solar Heating

Key Concepts: The color of an object affects the amount of solar energy that object absorbs.

Skills Focus: Observing, inferring, measuring, graphing

Time Required: 60 minutes

◆ Pre-Lab Discussion

It has been estimated that 1,000 times more energy reaches Earth's surface from the sun each year than could be produced by burning all the fossil fuels mined and extracted during that year. Imagine if people could use even a small fraction of that solar energy; many of our resource and pollution problems would be solved!

The idea of using the sun's energy is not new. Many ancient peoples used solar energy for heating their homes, including the Egyptians, the Greeks, the Romans, and Native Americans. These peoples built their homes facing the south or south-west, where the sun is located in the sky most often in the Northern Hemisphere. This passive solar-heating system, in which sunlight heats an area, is used today to provide renewable, nonpolluting energy. But the sun is not always shining, so the sun's heat must be collected and stored for later use during the night and on cloudy days. This task is usually part of an active solar-heating system, in which solar energy is collected and distributed throughout a building using fans and pumps.

Solar collectors are used to absorb and collect solar energy. A solar collector is basically a box mounted on a roof. The box is covered with a material that absorbs the sun's energy. This energy transfers to air or water in the box and moves into the building where it can be used. In this investigation, you will discover how the color of an object affects the amount of solar energy it absorbs.

1. What forms of energy are constantly given off from the sun?

   The sun constantly gives off energy in the form of light and heat.

2. What is the difference between a passive solar-heating system and an active solar-heating system?

   A passive solar-heating system converts light from the sun into thermal energy without using

   mechanical pumps or fans. An active solar-heating system captures the sun's energy, then uses

   fans and pumps to distribute the heat.

Advance Preparation: Collect metal or plastic containers with fitted plastic lids. The containers should all be about the same size. Tall containers, such as quart-size food containers, will be stable enough to support lab thermometers without tipping over. Each lab group will need two containers that are identical in size and are made of the same materials.

◆ Problem

How does the color of an object affect the amount of solar energy it absorbs?

This lab must be performed on a day when there is adequate sunshine.

SOLAR HEATING (*continued*)

◆ Materials (*per group*)

black and white construction paper
tape
scissors
2 metal or plastic containers with plastic lids
2 thermometers
tongs or gloves
clock or watch
colored pens or pencils

Teaching Tips:

Ask students to check that the containers are stable once the thermometers are inserted.

Have students plot the temperatures of the containers, using a different color for each line on the graph.

◆ Safety   *Review the safety guidelines in the front of your lab book.*

Be careful when using scissors.

◆ Procedure

1. Tape two layers of black paper completely around one container. Also tape two layers of black paper over one of the lids. Keep the edge of the lid paper-free so that it will fit on the can. Tape two layers of white paper completely around the other container. Cover its lid with two layers of white paper.

2. Using scissors, carefully punch a small hole through the center of each lid. Each hole should be just large enough to hold a thermometer.

3. Cover each container with its plastic lid of the same color. Place the containers on a sunny windowsill.

4. Carefully insert a thermometer through the hole in each lid as shown in Figure 1. Make sure the bulb of the thermometer is near but not touching the bottom of the container.

5. Record the temperature of the air in each container every 3 minutes for 30 minutes. Record your data in the Data Table. Then answer the questions in Observations.

6. Use the graph paper on page 151 to make a graph of your data. Plot temperature on the vertical axis and time on the horizontal axis.

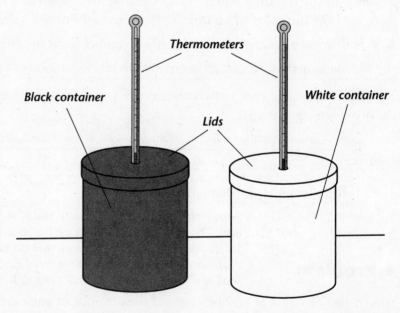

Thermometers
Black container
White container
Lids

Figure 1

SOLAR HEATING *(continued)*

Time (min)

SOLAR HEATING *(continued)*

◆ Observations

Data Table   Sample Data

Time (min)	Temperature in Black Container (°C)	Temperature in White Container (°C)
0	19	19
3	20	19
6	21	19
9	22	20
12	23	20
15	24	20
18	25	20
21	26	20
24	26	21
27	26	21
30	26	21

Temperature in black container will rise faster that that in white container.

1. During which time interval did the temperature in the black container begin to rise? During which time interval did the temperature in the white container begin to rise?

Time intervals will vary, depending on the specific conditions of the experiment, but the

temperature should begin to rise in the black container first.

2. What was the final temperature of the air in the black container? In the white container?

Final temperatures will vary, depending on the specific conditions of the experiment, but the final

temperature should be higher in the black container than in the white container.

◆ Analyze and Conclude

1. Did the color of the containers affect the amount of solar energy they absorbed? Explain your answer.

Yes. The container covered with black paper absorbed more energy and heated at a faster rate

than did the container covered with white paper.

SOLAR HEATING (*continued*)

2. Did your experiment represent a passive or an active solar-heating system? Explain.

It represented a passive solar-heating system because the container was heated directly by the energy of the sun, and pumps or fans were not used to distribute the heat.

3. What additional variables might have affected your results?

Variables might include the thickness or the composition of the containers, any cold drafts of wind near the windows, shadows cast on either container over the course of the experiment, and proximity to a heat source such as a radiator.

◆ Critical Thinking and Applications

1. Why was it important that both containers be the same size?

If both containers were not the same size, the difference in the amounts of air in each container would be an uncontrolled variable that could affect the results.

2. How would this system need to be modified if it were to be used to heat a home?

Answers will vary, but responses should include some method of transferring the heat to different areas of the home.

3. Based on the results of this experiment, what color clothing would best help you stay warm in the winter? Cool in the summer? Explain.

Wearing dark-colored clothing can help a person absorb more solar energy and so stay warmer in the winter; wearing light-colored clothing can help a person reflect solar energy and so stay cooler in the summer.

4. In what other situations would you be able to apply the knowledge you gained in this investigation? Consider surfaces used both indoors and outdoors, in which heat absorption or reflection is important.

Answers will vary. Some possible situations include choosing a color for an automobile, for the surface of a patio, deck, driveway, or paving stones, for a house or roof, for awnings, shades, or curtains, for a camping tent, or for cooking equipment that makes use of solar energy.

5. What are some advantages of solar energy compared with fossil fuels?

Answers will vary. Most students will conclude that solar energy is a cleaner energy source than fossil fuels are and that its renewability is also a strong advantage.

6

SOLAR HEATING *(continued)*

◆ More to Explore

New Problem What effect do different colors (other than black and white) have on the absorption of solar energy?

Possible Materials Consider which materials you can use from the lab. What other materials might you need?

Safety Be careful when using sharp scissors.

Procedure Make a hypothesis based on the question you want to investigate. Upon what do you base your hypothesis? Make sure to include a control for analyzing and comparing results. Write your procedure on a separate sheet of paper. Have the teacher approve your procedure before you carry out your investigation.

Observations Keep records of your observations on a separate sheet of paper.

Analyze and Conclude

How effective are the different colors at absorbing heat from the sun?

In general, the darker the color, the better is the energy-absorbing ability of the material.

Experiments will vary but should be designed to test the energy-absorbing abilities of different colors. Students may use the same setup of the laboratory but tape a different color of construction paper around each of the containers.

6

F-1   **LABORATORY INVESTIGATION**

Mapping a Future World

Key Concept: Earth's continents and oceans ride on plates that are moving at a slow rate and affect many of Earth's features, such as mountains and ocean basins.

Skills Focus: Model the continents' movement and use the model to predict future locations and features on Earth.

Time Required: 40 minutes

1

◆ Pre-Lab Discussion

You can't feel the land underneath you moving every day, but it is! The surface of Earth is divided into continents and oceans. These landmasses and water bodies are slowly but surely changing their positions and shapes. Scientists have measured these movements of a few centimeters a year.

What will Earth look like in the future? No one can be sure where the continents will end up. In this investigation, you will predict what Earth will look like as you map the movement of the continents.

1. What are plates in the Earth's crust?

Plates are separate sections of the lithosphere that fit closely together along cracks in the crust.

_____

2. What does plate tectonics mean?

Plate tectonics is the theory that the movement of convection currents in the mantle slowly shifts

pieces of Earth's lithosphere.

◆ Problem

Advance Preparation: Make a second copy of the map for each student.

Where will the continents be in the distant future, and how will their position affect mountains and oceans around the world?

◆ Materials *(per group)*

2 outline maps of the world showing
   latitude and longitude lines
scissors
colored pencils or markers
envelope
pencil or pen
clear tape
world map or globe

Teaching Tips: Encourage students to choose different cities on each continent so that differences in location can be compared.

Review proportions for the calculations. Have students set up the scale value on one side of the proportion and use 100 million as the time factor in the other part, e.g.: x/100 000 000 yr = 2.6 cm/1 yr. Remind students that 1 km = 100 000 cm.

Have slabs of modeling clay available to help students visualize what happens when plates move apart or are pushed together.

◆ Safety *Review the safety guidelines in the front of your lab book.*

Use caution in handling sharp scissors.

MAPPING A FUTURE WORLD (*continued*)

◆ Procedure

1. You will ignore the movement of Antarctica in this activity. Label the other continents and the oceans on the two outline maps.

2. You will need reference points when you start moving continents. Use a world map or globe to locate and label one city on each continent on both of the maps. In Data Table 2 in Observations, record the current latitude and longitude of each reference-point city.

3. From one map, carefully cut out the continents. Keep these pieces in an envelope when you are not using them.

4. Assemble a complete world map—the base map—by cutting out the map on one page and overlapping it with the map on the other page. The 20°W longitude lines (also called meridians) should overlay each other. Carefully tape the map together along the 20°W longitude line.

5. Lay the cutout continents on the base map in their current positions. You should be able to slide your cutouts easily over your base map.

6. Predict where the continents will be in 100 million years. Slowly move the continents to where you predict they will be. Trace their outlines lightly in pencil. Assume that the Indo-Australian Plate splits in a few million years, and India and Australia continue to move at the same rate.

7. Now, check your predictions. Use the plate speeds in Data Table 1 and the map in your textbook (p. 43) to find the direction and rate of movement for each plate that carries a continent. Calculate how far each continent will drift in 100 million years. Record these figures in Data Table 2 in Observations.

Data Table 1

Plate	Speed (cm/yr)
African	0.66
Eurasian	0.95
Indo-Australian	8.50
North American	2.31
South American	3.55

8. Use the scale on the base map to help you decide where the continents will be in 100 million years. Slowly move the cutout continents to their new locations. Trace their outlines on your base map, using a different color for each continent. Some continents may overlap in their new positions. Trace the outlines overlapping.

9. Mark and record the new location of each reference point.

10. Compare your completed map to your predictions. Then compare it to those of your classmates and discuss any differences.

Assuming constant motion, in 100 million years the African plate will move 660 km, the Eurasian plate will move 950 km, the Indo-Australian plate will move 8500 km, the North American plate will move 2310 km, and the South American plate will move 3550 km. Student maps should show these relative amounts of motion in the directions in the textbook map (p. 43).

MAPPING A FUTURE WORLD *(continued)*

◆ Observations

Data Table 2

Sample Data

These locations are approximations.

Continent	Reference Point	Location Now (Latitude and Longitude)	Distance Traveled in 100 Million Years	Location in 100 Million Years (Latitude and Longitude)
Africa	Tangier, Morocco	36°N, 6°W		40°N, 3°W
Asia	Beijing, China	40°N, 116°E		35°N, 125°E
Australia	Melbourne	39°S, 145°E		25°N, 145°E
Europe	Lisbon, Portugal	39°N, 9°W		35°N, 0°
North America	New York City	41°N, 74°W		50°N, 95°W
South America	Brasilia, Brazil	16°S, 48°W		16°S, 75°W

◆ Analyze and Conclude

1. How did your predicted locations of continents compare with the locations in Step 8?

   Predicted directions were more likely to be correct than the predicted distances.

2. What will happen to the location of North and South America as sea-floor spreading widens the Atlantic Ocean?

   North and South America will move farther west.

3. What will happen to the size of the Pacific Ocean as North America moves west?

   The Pacific Ocean will get smaller.

4. How did the latitude and longitude of your reference point in South America change?

   The latitude remains the same, and the longitude is farther west.

5. What might happen to the Himalayas over the next several million years? Give a reason for your answer.

   Answers will vary. Sample answer: The height of the Himalayas will increase because the Eurasian

   and Indo-Australian plates are colliding, crumpling the crust and pushing the mountains higher.

MAPPING A FUTURE WORLD *(continued)*

1

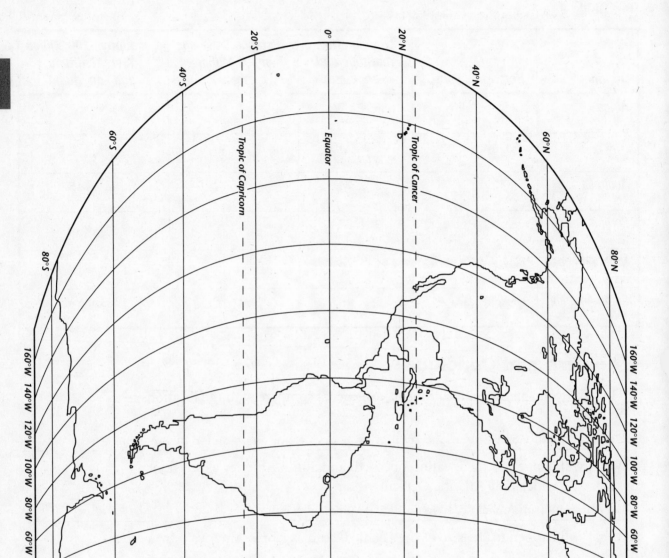

MAPPING A FUTURE WORLD *(continued)*

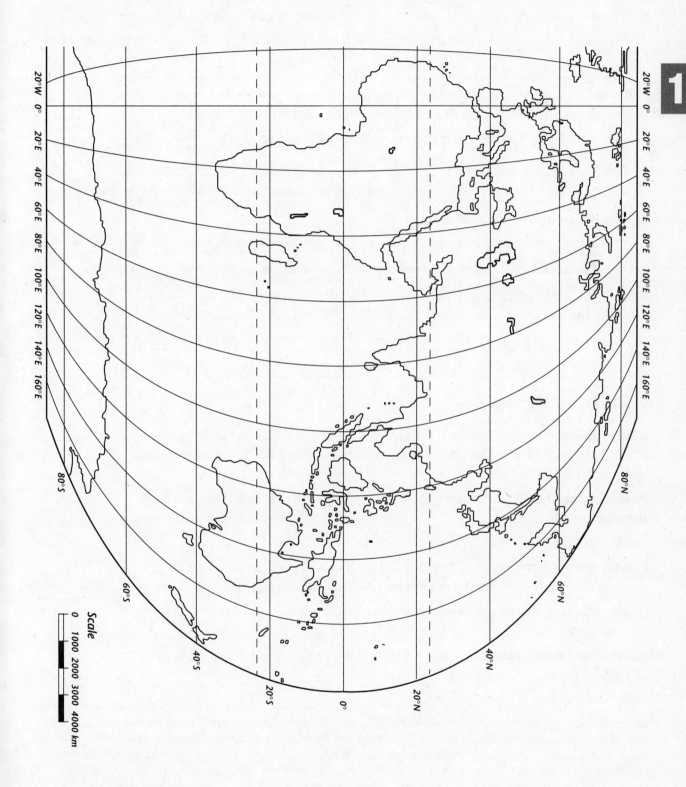

MAPPING A FUTURE WORLD *(continued)*

◆ Critical Thinking and Applications

1. Why did many scientists not accept the early theories of continental drift?

There was no satisfactory explanation for the force that pushes or pulls the continents, and the

movement is so slow that it is not obvious.

2. Based on your movements of the continents, where do you predict new mountain ranges will be forming in 100 million years? Explain your reasoning.

New mountain ranges will likely form in northern Africa or southern Europe as those two

continents collide. Mountains might also form in northern Australia as that continent collides with

Asia. Collisions will be evidenced on students' maps by overlapping outlines of the continents.

3. Why do continents move at different rates?

Answers will vary. Sample answer: Speed of movement depends on the fluidity of the underlying

matter and whether the plates are colliding with or pulling apart from surrounding plates.

4. Which is more important in determining the future location of a city—what continent it is on or what plate it is on? Give a reason for your answer.

Movement of a plate determines movement of any continent on it, so location on the plate is

more important. The size and shape of a continent may change over millions of years.

◆ More to Explore

New Problem Near what city's location will Los Angeles, California, be in about 17 million years? (Hint: The rate of plate movement along the San Andreas Fault is about 3.4 cm/yr.)

Possible Materials Use the same map and continent shapes as before. You may also need scissors again.

Safety Use caution in handling sharp scissors.

Procedure Predict where Los Angeles will be. Then develop a procedure to test your prediction. Get the teacher's approval before carrying out your investigation.

Observations Record your prediction. Also record any appropriate observations on your base map.

Analyze and Conclude Where do you think Los Angeles will be located in about 17 million years?

near San Francisco

Students could best model the movement of Los Angeles by cutting their North America continent shape along the San Andreas Fault and moving the Pacific Plate northwestward. The rate of 3.4 cm/yr equals 578 km in 17 million years, which would put Los Angeles near San Francisco. Students can estimate this distance by comparing 3.4 cm/yr to their calculations for Step 6. This comparison gives a distance of 3,400 km in 100 million years. Since 17 million is about $\frac{1}{6}$ of 100 million, students should move the plate $\frac{1}{6} \times 3,400 =$ about 566 km, which is still near San Francisco.

F-2   **LABORATORY INVESTIGATION**

Investigating the Speed of Earthquake Waves

Key Concept: Earthquakes produce primary and secondary waves, which travel at different speeds. The time between the arrival of each wave type can be used to locate the earthquake epicenter.

Skills Focus: Inferring, predicting, graphing

Time Required: 40 minutes

◆ Pre-Lab Discussion

An earthquake produces waves that travel away from the earthquake's epicenter, like ripples on a pond when you throw in a pebble. An earthquake produces three types of waves, primary (P waves), secondary (S waves), and surface waves. Seismologists track how far and how fast P and S waves travel to find the epicenter of the quake.

In this investigation, you will construct a travel-time graph for P and S waves. You will use the graph to answer some questions about earthquakes.

1. What causes an earthquake?

Stress in the subsurface rock causes the rock to break or slip, releasing energy stored in the rock.
_____

2. What is the epicenter of an earthquake?

The epicenter is the point on Earth's surface directly above an earthquake's focus.
_____

◆ Problem

Advance Preparation: Have yarn, spring toys, and stopwatches available for More to Explore.

How can you use a graph of earthquake waves' travel distance and time to find an epicenter?

Teaching Tips: Encourage students to use the Internet to learn more about earthquakes. A site at which students can track and predict earthquakes around the world is http://athena.wednet.edu/curric/land/todayqk.html

◆ Materials *(per group)*

pen or pencil

◆ Procedure

Students may have trouble graphing seconds. Using a transparency of the grid or a grid on the chalkboard, have students locate several points to emphasize that each division is equal to 20 s.

1. An earthquake produced P and S waves that were recorded by instruments at 20 stations. These waves are listed in the Data Table on the next page. The table shows the distance traveled and the travel time for each wave. Using these data, construct a graph showing the relationship between the distance traveled by P and S waves and their travel times. Label the curves *P wave* or *S wave*.

2. Use your graph to answer the questions.

INVESTIGATING THE SPEED OF EARTHQUAKE WAVES *(continued)*

Data Table

Wave Type	Distance Traveled From Epicenter (km)	Travel Time (min) (s)	
P	1600	3	20
P	6500	9	50
P	5400	8	40
P	2000	4	00
P	9600	12	40
P	700	1	30
P	7000	10	20
P	3400	6	10
P	8800	12	00
P	4000	7	00
S	2200	8	00
S	4000	12	40
S	5200	15	20
S	1700	6	30
S	6000	17	00
S	1100	4	20
S	7400	19	40
S	8200	21	00
S	500	2	10
S	9000	22	10

INVESTIGATING THE SPEED OF EARTHQUAKE WAVES *(continued)*

◆ Observations

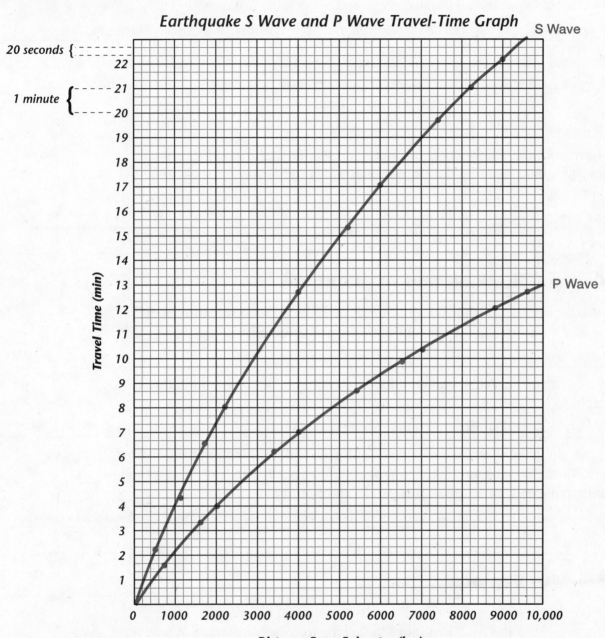

Earthquake S Wave and P Wave Travel-Time Graph

◆ Analyze and Conclude

1. If an earthquake occurred near you, would P waves or S waves reach you first? Give a reason for your answer.

P waves travel faster and would arrive first. However, if you were near the epicenter, the

difference might be negligible.

INVESTIGATING THE SPEED OF EARTHQUAKE WAVES *(continued)*

2. How long would a P wave take to travel 8000 km from an earthquake epicenter? How long would an S wave take to travel the same distance?

Interpolating from the graph of the data in the table, it would take 11 min 20 s for the P waves to

arrive and 20 min 40 s for the S waves to arrive.

3. Approximately how far is an observer from an earthquake epicenter if he or she observed a P wave 8 min after the earthquake?

Interpolating from the graph of the data in the table, the observer is 4,800 km away.

4. How could you tell which of two observers was farther from an earthquake epicenter by comparing the arrival times of P and S waves for the two locations?

The observer who clocked more time between the first arrival of P and S waves would be farther

from the epicenter.

◆ Critical Thinking and Applications

1. How far from an earthquake epicenter is an observer who measured a difference of 8 min 40 s in the arrival times of P and S waves?

7000 km

2. If a curve for surface waves was added to the graph, where would it appear? Explain.

The curve would be above both the P and S curves because surface waves travel the slowest.

3. States along the West Coast, such as California and Washington, have much earthquake and volcanic activity. What does this activity indicate about the underlying rock structure of this part of the country?

The underlying rock structure is close to a plate boundary and is subject to stress that may

break it.

◆ More to Explore

Tie a piece of colorful yarn to a coil near the middle of a spring toy. Move the spring to create a P wave. Then move the spring to create an S wave. Which wave travels faster? Which kind of wave produces the most overall motion of the yarn? Which wave would cause more damage as a seismic wave?

Students should observe that the speed of the compression wave is greater, but the overall movement of the yarn is greater in the transverse wave, reinforcing the concept that S waves cause more damage than P waves do.

F-3   # LABORATORY INVESTIGATION

Predicting Lava Flows

Key Concepts: The fluidity of magma and lava depend on both their temperature and the amount of silica they contain. The type of volcano produced by an eruption depends in part on the fluidity of the lava that forms it.

◆ Pre-Lab Discussion

Skills Focus: Observing, inferring, making models, communicating, designing experiments, creating data tables

You know that a liquid becomes a solid if its temperature is lowered enough that the substance freezes. If you freeze a mixture of cream, eggs, and flavoring in an ice-cream maker, the result is ice cream. When the molten wax on a candle cools, it turns into a solid. The type of material that results depends on the liquid you started out with.

Time Required: 40 minutes

Volcanic rocks form on Earth's surface when lava cools and "freezes." But are all rocks formed from lava the same?

Because different types of lava are made from different materials, they also behave differently when they flow on Earth's surface and harden into rock. Two main types of lava differ in how easily they flow because of their silica content. In this investigation, you will relate the ease of flow of different types of lava to the shapes of the volcanoes they form.

Alternative Materials: If graduated cylinders are not available, a metric measuring cup can be used.

3

1. In addition to silica content, what are two other differences between different types of lava?

   temperature and gas content
   _____

2. If you are comparing how easily different types of lava flow, why do you have to make sure that the temperature of each is the same?

   Ease of flow also depends on temperature. Cooler lava is thicker than hotter lava. To make an
   _____

   appropriate comparison, only one factor can be varied at a time.
   _____

Teaching Tips: [Step 1] Lab groups should be no smaller than three students. Be sure students protect themselves and all surfaces from spills. Caution students to add water gradually to the cornstarch, a little at a time, so that the result is somewhat runny.

◆ Problem

How do the temperature and composition of lava affect the way it flows?

[Step 3] Ask students to relate other examples of when the thickness (viscosity) of something matters. Answers might include motor oil, which can vary in viscosity depending on its use and temperature, and concrete, which varies in thickness before it sets, depending on its use and environmental conditions.

◆ Possible Materials (per group)

molasses, about 20 mL
cornstarch, about 25 mL
spoon
watch or clock with second hand
cookie sheet or food tray

graduated cylinder, 100 mL
water
paper towels
newspaper
meterstick
3 paper cups or beakers, at least 100 mL each

PREDICTING LAVA FLOWS *(continued)*

◆ Safety   *Review the safety guidelines in the front of your lab book.*

Wear a lab apron and safety goggles while doing this activity.

◆ Procedure

Part A: Modeling Types of Lava

1. Add about 25 mL of cornstarch to a cup or beaker. Add about 25 mL of water, a small amount at a time, to the cornstarch while mixing. A runny mixture, about the thickness of milk, should result. This mixture is a model of low-silica lava.

2. To model high-silica lava, use a spoon to place about 5 mL of molasses into a different cup or beaker.

3. Compare and contrast the thickness of the two types of "lava." Predict which type will move faster down a slope. Explain your reasoning.

   Students may predict that the "low-silica lava" will flow faster because it is thinner.
   _____

   Design an experiment to test your prediction. Write your procedure on another sheet of paper.

4. Decide what types of data you will need to collect. Add columns, rows, and headings to the Data Table in Observations as appropriate.

5. After the teacher has approved your procedure and Data Table, conduct your investigation.

Part B: Modeling Lava at Different Temperatures

Dispense hot samples of molasses from a hot plate to students once they have developed a satisfactory procedure.

1. Use molasses to investigate the effect of temperature on lava flow.

2. Predict whether a hot sample or a room-temperature sample of molasses will move faster down a slope. Explain your reasoning.

   Answers may vary. Sample: The hot molasses will flow faster because it will be thinner than the
   _____

   cool molasses.

3. Design an experiment to test your prediction. Write down your precedure on a separate sheet of paper. Repeat Steps 4 and 5 from Part A. Obtain a hot sample of molasses from your teacher.

4. Follow any special instructions the teacher gives you about cleaning up your work area. Throw any "lava" materials, paper towels, and newspaper in the trash can. Do not wash any materials down the drain. Wash your hands after everything else is cleaned up.

   The materials used are not caustic but might plug a drain.

PREDICTING LAVA FLOWS *(continued)*

◆ Observations

Data Table

Students should observe that "low-silica lava" is thinner and flows faster than does "high-silica lava." They should also observe that hotter "lava" flows faster than does cooler "lava."

◆ Analyze and Conclude

1. In Part A, which type of "lava" flowed slower, high-silica or low-silica "lava"? In Part B, which type of "lava" flowed slower, hot "lava" or room-temperature "lava"?

high-silica lava, room-temperature lava

2. Compare two types of lava: pahoehoe and aa. How are they similar? How are they different? How were these two types of lava represented in this experiment?

They are similar in that they are both low-silica lava. They differ in temperature; pahoehoe is

hotter than aa and flows more easily. The hot molasses represented pahoehoe; the room-

temperature molasses represented aa.

3. On the left below, sketch and name the type of volcano that would be formed from low-silica lava. On the right below, sketch and name the type of volcano that would be formed from high-silica lava.

Students' sketches should show a volcano with gentle slopes—a shield volcano—on the left and a volcano with steep slopes—a cinder cone volcano—on the right.

4. Describe the kind of eruptions you would expect as a volcano forms from low-silica lava.

The eruptions would be relatively quiet, with spurting and flowing lava but no explosions.

PREDICTING LAVA FLOWS *(continued)*

5. Describe the kind of eruptions you would expect as a volcano forms from high-silica lava.

The eruptions would be more explosive than with low-silica lava.

◆ Critical Thinking and Applications

1. How does the shape of a volcano help you draw conclusions about the type of magma near the surface beneath the volcano?

The shape of the volcano indicates the amount of silica in the magma that erupted to the

surface.

2. What type of magma occurs near the surface beneath a composite volcano? Give a reason for your answer.

Because the magma beneath composite volcanoes is high in silica, these volcanoes alternate

between explosive eruptions and eruptions of thick lava.

◆ More to Explore

3

New Problem How does the gas content in magma affect the shape of a volcano?

Possible Materials
  modeling clay
  vinegar
  baking soda
  paper towels

Procedures may include forming a cone from the modeling clay. Students may place varying amounts of baking soda in the cone and then add a consistent amount of vinegar each time.

Safety Wear safety goggles and laboratory aprons.

Procedure Develop a plan to determine how volcano shape depends on the gas content of the magma. Write the steps of your plan on another sheet of paper. Have the teacher approve your plan before you carry out your investigation. (*Hint:* Vinegar and baking soda will react to form a gas.)

Observations Record your observations in a data table on a separate sheet of paper.

Analyze and Conclude Based on your observations, write a statement of how the gas content of magma is related to the shape of the volcano.

Observations should show that the more baking soda used, the more gas formed, and the more

explosive the eruption. Observations should indicate that the more explosive the eruption, the

steeper the slope that formed.

F - 4

How Tessellating!

Key Concept: Repeating patterns, or tessellations, of atoms that have no gaps or overlaps form crystals.

Skills Focus: Observing, classifying, making models, forming operational definitions

◆ Pre-Lab Discussion

Time Required: 50 minutes

A floor covered with tiles may be made of repeated squares. A honeycomb is made of repeated hexagons. Crystal shapes within a mineral have definite repeating patterns, too. A pattern tessellates if it repeats and covers a plane (such as a sheet of paper, a floor, or a wall) with no gaps or overlaps. See Figure 1. In this investigation, you will model crystal shapes by creating patterns that tessellate.

Figure 1

Sample Tessellation

Advance Preparation: Gather several small mirrors for More to Explore. Mirrors should be unframed and have edges that aren't sharp.

4

1. Think about what makes up a mineral. Why isn't coal a mineral?

   Coal is naturally occurring and a solid, but it is not inorganic because it is made from plant

   matter. There are several types of coal, so it does not have a definite composition. Students

   may not be aware that coal has no crystal shape.

2. How many sides does a hexagonal figure have?

   Six

◆ Problem

What patterns tessellate?

◆ Materials *(per group)*

index cards
tape
scissors
plain white paper
colored pencils
ruler

Teaching Tips: Be sure that students don't choose final patterns that are too simple. Encourage students to use rectangles and triangles only until they understand how to tessellate patterns.

When students tape smaller pieces of paper together to make a shape, the tape should not extend over the edge of the pieces and affect the tessellation by causing overlap of the patterns.

Have more index cards available for students if they need them.

Tessellation models are not complete models of three-dimensional crystal shapes. After the activity, have students use identical three-dimensional shapes to model actual crystal structure. Another option is to show students pieces of rock salt, which are cubic crystals. Carefully break the rock salt into smaller pieces. Have students examine the pieces of salt with a hand lens and observe that the salt crystals remain cubic.

HOW TESSELLATING! *(continued)*

◆ Safety ✂ *Review the safety guidelines in the front of your lab book.*

Use caution in handling sharp scissors.

◆ Procedure

1. Use a ruler and scissors to carefully cut simple geometric shapes with straight edges from an index card. Begin with squares, rectangles, or hexagons. The simpler the shape, the easier it will be to get it to tessellate.

2. Tape the pieces of the card together to form an interesting new shape that you think will tessellate. Remember, if you make your shape very complicated, you will have trouble getting it to repeat.

3. Trace your new shape repeatedly onto a piece of paper. Does the shape tessellate? Sketch it in the appropriate space in the Observations section below. If it doesn't tessellate, try taping the pieces in a different arrangement or make a different pattern. Sketch shapes that do not tessellate in the appropriate space below.

4. Once you get a shape to tessellate, cover the entire area in the Observations section on the next page with your design.

5. Look for other patterns that tessellate in your design. Can you find any? Use colored pencils to outline several different shapes that tessellate.

◆ Observations

Patterns That Tessellate	*Patterns That Don't Tessellate*

HOW TESSELLATING! *(continued)*

<table>
<tr><td>*Tessellation*</td><td style="text-align:right">Sample Tessellation</td></tr>
</table>

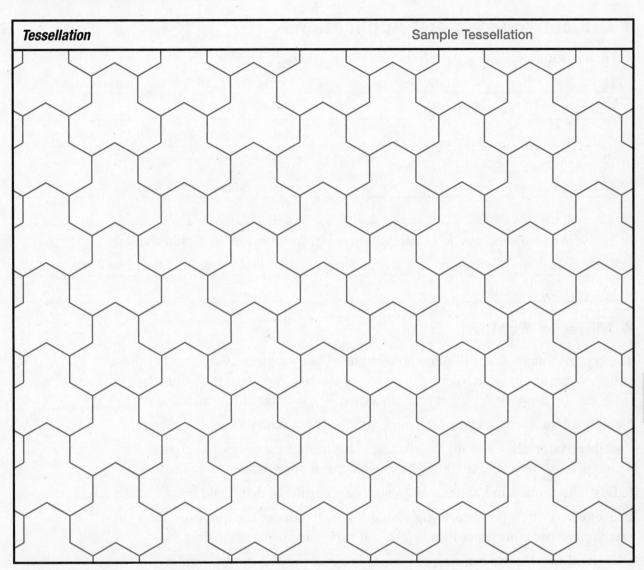

◆ Analyze and Conclude

1. Did your first pattern tessellate? With what basic geometric shape did you begin?

Answers will vary. Students might begin with rectangles and diamonds.

2. Could you use a circle or an oval to tessellate? Give a reason for your answer.

Circles and ovals won't tessellate. To tessellate, sides must line up. Because circles and ovals

have an infinite number of sides, they can't tessellate.

3. A mineral has a definite crystal shape, as shown in your textbook (p. 124).
Which crystal shapes tessellate? Are any of the shapes the same as the ones that
tessellated for you?

Any of the six crystal shapes will tessellate. Many of the shapes will likely be ones that

tessellated for students.

HOW TESSELLATING! (continued)

◆ Critical Thinking and Applications

1. How is your tessellating pattern like a crystal's shape?

The pattern repeats without overlaps or gaps. The atoms forming the crystal shape add on in

a pattern without overlaps or gaps.

2. List examples of tessellating patterns in your everyday life.

Answers will vary. Examples might include tile on a floor or bricks on a building.

3. How does your model of tessellating patterns differ from actual crystal shapes?

Answers will vary. Sample answer: The patterns are two-dimensional and the crystal shapes

are three-dimensional.

◆ More to Explore

The crystals found within all minerals form tessellating patterns. Almost all of these patterns have another interesting property—symmetry. A pattern has symmetry if it looks exactly the same on either side of a center line through the pattern.

New Problem How can you determine whether your pattern has symmetry?

Possible Materials Use your tessellating pattern from the previous activity. Think of how you could use a mirror to find out if your pattern tessellates.

Safety Use caution in handling any sharp items or items that could break.

Procedure Write a procedure you would follow to answer the question. Have the teacher approve your procedure before you carry out the investigation.

Observations Make a drawing of your shape that shows how the pattern does or does not have symmetry.

Analyze and Conclude

1. Does your shape have symmetry? How do you know?

Most likely the shape will have symmetry because it looks the same on either side of a center line.

2. What are some examples of symmetry in nature?

Students may say mineral crystals and the bodies of most animals.

Symmetry can be checked with a mirror in the center of the pattern. If the mirror image of the pattern makes it look complete, the pattern has symmetry. Caution students to handle mirrors carefully and to report any breakage to you instead of trying to clean it up.

F - 5   **LABORATORY INVESTIGATION**

Making Models of Sedimentary Rocks

Key Concepts: Sedimentary rocks are typically formed by particles undergoing erosion, deposition, compaction, and cementation. The three types of sedimentary rocks are clastic, organic, and chemical, based on what materials they contain and how they were formed.

Skills Focus: Observing, inferring, making models, designing experiments

Time Required: 40 minutes for planning and making rocks (break after Step 4); after "rocks" dry, 40 minutes for determining properties

◆ Pre-Lab Discussion

Layers of rock that formed at the bottom of ancient seas in some cases now lie exposed, thousands of meters above sea level. The processes that formed this rock lasted millions of years. So did the Earth movements that exposed the rock, pushing and tilting it into high mountains. To study such slow natural processes, scientists and engineers use models in their laboratories to imitate, or simulate, the real thing. They try to give their models the look and feel of actual rock.

The three types of rocks—igneous, metamorphic, and sedimentary—are all formed in different ways. In this investigation, you will create models of sedimentary rocks and explore their properties.

1. How do sedimentary rocks differ from other rocks?

Sedimentary rocks are formed from particles deposited by wind or water.

2. What four steps occur during the formation of a clastic sedimentary rock?

Erosion, deposition, compaction, and cementation

◆ Problem

How is sedimentary rock formed, and what are its properties?

Advance Preparation: Collect, or have students bring from home, materials that can be used to form the rocks. Have plenty of newspaper on hand for students to work on.

◆ Possible Materials *(per group)*

sand	pans
soil	spoons
gravel	water
fossils	paper towels
plaster of paris	streak plate
powdered chalk	materials of known hardness
salt	newspapers

Alternative Materials: The list of materials is a suggestion. Similar materials can be used. You might suggest students use a water hose to test resistance to weathering in Step 5. Some of the minerals found in actual sedimentary rocks are commercially available. Don't let students use materials that are toxic, corrosive, or caustic, such as Portland cement. Plastic fossil models can be substituted for real fossils.

Teaching Tips:

To speed drying, have students use paper towels to blot excess water out of newly made rocks. Review physical weathering and how it differs from chemical weathering. Students can explore chemical weathering in More to Explore.

MAKING MODELS OF SEDIMENTARY ROCKS (continued)

◆ **Safety** 🧥 🧤 🔥 *Review the safety guidelines in the front of your lab book.*

Wear safety goggles and lab aprons. Wash hands frequently during this activity.

◆ **Procedure**

1. Starting with the list of materials, brainstorm with other students how to create models of sedimentary rocks. You may also be able to collect natural materials outside of your school or near your home. You do not have to use all of the listed the materials. You may want to use other materials as well.

2. **CAUTION:** *Put on your safety goggles and lab apron.* Start to experiment with materials to create your model rocks. How will you form layers? How could your model imitate the pressures that cement particles and fragments into rock? Will the rock layers have fossils?

3. Start to record your rock-making procedures on a separate sheet of paper. Your plans should include all classes of sedimentary rock: clastic, organic, and chemical. What materials can you use to model clastic rock? How will you model layered formations? How can you simulate different-size particles for a conglomerate? How might you model an organic rock? A chemical rock?

4. After the teacher approves your procedure, create your rock models. If your models are not coming out the way you want, modify your procedures. Sketch your rock models in Observations. Set the models aside to dry. Wash your hands when you're finished.

5. When your model rocks are completely dry, explore their properties. Observe and record in the Data Table color, texture, overall hardness, pattern, and resistance to weathering. Resistance to weathering is determined by whether the rock remains intact or crumbles when tested. What type of test could show whether your rock is weak or strong? What other properties should you evaluate? Have the teacher approve any test before you conduct it.

6. Compare models with several classmates. For each model rock, state what type of sedimentary rock it represents, how it was made, and its properties.

◆ **Observations**

Sketches of Sedimentary Rock Models		
Clastic	*Organic*	*Chemical*
Sketches of clastic rocks should show the individual ingredients, such as gravel and sand.	If fossils are used, they should be in the organic rocks.	Chemical rocks should look uniform. Students will probably make chemical rocks out of concentrated salt water, allowing the water to evaporate.

MAKING MODELS OF SEDIMENTARY ROCKS (continued)

Data Table   Sample Data

Properties of Model Rocks			
	Type of Sedimentary Rock		
Property	**Clastic**	**Organic**	**Chemical**
Color	dark	white	colorless
Texture	rough	somewhat smooth	smooth
Hardness	relatively soft	relatively soft	relatively hard
Pattern	irregular	somewhat irregular	crystal structure
Resistance to Weathering	easily broken	easily broken	resistant
Students may test other properties.			

◆ Analyze and Conclude

1. What determines the properties of your model rocks?

The properties are determined by the composition of the rocks.

_____

2. Why might you choose to have fossils in your rock models?

Organic rocks are made from previously living organisms. Fossils could be found in this type of

rock.

3. How does compaction during the model-making process change the strength of the model rock?

Compaction increases strength.

_____

MAKING MODELS OF SEDIMENTARY ROCKS *(continued)*

◆ Critical Thinking and Applications

1. Compare and contrast the different types of sedimentary rocks.

All types are formed from particles by erosion, deposition, compaction, and cementation. They

differ in composition. Clastic rocks are made of broken pieces of other rocks. Organic rocks are

formed from previously living materials. Chemical rocks are formed from mineral solutions.

2. Would the actual rocks that your models represent be a good material to use to build bridges or buildings? Why or why not?

Many sedimentary rocks are useful building materials. They are soft enough to be easily cut and

hard enough to be relatively weather resistant as building materials.

3. What properties of your rocks make them useful or limit their usefulness?

Answers may include that soft rocks have limited uses because they weather easily.

◆ More to Explore

You have seen how sedimentary rocks differ in their resistance to physical weathering. How resistant are they to chemical weathering? Write a procedure you would follow to answer this question. Use actual sedimentary rocks and vinegar. Have the teacher approve your procedure before you carry out the investigation. Wear safety goggles and laboratory aprons while carrying out your procedure.

Most sedimentary rocks will react with the vinegar, indicating that they would be attacked by chemical weathering. Many chemical sedimentary rocks, such as salt, will not react with the acid. Encourage students to notice local buildings, tombstones, or statues that are made of sedimentary rock and have been affected by chemical weathering.

Using a Topographic Map

Key Concept: By examining contour lines on a topographic map, you can describe features of Earth's surface.

Skills Focus: Observing, inferring, communicating, measuring

Time Required: 40 minutes

1

◆ Pre-Lab Discussion

When was the last time you used a map? Perhaps you used a road map to help plan a trip. You may have looked at a world map to locate a country for a school assignment. Did you ever use a map mounted in a mall to find a certain store? Maps provide a variety of information. They can show not only where something is but what it looks like. That's what topographic maps do. They show the shape of the land by providing a three-dimensional view of Earth's surface. With a little practice, you can read a topographic map and picture the landscape as if you were flying over it in a plane.

Imagine that your class is completing a three-day outdoor education program. You've learned about the plants and animals that live near your town of Mountain View. You've learned about the landforms in the area and how to read them on a topographic map. As a final exercise, the program leader has arranged a treasure hunt. She will fly a plane over the area and drop a bright red canister attached to a bright red parachute. Inside the canister are all kinds of gift certificates for the class. In this investigation, you will use clues and interpret a topographic map to find the canister. To do so, you need to know that each degree of latitude and longitude is divided into units called minutes. One degree is 60 minutes. The number of minutes for a given latitude is listed right after the number of degrees. The symbol for minutes is an apostrophe. The map in Observations shows examples of latitude and longitude using minutes.

1. Explain what a contour line is.

A contour line is a line on a map that connects points of equal elevation on Earth's surface.

2. What kind of information do contour lines provide?

Contour lines show the elevation, relief, and slope of the land. Together, this information provides

a picture of the shape of the land.

3. How would you write the latitude of a point that is half way between 35° N and 36°N? Use degrees and minutes.

35° 30′ N

◆ Problem

Teaching Tips: You may want to refer students to their textbooks for a general discussion of topographic maps.

How can you use a topographic map to pinpoint a location?

◆ Materials *(per group)*

metric ruler
pencil

Before starting, ask students to describe the land shown on the map. For example, in which direction does the land slope? (north to south). Show students how to read latitude and longitude on the map. Consider having students trace a path on transparencies and present their results.

USING A TOPOGRAPHIC MAP *(continued)*

◆ Procedure

The Program Leader has sent the following radio message from her plane: "Attention outdoor ed. students . . . heading northwest . . . over crossroads and school . . . marsh on my left . . . following river . . . over woods now . . . cliff approaching . . . turning northeast . . . crossing river . . . winds are calm . . . tree-tops . . . CANISTER AWAY!"

1. Use the message and the topographic map in Observations to determine where the pilot started sending the message.

2. Trace on the map the probable path taken by the pilot.

3. On the map, shade in an area where you would concentrate your search for the canister.

◆ Observations

Sample Data

See the path and the shaded area shown on the map. Students' paths and areas may vary slightly, but all should be similar to that shown.

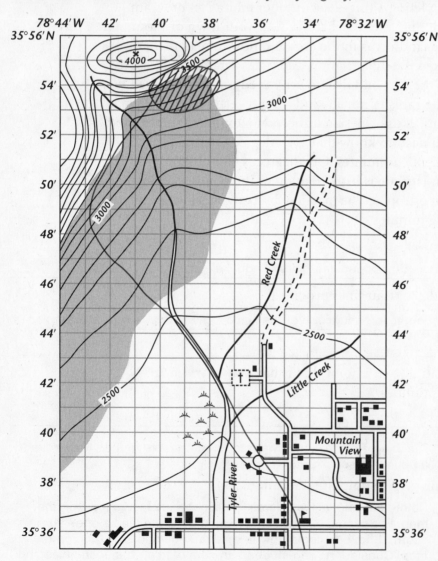

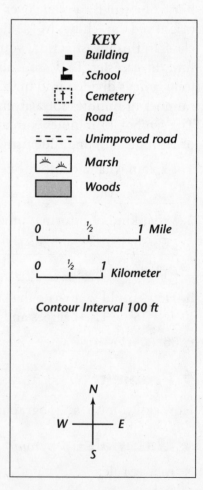

USING A TOPOGRAPHIC MAP *(continued)*

◆ Analyze and Conclude

1. What are the latitude and longitude of the highest elevation on the map?

35°55′ N, 78°41′ W

2. In which direction does the Tyler River flow? How do you know?

The river flows south because the contour lines that cross it point upstream—to the north—and

the elevation is higher to the north.

3. What clues in the pilot's radio message tell you where to start looking for the canister? What other clues might the pilot have given?

The pilot mentions directions and landmarks such as a crossroads, school, marsh, river, and cliff.

Other clues might have included the presence of the 4,000-ft peak and the lack of trees

near the peak.

4. What are the latitude and longitude of the most likely place to find the canister? Give a reason for your answer.

Answers should indicate a location near 35°54′ N, 78°39′ W. This location is where the pilot most

likely dropped the canister.

5. How far will you have to travel to reach the drop site? Assume that you will travel in a straight line.

about 7.5 kilometers

◆ Critical Thinking and Applications

1. Look at the area where the canister probably came down. What problems might you have retrieving the canister?

The area is relatively steep and wooded. Walking may be difficult on the steep terrain. Also, the

parachute may have gotten caught high in the trees.

USING A TOPOGRAPHIC MAP *(continued)*

2. Your class has decided to divide into teams to see which team could find the canister first. What suggestions would you make to your team for getting to the site quickly? Give reasons for your suggestions.

Suggestions might include following the unimproved road to its end, perhaps on bikes, then

hiking uphill from there. This might be a little farther than hiking in a straight line, but the terrain is

less steep and perhaps allows for faster hiking.

3. Suppose a steady wind is blowing from the west at 18 km/hr. How might this affect your search for the canister?

The search area would be extended to the east because the wind would likely blow the

parachute in that direction before landing. If the wind blows the parachute east of the trees, the

canister might be easier to find and retrieve—it will not get caught in the trees.

◆ More to Explore

In the space below, draw a topographic map of a small island. Use the following description. Show direction on the map and state the contour interval.

- The highest point of the island is 172 feet. The island is steeper on the east side than it is on the west side.
- A stream flows from the center of the island northwest to the coast.
- A marsh exists at the shoreline of the west side of the island.

The number of contour lines on students' maps will depend on the contour interval chosen. Contour lines should be closer together on the east side of the island. Contour lines should point to the southeast where they cross the stream. The symbol for a marsh should appear on the west side of the island. Below is one possible map.

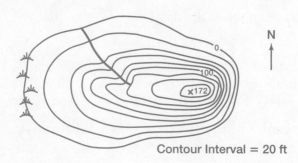

Contour Interval = 20 ft

LABORATORY INVESTIGATION

Investigating Soils and Drainage

Key Concepts: Soil permeability varies depending on the soil's composition. Relative permeability can be determined by measuring how quickly water passes through soil.

Skills Focus: Observing, making models, measuring, designing experiments, controlling variables

Time Required: 50 minutes

◆ Pre-Lab Discussion

Suppose that your community has a new soccer field, but it is hard to find a place to park. Many people park on the grass, which is now a muddy mess. Why didn't the water that created the mud just run off the land or soak into the soil? You think the answer to this problem lies in the soil. Different types of soil allow water to drain differently. Sandy soil drains differently than soil containing a lot of clay or soil that doesn't have much sand or clay. In this investigation, you will test how fast water drains through different types of soil.

1. What is soil made of?

Soil is a mixture of rock particles, minerals, decayed organic material, air, and water.

2. The size of soil particles gives soil its texture. List the four major types of soil particles in order from largest to smallest.

gravel, sand, silt, clay

◆ Problem

Advance Preparation: For the sake of time and safety, cut the bottles before the lab. Cut the tops off half the bottles and the bottoms off the other half. Punch a hole that will be above the water level and below where the two bottles meet.

How fast does water drain through different types of soil?

◆ Possible Materials (per group)

To ensure uniform initial dryness of the soils, heat the samples at a low temperature on a pan in an oven or let them dry in an area with low humidity.

4 plastic 2-L soft-drink bottles with bottoms removed
4 plastic 2-L soft-drink bottles with tops cut off and a hole punched high in the side
4 pieces of gauze or cheesecloth, about 8 cm × 8 cm
4 rubber bands
potting soil
sand
clay mixed with soil
gravel mixed with soil
plastic container, at least 1-L
timer or watch
permanent marker or wax pencil
graduated cylinder or metric measuring cup, 100-mL

Alternative Materials: Use large plastic or metal funnels instead of the upper bottle. Substitute coffee filters for cloth.

Teaching Tips: A good volume to mark on the side of the lower bottle is 500 mL. Students should fill the upper bottle about half full of soil and pat it lightly.

Students should plan to pour considerably more than the marked volume of water through the setup; the soil will absorb and retain some water.

INVESTIGATING SOILS AND DRAINAGE *(continued)*

◆ **Safety**   🗒 *Review the safety guidelines in the front of your lab book.*

Wear safety goggles and lab aprons throughout the activity. To prevent slips or falls, wipe up spills immediately.

Encourage students to use consistent quantities of all materials and to use metric measurements.

◆ **Procedure**

1. Read through the entire lab before carrying out your investigation.

2. Design a way to compare how quickly water flows through different soils. Figure 1 shows one possible setup. Write your procedure on a separate sheet of paper. Your procedure should address the following questions:

- What types of soil will you test?

- How much soil and water will you use?

- How will you pour the water: quickly and all at once, or more slowly and continuously?

- When will you start and stop timing?

- What variables will you control?

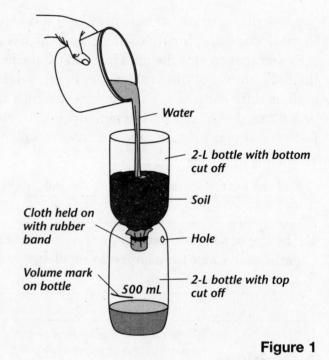

Figure 1

3. Predict which soil will drain most slowly and which soil will drain most quickly. Give reasons for your predictions.

Students may predict that gravel will drain most quickly because of the air spaces between the

particles of gravel. Similarly, students may think clay soil will drain most slowly because the clay

particles are so small that they don't allow much space between particles.

_____

4. Have the teacher approve your procedure before you carry out the investigation.

5. Fill in the first column of the Data Table in Observations. Record your data in the second column.

INVESTIGATING SOILS AND DRAINAGE *(continued)*

◆ Observations

Data Table

Soil Type	Draining Time

Sample Data

Data should show that a gravel/soil mixture drains most quickly, followed by sand, potting soil, and clay soil.

2

◆ Analyze and Conclude

1. Describe what happens to the water from the time you pour it into the soil until the time it drains into the plastic bottle.

The water moves through the spaces between the soil grains. The spaces are connected, which

allows the water to pass through the soil.

2. Through which soil did water drain the fastest? Why do you think this happened?

If students tested the gravel/soil mixture, they should find that water passed fastest through this

material. The water can pass relatively quickly through the large spaces between the pieces of

gravel.

3. Do your results agree with your predictions? If they do not, explain why you think they don't agree.

Results may not agree with predictions because students may not have been considering grain

size in their predictions. Procedural factors, such as inconsistency in pouring the water, packing

some soils too tightly, and using soils too similar to one another, may also have accounted for

disagreement between predictions and results.

4. What was most surprising about your results?

Answers will vary. Students may have been surprised by how quickly or how slowly water

traveled through the different soils and by how close or far apart the draining times were for

different soil types.

INVESTIGATING SOILS AND DRAINAGE *(continued)*

◆ Critical Thinking and Applications

1. Why did water drain through the soils at different rates?

The soils differ in particle size and amount of space between the particles. Water can move

through larger spaces faster than through smaller ones.

2. If you wanted to test other soils, what might you change in your experimental procedure?

Students might suggest having more samples of each soil type and running more trials.

3. Why do you think people put gravel on parking lots?

Gravel particles are relatively large, so gravel has relatively large spaces between the particles

through which water can travel quickly. Water would drain quickly through the gravel and would

not gather in puddles.

4. Think of what happens to rain that lands on a paved parking lot. What would be an advantage of paving a lot? What would be a disadvantage?

An advantage is that the lot would not become muddy. A disadvantage is that water would not

drain through the paving material; any depression would contain standing water.

5. Suppose another sports field is being built. What kind of soil should be used for the best drainage? Give a reason for your answer.

A soil with lots of sand would produce less mud after a rain because water would drain through it

more quickly. Students may also suggest including some gravel in the soil to improve drainage.

Too much gravel, however, might interfere with the growth of the grass.

◆ More to Explore

Drainage is only one of many considerations when building a sports field. Another concern is how well grass will grow on the field. Is the soil that drains the best able to support a healthy crop of grass? What soil would be best to use for a new field? On a separate sheet of paper, write a procedure to answer these questions. Have the teacher approve your procedure before you carry out your investigation. Be sure to wear safety goggles and a lab apron.

Students should use the same soils as before and find out how well grass grows in each. Plastic cups or margarine tubs are adequate containers in which to grow grass. Students may suggest using sod instead of growing grass because most sports fields use sod. Sod will require containers with a larger area such as baking pans. Be sure students consider the criteria they will use to evaluate the effectiveness of the soil in supporting grass.

The Daily Grind

Key Concept: The amount of rock erosion that occurs through abrasion depends on time and the properties of the rock.

Skills Focus: Making models, observing, measuring, interpreting data

Time Required: 45 minutes

◆ Pre-Lab Discussion

A river or stream is more than just water in motion. Such moving bodies of water also carry along rocks and other materials, which change as they move. One kind of change is called mechanical weathering. As the water moves, it repeatedly tosses the rocks against each other and against the sides of the streambed. Each day, little by little, the rocks are ground into smaller and smaller pieces in a process called abrasion. Abrasion is one cause of the mechanical weathering of rocks.

In this investigation, you will model one way that abrasion causes the erosion of rocks. You will also find out how different kinds of rocks are affected by this process.

1. What provides the energy for the abrasion of rocks by rivers and streams?

Water at higher locations possesses potential energy because of the force of gravity. As the

water moves down a slope, the potential energy changes into kinetic energy, and some of this

energy wears down the rocks.

3

◆ Problem

How do time and the properties of specific rocks affect the way abrasion weathers rocks?

◆ Materials *(per group)*

balance
large plastic spoon
100-mL graduated cylinder
plastic jar, approximately 500 mL, with screw-on lid
limestone chips, pre-soaked
granite chips, pre-soaked
rock salt, coarse (dry)
fine wire screen
paper towels
water
watch or clock with second hand
graph paper
wide-mouthed plastic jar, approximately 1 L
newspapers
paper cups

Advance Preparation: The limestone and granite chips must be soaked for at least 1 hour before the lab. The rock salt must be dry at the beginning of the lab. Using "solar salt," a form of rock salt used in water softening systems, usually gives better results than using crushed rock salt. For optimal results, use rock chips that are about 10 mm in length. Use only fresh rock chips at the outset of the lab.

Teaching Tips: Determine in advance whether any students will carry out the More to Explore activity. They will need to collect the runoff water from each type of rock carefully, being sure to clean all the equipment between uses.

Music with a regular beat can help students maintain a consistent rhythm as they shake the rocks. Stress also that to control variables, students must always determine the mass of limestone and granite with the rocks damp but not dripping.

Alternative Materials: Bluestone chips may be used in place of granite and marble chips may be used in place of limestone.

THE DAILY GRIND (*continued*)

◆ **Safety** 🧍 🧤 🔲 🧴 *Review the safety guidelines in the front of your lab book.*

Use caution in handling any glass equipment. Do not touch broken glass. Report any breakage to your teacher.

◆ **Procedure**

Part A: Modeling Rock Erosion Over Time

1. Cover your work area with newspaper in case of spills. Obtain two large spoonfuls of pre-soaked limestone chips. Dab them briefly with a paper towel to remove any dripping water. Then use the balance to find the initial mass of the rocks, and record it in Data Table 1. (*Hint:* Find the mass of a dry container such as a paper cup, find the mass of the container plus the rocks, and then subtract to find the mass of the rocks.)

2. Observe the appearance of the rock chips, and record your observations on a separate sheet of paper. Read over the rest of the procedure for Part A. Then, on the same sheet of paper, write a prediction for the way the rocks will change as they are weathered mechanically.

3. Place the rock chips in a plastic jar with a screw-on lid. Add 250 mL of water. Cover the jar, and seal it tightly.

4. Decide on the motion with which you will shake the jar, for example, up and down. You must use that same shaking motion throughout this lab. Shake the jar for exactly 3 minutes.

5. Place a fine wire screen over a second, wide-mouthed jar. Pour the rocks and water onto the screen, letting the water flow into the wide-mouthed discard jar. Be careful not to lose any chips. Briefly dab the wet chips with a paper towel to remove any dripping water. Then measure and record the mass of the rock chips.

6. Return the rocks to the first jar, and repeat Steps 4 and 5 three times. You should have a total of five mass readings in Data Table 1.

7. Observe the appearance of a few of the rocks. Record your observations on a separate sheet of paper.

Part B: Comparing the Erosion of Different Kinds of Rocks

1. In Part B, you will follow the overall procedures from Part A, but you will shake each type of rock for one 3-minute period only. Use Data Table 2 to record the results for Part B.

2. For limestone, find the initial mass of the chips you used in Part A by reading the mass at time 0 in Data Table 1. Record that mass as the original mass of the limestone chips in Data Table 2.

THE DAILY GRIND *(continued)*

3. Find the mass of the limestone chips after 3 minutes in Data Table 1, and record this in Data Table 2 as the Final Mass of the limestone chips.

4. Obtain two spoonfuls of pre-soaked granite chips, dab them briefly with a paper towel to remove excess water, and then find their initial mass. "Weather" the rocks by shaking them for 3 minutes, dab them briefly with a paper towel, and then find their final mass. Record your data in Data Table 2.

5. Obtain two spoonfuls of dry rock salt chips, and find their initial mass. "Weather" them by shaking for 3 minutes. Dab them dry with a paper towel, and then find their final mass. Record your data in Data Table 2.

6. For each type of rock in Data Table 2, find the mass of the rocks lost to weathering by subtracting the final mass from the original mass. Record the results in the fourth column of the data table.

7. For each type of rock in Data Table 2, determine the percent of change in mass using the equation below. Enter the results in the last column of your data table.

$$\frac{\text{mass lost to weathering}}{\text{original mass}} \times 100\% = ?\%$$

3

◆ Observations

Data Table 1

Weathering Time (min)	Mass of Rocks (g)
0	54.5
3	54.3
6	54.1
9	54.0
12	53.9

Data Table 2

Type of Rock	Original Mass of Rocks (g)	Final Mass of Rocks (g)	Mass of Rocks Lost to Weathering (g)	Percent of Change
limestone	54.5	54.3	0.2	0.4%
granite	54.3	53.2	1.1	2.0%
rock salt	34.3	1.3	31.7	92.4%

THE DAILY GRIND *(continued)*

◆ Analyze and Conclude

1. Graph the results from Part A. Place time on the horizontal axis and mass on the vertical axis. How did the mass of the limestone chips change over time?

    The graph should show that the mass of the chips decreased after each period of weathering,

    but the amount of decrease became less each time they were weathered.

2. In Part A, how did the appearance of the limestone chips change over time?

    At first, the limestone chips had irregular shapes, and many of their points were

    sharp. At the end, the chips were smoother, and they had fewer sharp points.

3. In Parts A and B, what happened to the rock that was "lost" to mechanical weathering? In your model, where did that lost rock go?

    The process of abrasion broke off small sections of rock, changing them into particles of

    sediment. That sediment was poured off with the water into the discard jar.

◆ Critical Thinking and Applications

1. Based on your results from Part A, what can you conclude about the mechanical weathering of rocks carried along by the water in rivers and streams?

    In the beginning, the rocks are relatively large and have irregular shapes. As

    mechanical weathering occurs, the rocks become smaller and smoother. The rate of

    weathering decreases after the initially irregular rocks become smoother.

2. Based on your results from Part B, what can you conclude about the mechanical weathering of rocks carried by moving water? How might those results be explained?

    Different rocks weather at different rates. The differences in weathering might be caused by the

    hardness of the rocks, the initial shapes, and how rapidly the rock dissolves in water.

◆ More to Explore

How does the amount of rock "lost" during abrasion by water compare with the amount of sediment produced? Use ideas from the lab just completed to design an experiment to investigate that question. Your teacher must approve your procedure before you begin. Remember to wear your safety goggles and lab apron while carrying out your procedure.

In one method, students could use filter paper to find the mass of rock in the discard bottle and

compare it to the amount of rock "lost" by the rock chips; they must wet the filter paper before

finding its mass. In another method, they could pour a given amount of the discard water into

an evaporating dish and find the mass of the material remaining when the water evaporates.

G-4   LABORATORY INVESTIGATION

Exploring Geologic Time Through Core Samples

Key Concepts: Geologists use core samples to learn about the thickness and composition of rock beneath the earth's surface.

Skills Focus: Observing, making models, communicating, measuring

Time Required: 40 minutes

◆ Pre-Lab Discussion

One way in which scientists study past geologic events is to examine rock layers that are buried beneath Earth's surface. Over a long period of time, sediment and the remains of organisms have been deposited, layer upon layer, and have hardened into rock. Scientists collect rock samples by driving hollow tubes into the rock and withdrawing the tubes with the rock and their fossils inside. This process is called coring. Scientists examine and interpret the core samples, which show the various layers of rock and fossils they contain. In this investigation, you will create sediment deposits to represent rock layers and fossils. You will then take core samples of such deposits and interpret them—just as scientists do.

1. Define the law of superposition.

The law of superposition states that each horizontal layer of sedimentary rock is younger than

the layer below it if the layers have not been overturned.

2. Define index fossils and tell how they help scientists date rocks.

Index fossils are fossils of organisms that lived during only one short period of time. Index fossils

help scientists date sedimentary rock layers because they are easy to recognize, limited to a

particular time period, and occur widely in different areas.

◆ Problem

How are core samples collected and interpreted?

◆ Possible Materials *(per group)*

1-L milk carton, clean and empty
sediments:
    loose clay or red-colored sand
    white-colored sand
    potting soil or mud
    ground-up leaves or grass
fossils (variety of small grains and seeds
    such as rice, barley, millet, lentils,
    and split peas)
mixing bowl
thick plastic drinking straws
wooden or plastic rod that fits into the straw
several sheets of paper
metric ruler

Advance Preparation: Assemble sediments and "fossils." The fossils should be small enough to fit in the drinking-straw "corers." Examples might include grains, beans, seeds, small beads, or any other small, hard item that will not dissolve or break down in water. Each type of fossil should be separate from all others.

Obtain drinking straws that are sturdy and totally smooth. They should have as large a diameter as possible.

Alternative Materials: Any tall, narrow container, such as potato chip cans, can be used instead of milk cartons. Whatever kind of containers you provide, they should be opaque, so that students must obtain information about the layers from the core sample, not from being able to see the layers through the container.

Sediments and fossils must be small enough to fit into the straw.

A pencil or pen can be used as a rod as long as it can fit into the straw.

EXPLORING GEOLOGIC TIME THROUGH CORE SAMPLES (continued)

◆ **Safety**   ![icon] *Review the safety guidelines in the front of your lab book.*

Immediately sweep up or wipe up any materials that spill.

Teaching Tips:

To simplify the lab, you might assign each group to include only one type of index fossil.

◆ **Procedure**

1. Decide on the type and order of the sediments that will be placed in your milk carton. Use at least two different types of sediments. Also decide how you will use fossils in your model. Include at least one type of index fossil.

2. Build your model of sediment layers with fossils. For your bottom layer, take two or three handfuls of the chosen sediment. Mix in a few pinches of "fossils." Place the mixture in the bottom of the milk carton. Add a small amount of water so that the sediments become slightly damp.

3. Continue this process, following your sediment order, until the carton is almost full. You can make the sediment layers of different thicknesses but keep them horizontal. As you build your model, record the sediment order and width, and the type and placement of fossils in the first milk carton in Observations.

4. Exchange your milk carton for a milk carton prepared by another group.

5. Collect a core sample from this container by holding a straw with your fingers near the soil surface and slowly pushing the straw "corer" straight down into the sediments. Push until your straw is close to the bottom of the milk carton.

6. Fold a sheet of paper in half lengthwise. Write *Top* at the top and *Bottom* at the bottom of the paper. You will use the crease to hold the core sample after you have removed the sample from the straw.

7. Gently remove the straw with the sample from the sediment container. Using the rod, carefully push the sediment out of the bottom of the straw into the crease of the folded paper so that the core sample rests in the crease. The top of the sample should be near the top of the paper. See Figure 1.

Students might want to lightly pack the sediments so the layers more closely resemble hardened layers of rock. However, the layers should be kept loose enough so that the straw can go through them.

Be sure students push the straw straight down into the sediments, not at an angle.

Be sure students are careful when removing the straw from the milk carton so that they do not scatter any of the remaining contents out of the milk carton.

8. Record the sediments in their correct order by drawing them in the second milk carton in Observations. Measure the height of each layer in centimeters and write the measurements next to the recorded layers.

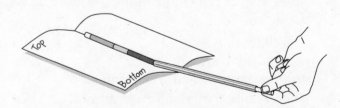

Figure 1

9. Look through the sediment layers one at a time for fossils. Since the fossils are small, you may need to take several core samples to find any fossils. Record the type of fossil (type of bean, seed, and so on) you found and the sediment layer you found it in.

10. Check your results with the group that set up the sediment carton.

EXPLORING GEOLOGIC TIME THROUGH CORE SAMPLES *(continued)*

◆ Observations

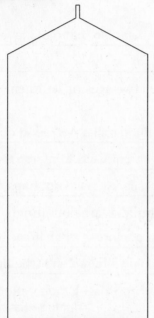

Your group's layers

Layers from other group

◆ Analyze and Conclude

1. In the carton you examined, which layer is the oldest? How do you know?

According to the law of superposition, the layer on the bottom is the oldest because it was

deposited first.

2. Which layer is the youngest? How do you know?

According to the law of superposition, the layer on the top is the youngest because it was

deposited last.

3. What conclusions can you make from studying the "fossils" in your core samples?

Students can conclude when the fossils were deposited in relation to the formation of other rock

layers. Depending on whether the same fossils appear in other rock layers, students can

conclude whether that fossil would be useful as an index fossil.

◆ Critical Thinking and Applications

1. Why should a geologist exercise great care and patience when taking and preparing a core sample?

Answers might include that the thickness of the layers could be affected by pressure of the tube

or that if layers are disturbed by the coring process, their order could be mixed up. Rough

handling of core samples could also damage delicate fossils included in the layers.

2. If an earthquake causes a fault to form in these sediments, how could the fault affect the core sample?

Faults could tilt sediment layers or displace them along the fault, so that older layers might be

found above younger layers.

3. How could index fossils help a geologist figure out the relative ages of sediment layers after an earthquake?

Index fossils can give the relative age of rock layers, even if the rocks are found out of their

normal order based on superposition. Geologists can use index fossils to match the layers in a

disturbed sample with rock layers that have those same fossils but have not been disturbed.

4. How could a core sample be useful in choosing a site to build a large building?

A large building should be built on materials that would not compress or shift easily. A core

sample would indicate how firm the layers beneath the building site are and whether faults exist.

◆ More to Explore

New Problem How can you make a model of a fossil?

Possible Materials empty quart or half-gallon milk carton, modeling clay, petroleum jelly, plaster of paris, water, bowl, spoon

Safety Wear safety goggles and lab aprons during the activity. Wash your hands when you are finished.

Procedure

1. Choose an extinct animal or plant to represent in a fossil exhibit. Research this organism in the library.

2. Design a procedure for making a fossil by creating a mold of the organism or traces of the organism, such as a footprint. Write the steps for your procedure on a separate sheet of paper.

3. Design a procedure for making a fossil by creating a cast of the organism or traces of the organism from the mold. How will you keep your mold and your cast from sticking together? Write the steps for your procedure on a separate sheet of paper.

4. When the teacher has approved your procedures, carry out the lab.

5. Prepare an information card that includes the name of the organism and the geologic era in which the organism lived. Use your card, your mold, and your cast in a classroom display of fossils.

Analyze and Conclude In terms of fossils, compare and contrast molding and casting.

Student procedures could include making a mold by pressing a layer of clay in the bottom of a container. They could use an existing model or make a model of the organism or its trace out of a material that is harder than clay. To make the mold of the organism, they could use the model to make an impression of the organism or its trace in the clay. They could then make a cast by pouring plaster of paris into the mold. A layer of plaster of paris about 5 cm thick is a good amount for a cast. Spreading a thin layer of petroleum jelly on the mold before pouring the plaster of paris prevents the two layers from sticking together. When the plaster of paris has hardened, students can separate the mold and cast.

Students might indicate that both molds and casts can give a good indication of shape, size,

texture, and surface features of fossil organisms or traces of such organisms. Accept other

comparisons based on students' observations or reflections on the procedure they followed.

4

H-1   **LABORATORY INVESTIGATION**

Properties of Water

Key Concept: The properties of water make it a unique substance on Earth.

Skills Focus: Observing, inferring, predicting

Time Required: 60 minutes

◆ Pre-Lab Discussion

Water is the only substance on Earth that commonly exists in all three states— solid, liquid, and gas. Water also has some other unusual properties. In this investigation, you will examine some properties of the substance that covers most of Earth's surface.

1. What are three properties of water that are caused by the attractions among water molecules?

Surface tension, capillary action, and high specific heat

2. Why can water dissolve so many other substances?

The water molecule is polar, so its charged ends attract the molecules of other polar substances.

◆ Problem

What are some of the unique properties of water?

Advance Preparation: You may want to form the screening containers for Part A ahead of time. Consider setting up separate stations for Parts A, B, and C.

◆ Materials *(per group)*

plastic cup
tap water
3-cm square of metal
  window screening
dark food coloring
paper towel
scissors
250-mL beaker

distilled water
hot plate
thermometer, metal
spoon
salt
hot pad
wax pencil

Alternative Materials: If possible, use alcohol thermometers rather than mercury thermometers.

Teaching Tips: Dark food coloring will make the water movement easier to see.

Students can complete Part C while waiting to observe the results from Part B.

◆ Safety   *Review the safety guidelines in your lab book.*

Handle the thermometer carefully. If it breaks, do not touch it and immediately tell your teacher. Use tongs or a hot pad when handling hot objects. Always wear safety goggles when heating objects.

PROPERTIES OF WATER *(continued)*

◆ Procedure

Part A: Surface Tension

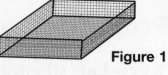

Figure 1

1. Fill a plastic cup three-fourths full with tap water.

2. Bend up the sides of the window screening to form the shape shown in Figure 1. Be careful of any sharp edges on the screen.

3. Predict what will happen if you place the screening on the water's surface. Explain your reasoning.

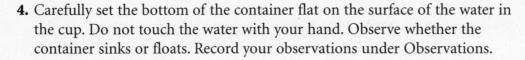
Unless students consider surface tension, they may predict the screening will sink.

_____

4. Carefully set the bottom of the container flat on the surface of the water in the cup. Do not touch the water with your hand. Observe whether the container sinks or floats. Record your observations under Observations.

Part B: Capillary Action

1. Put about 2 cm of tap water in the plastic cup. Add 2 or 3 drops of food coloring to the water.

2. Cut a strip of paper towel about 1 cm wide. Drape it over the lip of the glass so that one end is in the water. See Figure 2.

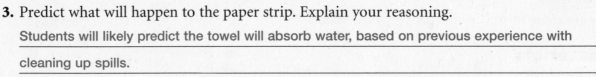

Figure 2

3. Predict what will happen to the paper strip. Explain your reasoning.

Students will likely predict the towel will absorb water, based on previous experience with

_____

cleaning up spills.

4. Set the cup aside. After about 20 minutes, observe the strip of paper towel. Record your observations under Observations.

Part C: Changing States

1. **CAUTION:** *Put on your safety goggles and apron.* Fill a 250-mL beaker two-thirds full of distilled water. Place the beaker on a hot plate.

2. Heat the water until it boils. Measure the temperature of the boiling water. **CAUTION:** *Handle the thermometer carefully; it is breakable.*

3. Let the water cool slightly. Add a spoonful of salt to the water. Predict how you think adding salt will affect the water's boiling point. Explain your reasoning.

Students will likely think adding salt will affect the water's boiling point in some way.

_____

4. Heat the water until it boils and record the temperature of the boiling water in the Data Table under Observations.

5. Repeat Steps 3 and 4 three more times. **CAUTION:** *Use a hot pad or beaker tongs to handle the beaker.*

PROPERTIES OF WATER (continued)

◆ Observations

Part A

1. What happened when you placed the screening on the water's surface?

If the screening is set carefully on the water, with the flat bottom touching the surface of the

water, it will float.

Part B

1. What did you observe about the end of the paper towel that was outside the glass?

After 20 minutes, the end of the paper towel that was outside the glass was wet.

Part C

Data Table

	Boiling-Point Temperature
Distilled water	100°C
Distilled water + 1 spoon of salt	
Distilled water + 2 spoons of salt	
Distilled water + 3 spoons of salt	
Distilled water + 4 spoons of salt	

Boiling-point temperatures may vary, depending on the accuracy of the laboratory thermometers and altitude, but in general, the more salt that is dissolved in the water, the higher its boiling point.

◆ Analyze and Conclude

1. Explain your observations in Part A based on what you know about the surface tension of water.

The container floated because it isn't heavy enough to break the surface tension of the water.

2. Explain your observations in Part B based on what you know about capillary action.

Water moves through the small spaces in the paper towel because of capillary action.

3. How does dissolving salt in water affect the temperature at which the water boils?

The more salt dissolved in the water, the higher the boiling point of the solution becomes.

PROPERTIES OF WATER *(continued)*

◆ Critical Thinking and Applications

1. What do you think would happen if you put a penny on the screening? Give a reason for your answer.

The container would sink because the penny made it heavy enough to break the surface tension

of the water. Suggest students test their hypothesis by performing this experiment.

2. If you cut off a centimeter from the bottom of a celery stalk and put the cut end into water colored with blue food coloring, in about an hour the stem would be streaked with blue. Explain what happens in terms of capillary action.

The colored water travels up tiny tubes in the celery stalk. Capillary action causes water

molecules to cling to the insides of the narrow tubes and move through them.

3. When some people cook vegetables, they add salt to the cooking water. They say this makes the vegetables cook faster. Are they correct? Give a reason for your answer.

Adding salt to water makes water boil at a higher temperature, and a higher temperature will

cook the vegetables a little faster.

◆ More to Explore

New Problem Does dissolving salt in water change the freezing point of the water?

Possible Materials Consider what materials you will need to use. Write a list of your materials.

Safety Handle thermometers carefully. Wear your safety goggles and apron.

Procedure Write a procedure you could follow to find the answer to the problem. Have the teacher approve your procedure before you carry out the investigation. (Hint: You do not necessarily need to make salt water freeze to answer this question.)

Students will need access to a freezer for this investigation. It will probably take several hours for the salt water to freeze, depending on the concentration. If a freezer isn't available or to save class time, have students do the project at home.

Observations Make a data table and record your observations.

Analyze and Conclude

1. How does dissolving salt in water affect its freezing point?

The more salt that is dissolved in the water, the lower the freezing point of the water will be.

2. Why do some communities spread salt on icy roads in winter?

Salt lowers the freezing point of water, so the ice will change to water even when the air

temperature is below 0°C.

H-2   LABORATORY INVESTIGATION

Field Testing a Body of Fresh Water

Key Concept: Fresh water found in streams, ponds, rivers, and lakes can have different properties.

Skills Focus: Observing, inferring, predicting, measuring, creating data tables, designing experiments, controlling variables

Time Required: two or three 40-minute classes

◆ Pre-Lab Discussion

Fresh water in streams, ponds, rivers, and lakes is far from pure. Fresh water usually contains dissolved substances and a range of sediments suspended in the water. Some suspended substances can make fresh water look dirty and murky. The amount of acid in a substance is measured by pH values. Dissolved substances can sometimes change the pH of water.

Oxygen dissolved in water is necessary for fish to live. Around 4 to 5 mg/L of dissolved oxygen is the lowest amount that will support fish. The presence of nitrogen in the form of nitrate indicates pollution. Nitrates cause the growth of plankton and water weeds that provide food for fish. However, if algae grow too much, oxygen levels will be reduced and fish will die. Nitrate levels below 90 mg/L have little effect on warm-water fish, but cold-water fish are more sensitive to nitrate levels.

Phosphorus can come from phosphate-containing rocks or from fertilizers, detergents, and pesticides. Too much phosphorus causes overgrowth of algae and reduces dissolved oxygen. The recommended maximum for phosphorus is 0.1 mg/L. Most freshwater organisms can live only in water between 0°C and 35°C.

When determining water quality in a body of fresh water, the factors described above are only some of those that must be considered. In this investigation, you will examine a body of fresh water near your school.

1. How do sediments get into fresh water?

Moving water causes erosion, so fresh water picks up sediments. Some of these sediments are

suspended in fresh water, while others dissolve in the water.

2. How is the amount of oxygen in a body of water affected by a large amount of algae in the water? Explain how this might occur.

When the algae layer becomes so thick that it begins to block out the sunlight, some plants in

the water cannot carry out photosynthesis. They stop producing food and oxygen and die. The

amount of oxygen in the water decreases.

◆ Problem

What is the quality of a nearby body of fresh water?

FIELD TESTING A BODY OF FRESH WATER (continued)

◆ Possible Materials

(per group)

water samples of a stream, pond, river, or lake
thermometer
pH paper
graduated cylinders
large test tubes with stoppers
beakers
large jars
hand lens
petri dishes with agar
plankton net
water quality test kits
waterproof boots

Advance Preparation: Be sure you have signed permission slips from parents or guardians for this field trip. Use a buddy system near the water.

You may want to examine a topographical map of the region that includes the body of water to be studied. Determine the source or sources of the water and discuss how the body of water's location might affect the water quality.

Alternate Materials: If you do not wish to do this investigation as a field study, you can collect and label water samples from different sources, such as streams, ponds, rivers, and lakes, and have students test the samples in class.

In addition to the materials listed in the student lab, the following materials should be made available: droppers, spoons, funnels, filter paper, balances, microscopes, slides and coverslips, field guides to plants and animals, heavy twine, hydrometer, tweezers, and sorting trays. Small baby food jars with lids can be substituted for test tubes.

◆ Safety   *Review the safety guidelines in the front of your lab book.*

Use caution when near a body of water. Wear waterproof boots. Wash all equipment thoroughly before taking water samples and doing tests. Wash your hands thoroughly after completing this investigation.

◆ Procedure

1. As a class, discuss the bodies of fresh water in your community. Determine which body of water you will examine. The type of water body chosen may influence some of the tests you want to do. For example, if you are investigating a stream or river, you may want to measure water velocity.

2. Some of the tests you may want to perform include the following: temperature, pH, dissolved oxygen, nitrate, phosphorus, suspended solids, dissolved solids, bacteria content, salinity, and types of microorganisms present in the water.

3. With your group, decide what tests you will perform. List the different tests you plan to do in the Planning Table on the next page. Research the methods of doing these tests and read the instructions in the water-testing kits to determine how much water you need to test and what materials you will need.

4. Decide how you are going to gather your water samples. What observations can you make at the water site? You may also want to examine the soil at the water's edge and complete a plant and animal survey in the immediate area around the water.

Teaching Tips:

You may want to have several parents or other adults accompany the class on the field trip.

Student groups may share water sites and share the test-taking procedures.

You may want each group to do 2 or 3 tests and share results so that a variety of tests can be done more manageably.

FIELD TESTING A BODY OF FRESH WATER *(continued)*

Planning Table

Water Test	Amount of Water Needed	Materials Needed to Complete Test
		Data will vary depending on the body of water tested and the tests students choose to perform. Most tests done with test kits, such as pH and nitrates, require 5–10 mL of
		water sample. Tests for dissolved oxygen require about 60 mL.

5. Predict whether the water site is polluted. What were the reasons behind your prediction?

Students might base their predictions on the clarity of the water, odors from the water, presence

or absence of wildlife, or presence of nearby sources of pollution such as factories or farms.

_____

6. On a separate sheet of paper, write a procedure to follow to complete your water quality investigation. After the teacher approves your investigation plan, gather your material for the field study. Be sure all of your water-sampling equipment is clean before you use it. You do not want to contaminate your samples.

7. Complete the tests you have decided to do. Use the Data Table provided on the next page to record your observations and the data you gather. If you are doing a plant and animal survey, record your results on a separate sheet. Compare your data with that of other groups in your class.

FIELD TESTING A BODY OF FRESH WATER *(continued)*

◆ Observations

1. What observations can you make at the water site? Is the water clean or dirty?
   What plants and animals are in the immediate area around the water?

   Students should make qualitative observations of the water, including comments about the color

   and whether the water is clean. Diagrams and notes on the plants and animals in the

   immediate area can be taken and later classified, using a field guide.

   _____

   _____

   _____

Data Table Sample Data

Water Test	Observations	Test Results
Dissolved oxygen	Numerous fish observed in pond. Therefore, expect D.O. is at least 4 mg/L.	8 mg/L
pH	Extensive variety and number of plants at water's edge. Numerous fish. Expect pH within range of 6.0 to 8.0.	7.2

FIELD TESTING A BODY OF FRESH WATER *(continued)*

◆ Analyze and Conclude

1. The pH of most rivers, lakes, and streams in the United States falls within the range of 6.0 to 8.0. Many species of fish can live in water with this pH range. Would the water in your sample support fish life? Explain.

Answers will vary. If the pH of the water is below 6.0 or above 8.0, the water sample would most

likely not support fish life.

2. Which of your tests indicates a problem with the body of water you tested? Which did not?

Answers will vary. Dissolved oxygen levels below 4 mg/L, nitrate levels above 90 mg/L, and

phosphate levels above 0.1 mg/L indicate water problems. Students should determine which

tests indicated water pollution and which values fell within normal levels.

3. How did the plants and animals found in and around the body of water give an indication of water quality?

Answers will vary. The presence of a variety of plants and animals in and around the body of

water would indicate that the water pollution level may not be extremely high.

◆ Critical Thinking and Applications

1. How might the amount of suspended solids in a stream or pond differ if you measured them right after a heavy rainstorm?

After a heavy rainstorm, the water is likely to contain more suspended and dissolved solids

because of runoff.

2. Different fish have different temperature requirements. The following list contains the maximum water temperature in which each species of fish can survive.

brook trout	25.5°C
carp	41.0°C
bluegill sunfish	34.3°C
yellow perch	30.8°C
fathead minnow	33.7°C
brown bullhead	34.8°C

2

Would any of these fish be able to survive in the water you tested? If so, which ones?

Answers will vary. Students should report the water temperature of the body of water they tested.

Any species of fish with a maximum water temperature tolerance above the stated water

temperature would be able to survive in the water tested assuming that all of its other needs

were met.

3. Water in a swampy or boggy area is usually very acidic, or has a low pH. Imagine that water from a swamp flows into a stream at point A. How do you think the pH of water samples taken upstream and downstream from point A would compare?

The pH of the water sample taken downstream from point A would be lower than the pH of the

water sample taken upstream.

◆ More to Explore

If the conditions you found in the fresh water you investigated need improvement, write a plan for steps that should be followed to improve the water quality. Share your plan with the class and mail it along with a cover letter to an appropriate local official or environmental agency.

Student plans will vary depending on what problems students found with the body of water tested. Plans should indicate specific directions for raising or lowering unacceptable levels of acidity, minerals, or sediments present. If unacceptable levels are found, students should investigate the source or sources of the pollutants.

H-3 **LABORATORY INVESTIGATION**

Pollution of a Water Supply

Key Concept: Pollutants can travel through the groundwater in an aquifer.

Skills Focus: Observing, inferring, making models

Time Required: 40 minutes

◆ Pre-Lab Discussion

Many communities get their water from sources deep in the ground. This groundwater seeps slowly through the pores of sediment and rock layers. The rate of movement depends largely on the slope of the rock layers and the permeability of the rock.

People bring groundwater to the surface in wells. If water is pumped out too fast, a well can go dry. Besides the quantity of groundwater, its quality is also a concern. Many pollutants that contaminate surface water also contaminate groundwater.

In this investigation, you will create a model of a well system and add pollutants. You will study the spread of the pollutants and their effect on the water supply.

1. What are three sources of groundwater pollution?

Possible answers include human wastes, industrial wastes, agricultural wastes, and runoff from

roads.

2. What is the difference between point sources and nonpoint sources of water pollution? Give an example of each.

Point sources are specific sources of pollution; industrial outfall pipe. Nonpoint sources are

widely spread sources of pollution that cannot be pinpointed; runoff.

◆ Problem

How does groundwater pollution affect a community's water supply?

◆ Materials *(per group)*

plastic or transparent glass loaf pan, approximately 10 cm × 20 cm
2 blocks of modeling clay
2 cups of coarse sand
14 heavy plastic drinking straws
red food coloring

blue food coloring
paper towels
medicine dropper
watering can
metric ruler

Advance Preparation: Collect clear plastic loaf pans used as packaging by grocery stores. Be sure to clean them thoroughly before using them.

Alternative Materials: Use dropper bottles of food coloring to eliminate the need for plastic droppers.

POLLUTION OF A WATER SUPPLY (continued)

◆ Safety 🧑‍🔬 🥽 🧤 🔥 *Review the safety guidelines in the front of your lab book.*

To prevent slips or falls, immediately wipe up any water spilled on the floor.
Handle glass objects carefully. If they break, tell the teacher. Do not pick up
broken glass. Wear safety goggles and an apron at all times.

◆ Procedure

1. Cover the bottom of the pan with a layer of modeling clay to a depth of
   1–2 cm. Build it up at one end to create a slope. See Figure 1. Press the clay
   tightly against the bottom and sides of the pan.

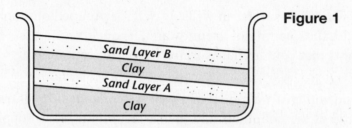

Figure 1

2. Cover the clay with sand. The sand layer should be about 1–2 cm thick and
   follow the slope of the clay. Lightly sprinkle the sand with water, using the watering can. This is sand layer A.

3. Place a thin layer of modeling clay (about 1 cm thick) on top of the sand, following the slope of the layers below. Press the clay tightly against the sides of the pan.

4. Finally, cover the clay with about 1 cm of sand, following the slope of the layers
   below. Lightly sprinkle the sand with water. This is sand layer B. Your final
   model should resemble Figure 1.

5. Hold your finger over the top of a drinking straw. Insert the straw on one side
   of the model about 5 cm from the highest spot. See Figure 2. The end of the
   straw should just go into the bottom layer of clay. Withdraw the straw. A slight
   twist will help to remove it. The clay and sand should come out with the straw,
   leaving a hole.

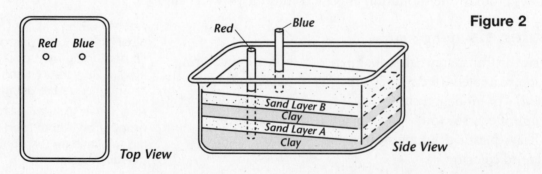

Figure 2

POLLUTION OF A WATER SUPPLY (*continued*)

6. Carefully insert another straw in the same hole to about the same depth. Put five or six drops of red food coloring in the straw. Do not drip the food coloring on the surface of the sand. Remove the straw. Rinse the plastic dropper.

7. Using the same method as in Step 5, insert a third straw in the other side of the pan, but this time just until it touches the **top** layer of clay. Withdraw the straw. Again, the clay and sand should come out with the straw.

8. Carefully insert another straw in the same hole. Put five or six drops of blue food coloring in this straw. Remove the straw carefully.

9. The food coloring represents pollutants that have been introduced into a shallow well (blue) and a deep well (red).

10. Lightly, but thoroughly, sprinkle the surface of the sand with water. This process simulates rainfall. Wait a few minutes for the water to soak into the layers.

11. Insert another straw to the bottom of the pan, uphill or downhill from a well. See Figure 3. Remove it and lay it on a paper towel. Record the sample distance from the original well in the Data Table, and label it *uphill* or *downhill*.

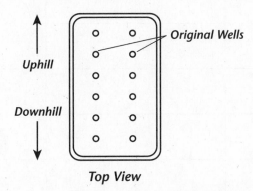

Figure 3

Uphill

Downhill

Original Wells

Top View

12. Predict the color of the sand from each sand layer the straw passed through. Record your predictions in the table. Ask your teacher to cut the side of the straw. **CAUTION:** *Do not cut the straw yourself.* Examine the contents of the core, and record your observations in the table. Note any color, how strong the color is, and in which sand layer the color appears.

13. Using the method in steps 11 and 12, take ten core samples uphill and downhill in a straight line from both wells. See Figure 3. Record your predictions and your observations.

Use a razor blade, box knife, or scalpel blade to slit the straw and reveal its contents.

POLLUTION OF A WATER SUPPLY (continued)

◆ Observations

Data Table

Core Sample	Distance From Well (Indicate Uphill or Downhill)		Color			
			Sand Layer A		Sand Layer B	
	Red Well	Blue Well	Prediction	Actual	Prediction	Actual
1						
2						
3						
4						
5						
6						
7						
8						
9						
10						

Distances uphill and downhill from the original wells will vary. Data should indicate stronger colors of pollutants downhill from the original wells, and mostly red in sand layer A and blue in sand layer B.

1. In which direction do the pollutants travel faster? Why?

The pollutants travel faster downhill because of gravity.

_____

_____

_____

POLLUTION OF A WATER SUPPLY *(continued)*

2. In which sand layer do the pollutants travel faster? Why?

The pollutants travel faster in sand layer B because this layer is closest to the top and absorbs

most of the rain.

◆ Analyze and Conclude

1. What does the modeling clay represent?

Rock layers that are not permeable

2. Did you find any red coloring in sand layer B? Why or why not?

No, because the pollutant does not rise.

3. Did you find any blue coloring in sand layer A? Why or why not?

No, because the blue coloring could not permeate the clay.

4. Which sand layer is harder to pollute from the surface? Why?

Sand layer A, because the layer of clay would block the flow of surface pollution.

5. Which sand layer is harder to purify if it does become contaminated? Why?

Sand layer A, because it is deeper and the layer of clay would block some cleaning efforts.

◆ Critical Thinking and Applications

1. How could wastes buried in soil eventually pollute the groundwater?

The wastes could seep through permeable layers of soil and rock and eventually reach the

groundwater.

2. How does the pollution of groundwater differ from the pollution of surface water?

Surface water is usually polluted directly by point sources, such as a pipe dumping pollutants

into a river. Groundwater is usually polluted by nonpoint sources, such as agricultural chemicals

that seep into the ground. Groundwater pollution is also more difficult to detect.

POLLUTION OF A WATER SUPPLY *(continued)*

3. Do you agree that water in deep wells is less likely to be polluted than water in more shallow wells? Give a reason for your answer.

Answers will vary. Deep wells are more likely to be protected by impermeable rock layers

that prevent pollution from seeping down to them. However, if water from deep sources does

become polluted, it is harder to purify than water from more shallow wells.

◆ More to Explore

New Problem How do different kinds of sediments affect the movement of pollutants?

Possible Materials Consider which materials you can use from the previous part of this lab. Choose additional materials to represent different sediments.

Safety Wipe up spills immediately. Handle glass objects carefully. Be sure to wear your safety goggles and apron.

Students may suggest using various sizes of sand and gravel in layers among the layers of clay.

Procedure Develop a procedure to solve the problem. Write your procedure in your notebook. Have the teacher approve your procedure before you carry out the investigation.

Observations In your notebook, make a data table similar to the one in the previous part of this lab in which to record your data and observations.

Analyze and Conclude Do certain types of materials act as filters for pollutants? Describe the evidence for your answer.

Be sure students state the evidence from their results that justifies their answer to Analyze and

Conclude. Students will likely find that the finer the sediments, the more effective they are at

blocking the movement of pollutants.

H-4   **LABORATORY INVESTIGATION**

Density and Salinity

Key Concept: Water of different densities, caused by different salinity, forms layers.

Skills Focus: Observing, inferring, predicting, measuring

Time Required: 90 minutes

◆ Pre-Lab Discussion

The average salinity of ocean water is 35 parts of salt per thousand parts of water. Ocean salt comes from minerals on land, which dissolve into water that flows over them. Dissolved salts affect water density, and density affects the way ocean waters move and form layers. By studying the salinity of water, oceanographers learn about ocean layers and currents.

In this investigation, you will model ocean water of different salinity and use the models to determine how ocean waters form layers.

1. Define salinity.

Salinity is the total amount of dissolved salts in water. _____

_____

2. What causes differences in the salinity of ocean water in different areas?

Rain, snow, melting ice, and fresh water from rivers lower the salinity of ocean water. Evaporation

and the freezing of surface water increase the salinity.

4

◆ Problem

How do differences in salinity create layers in ocean water?

◆ Materials *(per group)*

salt	red food coloring
spoon	blue food coloring
balance	3 small plastic foam cups
4 1000-mL beakers	metric ruler
graduated cylinder	tape
water at room temperature	toothpick
250-mL beaker	

Advance Preparation: Fill a large container with tap water several hours before the lab and let it reach room temperature. Each group will need about 4 L of this water.

Alternative Materials: You can use large jars instead of beakers, and measuring cups instead of graduated cylinders.

Teaching Tips: Remind students not to bump the beakers and plastic-foam cups while the colored water is leaving the cup.

◆ Safety   *Review the safety guidelines in the front of your lab book.*

To prevent slips and falls, immediately wipe up any water spilled on the floor. Handle glass objects carefully. If they break, tell your teacher. Do not pick up broken glass.

To save time, prepare 5% and 10% salt solutions ahead of time.

DENSITY AND SALINITY (*continued*)

◆ Procedure

1. Make a 5% salt solution: Measure 50 g of salt and pour it into a 1000-mL beaker. Add 950 mL of water to the beaker. Stir until all the salt dissolves.

2. Make a 10% salt solution: Measure 10 g of salt and pour it into the 250-mL beaker. Add 90 mL of water to the beaker. Stir until all the salt dissolves. Add enough blue food coloring to make the water deep blue.

3. Fill a second 1000-mL beaker with 400 mL of water.

4. Pour 10 mL of the 5% salt solution into a plastic foam cup. Add enough red food coloring to make the water deep red. Tape the cup inside the beaker of water, so that the bottom of the cup is just below the water level. See Figure 1.

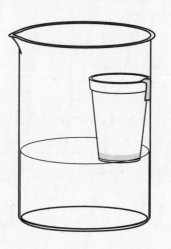

Figure 1

5. Holding the plastic foam cup steady, use a toothpick to poke a small hole near the bottom of the cup.

6. Be careful not to bump the beaker. Observe what happens to the colored water. Record your observations in the Data Table. Sketch and color what you observe.

7. Fill the third 1000-mL beaker with 5% salt solution to within 10 cm of the top.

8. Pour 10 mL of the blue 10% salt solution into the second plastic foam cup. As before, tape the cup inside the beaker so that the bottom of the cup is just below the water level.

9. Repeat Steps 5 and 6.

10. As a control, fill the fourth 1000-mL beaker with 5% salt solution to within 10 cm of the top. Pour 10 mL of tap water into the third plastic foam cup. Add blue food coloring to the tap water until the tap water is the same color as the 10% salt solution in Step 2. Tape the cup to the inside of the beaker as before. Repeat steps 5 and 6.

DENSITY AND SALINITY *(continued)*

◆ Observations

Data Table

	Observations	*Sketch*
5% red salt solution in tap water	The red water sank to the bottom of the clear water and formed a separate layer.	Drawings should show a layer of red water at the bottom of the beaker.
10% blue salt solution in 5% salt solution	The blue water sank to the bottom of the clear water and formed a separate layer.	Drawings should show a layer of blue water at the bottom of the beaker.
Blue tap water in 5% salt solution	The blue water floated on the clear water and formed a separate layer.	Drawings should show a layer of blue water on top of the clear water in the beaker.

◆ Analyze and Conclude

1. Which water was the least dense? The most dense? Explain your reasoning.

   The plain tap water was the least dense, and the blue 10% salt solution was the most dense.

   _____

   _____

2. How does the amount of salt dissolved in water affect its density? Give the evidence that supports your answer.

   The more salt that is dissolved in the water, the denser the water is. Evidence for this conclusion

   is that the water with the greatest concentration of salt always sank beneath the water with the

   least concentration of salt.

DENSITY AND SALINITY (*continued*)

3. In the ocean, where would you expect to find water with the greatest salinity? Give a reason for your answer.

Water with the greatest salinity is at the bottom of the ocean because it has the greatest density

and will sink.

◆ Critical Thinking and Applications

1. Predict how the following kinds of water would form layers: (1) warm, slightly salty water; (2) cold, slightly salty water; (3) cold, very salty water; (4) warm rainwater. List them in order, starting with the deepest layer. Give a reason for your answer.

From bottom to top: 3, 2, 1, 4. As water's temperature decreases and its salinity increases, it

becomes more dense and sinks. Rainwater is fresh water and, therefore, would form the top

layer.

2. Why was it important that all the water in the experiment was the same temperature?

If the water had been different temperatures, the temperature, not just the salinity, might also

have affected how the water formed layers.

3. Would you expect the salinity to be high or low in the ocean off the coast of a hot, dry area? Give a reason for your answer.

The salinity would be high because as warm water evaporates, salts are left behind. Also, in a dry

area, little rain falls to dilute the salinity of the ocean in that area.

◆ More to Explore

What would happen if you added red 5% salt solution and blue 10% salt solution from two cups at the same time to a container of tap water? Develop a hypothesis for this problem. Then write a procedure you would follow to test your hypothesis. Have the teacher approve your procedure before you carry it out. Remember to wear your safety goggles and apron.

If the water is not disturbed, three separate layers should form, with the blue 10% salt solution on the bottom, the red 5% solution above that, and the clear tap water on top.

H - 5 **LABORATORY INVESTIGATION**

Microscopic Marine Life

Key Concept: Microorganisms are part of the ocean's food webs.

Skills Focus: Observing, inferring

Time Required: 60 minutes

◆ Pre-Lab Discussion

Much marine life is too small to see without a microscope. But these tiny organisms play an important role in marine habitats. They serve as food for larger organisms. At the base of all food webs are algae plankton that use sunlight to produce their own food. Their cells contain chlorophyll, a green pigment. In turn, these plankton become food for other organisms.

In this investigation, you will examine and compare microscopic organisms that live in the ocean.

1. What are plankton?

Plankton are tiny algae and animals that float in water.
_____

2. Describe the two major groups of plankton.

Algae plankton include diatoms and other organisms that make their own food. Animal plankton,

such as copepods, crustacean larvae, and fish larvae, eat other organisms.
_____

◆ Problem

What can you learn about plankton by observing them?

Advance Preparation: Obtain prepared slides of a variety of marine plankton, such as diatoms, dinoflagellates, foraminiferans, copepods, fish larvae, and crustacean larvae.

◆ Materials *(per group)*

prepared slides of
    marine plankton
compound microscope
colored pencils

Alternative Materials: If microscopes are not available, you could use a microprojector and have students sketch from the projected images. Live samples may be collected with a plankton net if you live near the ocean.

Teaching Tips: Before beginning the investigation, review the parts of the microscope and its proper use. Have reference books available to help students identify the plankton they observe.

◆ Safety *Review the safety guidelines in the front of your lab book.*

Always use both hands to pick up or carry a microscope. Hold the microscope base with one hand and the microscope arm with your other hand. Handle glass slides carefully.

Remind students to handle glass slides with care and to tell you if they break a slide.

◆ Procedure

1. Place a slide under the clips on the microscope stage. Adjust the mirror or lamp to shine light through the slide. **CAUTION:** *If the microscope has a mirror, do not use direct sunlight as a light source. Direct sunlight can damage your eyes.*

MICROSCOPIC MARINE LIFE *(continued)*

2. Watching the microscope from the side, use the coarse-adjustment knob to lower the low-power objective slowly until it is close to the slide. Do not let the objective touch the slide. Look into the eyepiece and raise the tube until you can see the organism. You may need to move the slide slightly to center the organism. Use the fine-adjustment knob to focus the image.

3. In Observations, record the name of the organism. Then draw and color what you see under the low-power lens. Record the magnification of the low-power lens.

4. Turn the revolving nosepiece to move the high-power objective into place. Carefully focus the image with the fine-adjustment knob. **CAUTION:** *Never focus the high-power objective with the coarse-adjustment knob. The objective could break the slide.*

5. Draw and color what you see under the high-power lens. Record the magnification of the high-power lens.

6. Repeat steps 1–5 with each slide.

Diatoms are one-celled aquatic protists. They have delicate shells that come in many different shapes. Diatom shells are classified into two groups—those with radial symmetry and those with bilateral symmetry.

◆ Observations

Name of Organism	View Under Low Power Magnification: _____	View Under High Power Magnification: _____
_____ _____		
_____ _____		

Dinoflagellates are one-celled algae that have thick cell walls made up of thick cellulose plates that sometime resemble helmets or suits of armor. Dinoflagellates have whip-like flagella located in grooves at right angles to each other.

Foraminiferans are one-celled amebas that live inside shells. They extend pseudopodia through tiny holes in their shells.

MICROSCOPIC MARINE LIFE *(continued)*

Name of Organism	View Under Low Power Magnification: _____	View Under High Power Magnification: _____
_____ _____		
_____ _____		
_____ _____		
_____ _____		

5

Distinct green structures called chloroplasts will be evident in some marine plankton capable of photosynthesis, such as green algae, while some species may only show a general green color.

MICROSCOPIC MARINE LIFE *(continued)*

◆ Analyze and Conclude

1. Were all the organisms you observed single-celled? If not, which ones were not?

Answers will vary. Fish larvae, crustacean larvae, and copepods are multicellular.

2. What similarities did you observe in the organisms?

Answers will vary. Sample answer: All are too small to be seen without a microscope, and all are

made of cells.

3. What differences did you observe in the organisms?

Answers will vary. Sample answer: The organisms have different colors and shapes. Some have

whip-like external structures. Some are algae plankton, and some are animal plankton.

◆ Critical Thinking and Applications

1. Which of the organisms you observed produced their own food through photosynthesis? Give a reason for your answer.

Algae plankton, such as diatoms and dinoflagellates, make their own food. Algae contain

chlorophyll.

2. Which of the organisms you observed relied on other plankton as a food source? Give a reason for your answer.

Copepods, crustacean larvae, and fish larvae; any organism that does not have chlorophyll

probably relied on other plankton as a food source.

3. Explain how an organism can be part of the plankton at one stage of its life and part of the nekton at another stage.

Answers will vary. Sample answer: Some fish larvae are plankton. They are microscopic and are

moved by waves and currents. When they grow larger, they become free-swimming animals that

control their own motion.

◆ More to Explore

What do snails in an aquarium eat? Observe the activity of snails in an aquarium. Using toothpicks, scrape some green film from an aquarium glass and other surfaces. Make slides of your samples and examine them using a microscope. Wear your safety goggles. Wash up after completing the activity.

Allow a classroom aquarium to become slightly overgrown with algae and monerans before the lab begins. Students should observe that the snails leave a clear trail on the aquarium sides as it scrapes off and consumes the underlying growth of protists and monerans. Students will observe a variety of algae, including different diatom species. Cyanobacteria should also be present.

I-1

Key Concept: Acid rain can damage various materials.

Examining Acid Rain

Skills Focus: Observing, inferring, predicting, making models, measuring

◆ Pre-Lab Discussion

Time Required: two 30-minute periods on 2 consecutive days

Moisture in the air dissolves many pollutants. When the moisture falls as rain or snow, it removes the pollutants from the air. In many cases, this process is beneficial because it cleans the air. When the pollutants in the moisture are nitrogen oxides and sulfur oxides, however, the result is acid rain.

How can you tell whether rain is acidic? The process is simple. You dip specially treated paper in rainwater and compare the color of the paper to a pH color scale. The pH scale ranges from 0 to 14 and is a measure of how acidic or basic a substance is. Pure water is neutral and has a pH of 7. Solutions with a pH greater than 7 are basic, and those with a pH less than 7 are acidic. The lower the number, the more acidic the solution is. Grapefruits, lemons, vinegar, and other sour foods are acidic.

In this investigation, you will use pH indicator paper to determine the pH of some common substances. You will examine how acids affect materials used for buildings, statues, and other structures.

Advance Preparation: Each group will need 200 mL of the acid solution they choose to test and 200 mL of a control solution.

1. What acids are likely to be in acid rain?

nitric acid and sulfuric acid

2. What is the main source of the pollutants that cause acid rain?

The main source of nitrogen oxides is the burning of fossil fuels at high temperatures. The main

source of sulfur oxides is the burning of high-sulfur coal.

◆ Problem

How can acid rain affect building materials?

Equipment-supply houses or garden centers sell rocks that you can use for samples. You can also have students help you gather rocks from the environment.

Alternate Materials: Substitute large plastic cups for the beakers. You could add other building materials to the samples: concrete chunks, roof tiles, stucco samples, steel, and so on.

◆ Possible Materials *(per group)*

distilled water
lemon juice
white vinegar
carbonated water
pH scale
balance

pH indicator paper
8 beakers, 100 mL
glass marker
2 small samples each of limestone,
    sandstone, marble, and granite

Teaching Tips: Demonstrate how to test using indicator paper and comparing the color to a scale, usually found on the paper container.

◆ Safety   *Review the safety guidelines in this lab book.*

To prevent slips or falls, immediately wipe up any water spilled on the floor. Notify the teacher immediately if any glass breaks.

EXAMINING ACID RAIN *(continued)*

◆ Procedure

Part A: Modeling Acid Rain

Tell students that the solutions in the materials list are more acidic than acid rain. Therefore, the effects of these solutions on building materials will be greater than with actual acid rain.

1. Read the entire lab before continuing your investigation.

2. You will design an experiment to test the effects of acid rain on building materials. First, you need to decide what you will use for acid rain. Experiment with different solutions. Use the indicator paper to determine the pH of each solution to find out if it is a good model of acid rain. Record your data in Data Table 1.

3. Decide what you will use as a control. Your control should be a solution that has a pH of typical rainwater (5–5.6). Add this information to Data Table 1.

4. Get the teacher's approval of your models before going on to Part B.

To make a control solution, students could start with distilled water (pH 7.0) and add drops of lemon juice until the pH becomes that of rainwater (5–5.6)

Part B: Testing Acid Rain on Materials

1. Brainstorm some materials that buildings, monuments, and other structures are made of. Then decide what building materials you will test and how you will test them. Write your procedure on a separate sheet of paper.

2. Use Data Table 2 to record your observations and other data. Add headings to the data table. Plan to make observations today and tomorrow. You may need to make another data table on a separate sheet of paper for tomorrow's observations.

3. Have the teacher approve your procedure before carrying out your experiment.

4. Predict which building material will be the most affected by acid rain. Which material will be least affected? Give reasons for your predictions.

Students may base their predictions on how strong they think the material is. They may think that a heavyweight material with a smooth texture is stronger than a lightweight material with a grainy texture. The masses of the samples before and after they sit in acid will vary, but all rock samples will be affected. Of the materials listed, limestone will be the most affected, and granite the least.

◆ Observations

Data Table 1

Acid Rain Model (description)	Acid Rain Model (pH)	Control (description)	Control (pH)
	lemon juice: 2.0 white vinegar: 2.5 carbonated water: 3.0		

EXAMINING ACID RAIN *(continued)*

Data Table 2

Day: 1	Building Material			
	Limestone	Sandstone	Marble	Granite
Acid Rain Model				
Control				

Limestone will immediately effervesce in acid. It and marble will likely lose the most mass. Besides changes in mass, students may observe visible changes in the size and shape of some materials over the two days.

◆ Analyze and Conclude

1. Did any building material have an immediate reaction that you could see? If so, which one(s), and what was the reaction?

    If students test limestone, it will immediately start fizzing.

2. Which building material changed the most in a day? How did you measure the change?

    Limestone in acid will change the most. Students should be able to measure a change in the

    sample's mass. They should also recognize the change visually.

3. Which building material changed the least? How did you measure the change?

    Granite will change the least. It isn't likely to lose much mass in a day.

4. How can acid rain affect buildings, statues, and other structures made of the materials you tested?

    Answers will vary. Students should recognize that, among the listed materials, limestone will be

    most affected by acid rain, so buildings made from limestone are most likely to suffer

    deterioration from acid rain.

◆ Critical Thinking and Applications

1. How would your results have been affected if your acid rain had been more acidic? Less acidic?

    The more acidic the rain, the faster the material would have deteriorated. Rain that was less

    acidic would not change the material as much in the same amount of time.

EXAMINING ACID RAIN (*continued*)

1

2. Cleopatra's Needles are large obelisks, each weighing about 200 tons. They are made of red granite and carved with hieroglyphics. Figure 1 shows an obelisk. One of the Needles was shipped from Egypt to New York City in 1880. The New York monument's hieroglyphics have almost disappeared, while a similar monument in the Egyptian desert has changed little over the past 3,000 years. Explain one of the probable reasons this difference exists.

The obelisk in New York City is probably being destroyed, at

least in part, by acid rain. Acid rain would affect it more than

the Egyptian obelisk, since New York City has more rain and

probably more pollutants than the Egyptian desert.

_____

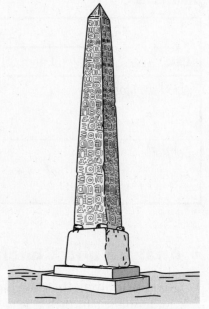

Figure 1

◆ More to Explore

New Problem How is *Elodea*, a freshwater plant, affected by acid rain falling into a pond where it grows?

Possible Materials Consider which materials you can use from this lab. What other materials will you need?

Safety To prevent slips or falls, immediately wipe up any liquid spilled on the floor. Handle glass objects carefully. If they break, tell the teacher. Do not pick up broken glass. Be sure to wear safety goggles and an apron and wash up after you're done.

Procedure Write a hypothesis about the effects that acid rain has upon *Elodea* plants. Then write a procedure you could follow to test your hypothesis. Have the teacher approve your procedure before you carry out the investigation.

Observations Keep careful records of your observations on a separate sheet of paper.

Analyze and Conclude

1. Does acid rain affect *Elodea*? Support your conclusions with data collected during the investigation.

   Elodea plants will show signs of distress and may die while growing in acidic conditions. Elodea

   in distilled water should not show any appreciable changes.

2. How might acid rain affect other plants and animals that live in fresh water?

   Other living things in water bodies that collect acid rain may show signs of distress.

   _____

Elodea plants and aquarium gravel are available in pet stores that sell fish. If *Elodea* is not available, provide *Cabomba* or *Sagittaria* (grassleaf).

Using a Psychrometer to Determine Relative Humidity

Key Concept: Relative humidity is the amount of water vapor in the air compared to the maximum that air can hold at a given temperature.

Skills Focus: Observing, inferring, predicting, measuring, designing experiments

Time Required: 40 minutes

2

◆ Pre-Lab Discussion

Even without rain, the air can be very wet because it contains invisible water vapor. The amount of water vapor in the air is known as humidity. As air gets warmer, it can hold more moisture. Meteorologists usually speak of relative humidity—the amount of water vapor in the air compared to the maximum amount that air can hold at a particular temperature.

You can measure relative humidity with a psychrometer, which consists of two thermometers. One thermometer has a dry bulb, and one has a wet bulb. A piece of wet cloth surrounds the bulb of the wet-bulb thermometer. When the wet bulb is exposed to air, water in the cloth evaporates, just as it does from wet clothing. Water evaporation requires heat energy, so it cools the wet bulb.

In this investigation, you will construct a sling psychrometer and use it to measure the relative humidity of the classroom.

1. What is the difference between humidity and relative humidity?

Humidity is the amount of water vapor in the air at a given time. Relative humidity is the amount

of moisture in the air compared to the maximum possible air moisture at that temperature.

2. Would you expect the temperature of the wet-bulb thermometer to be higher on a humid day or on a dry day? Give a reason for your answer.

The temperature of the wet-bulb thermometer would be higher on a humid day because not

much evaporation will cool the wet-bulb thermometer.

◆ Problem

How can you use a psychrometer to find the relative humidity of the classroom?

USING A PSYCHROMETER TO DETERMINE RELATIVE HUMIDITY *(continued)*

◆ Materials *(per group)*

2 identical thermometers
strip of gauze, 10 cm
piece of thread, 20 cm
piece of cardboard, approximately
    20 cm × 30 cm
water at room temperature
transparent tape
bucket
small plastic cup
plastic dropper
large index card

Advance Preparation: Cut a gauze strip and a piece of thread for each group. Collect shirt cardboard or the cardboard backing from notepads, one for each group. Let water sit in a bucket for a few hours prior to the lab so that it is at room temperature.

Alternative Materials: Use cotton cloth instead of gauze.

Teaching Tips: Use only alcohol thermometers if at all possible.

Remind students to tape the thermometers *securely* to the cardboard before picking it up.

The gauze surrounding the wet-bulb thermometer must be saturated with water before fanning begins.

Use the provided sample data to show students how to use the relative humidity table prior to starting the lab.

◆ Safety   *Review the safety guidelines in the front of your lab book.*

Handle the thermometer carefully. If it breaks, tell your teacher. Do not pick up broken glass.

◆ Procedure

1. **CAUTION:** *Handle the thermometer carefully; it's breakable.* Wrap the gauze around the bulb of one thermometer and tie it in place with the thread.

2. Tape the thermometers side by side with the two bulbs extending over the edge of the cardboard. See Figure 1.

Figure 1

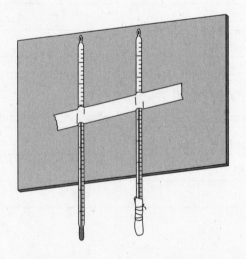

3. Scoop some water from the bucket into a small plastic cup. Use this water and the plastic dropper to thoroughly wet the gauze.

USING A PSYCHROMETER TO DETERMINE RELATIVE HUMIDITY *(continued)*

4. Hold the cardboard up in the air. Carefully fan the thermometer bulbs with the index card until the temperature of the wet-bulb thermometer stops dropping. Predict the difference in temperatures between the two thermometers. Explain your reasoning.

If the relative humidity feels low, students may predict a difference of at least 5 degrees,

reflecting the ability of the water on the wet bulb to evaporate quickly.

Read the temperatures on both thermometers. Record these numbers in the data table next to the sample data. Calculate the difference between the two readings.

5. Find the relative humidity in Data Table 1 below, using the temperature difference between the dry bulb and the wet bulb. Express relative humidity as a percentage. For example, suppose the dry-bulb reading is 21°C and the wet-bulb reading is 15°C. The difference is 6°C. The number on the table where the row of the dry-bulb reading (21) and the column of the difference (6) intersect shows the relative humidity (53%). These numbers are included in Data Table 2 as sample data. Record your own data next to them.

Data Table 1: Relative Humidity (%)

Dry-Bulb Reading (°C)	Difference Between Dry-Bulb and Wet-Bulb Readings (°C)									
	1	2	3	4	5	6	7	8	9	10
10	88	76	65	54	43	34	24	15	6	
11	89	78	67	56	46	36	27	18	9	
12	88	78	67	57	48	39	29	21	12	
13	89	79	69	59	50	41	32	23	15	7
14	89	79	69	60	50	42	34	26	18	10
15	90	80	71	61	53	44	36	27	20	13
16	90	80	71	62	54	46	38	30	23	15
17	90	81	72	64	55	47	40	32	25	18
18	91	81	72	64	56	49	41	34	27	20
19	91	82	74	65	58	50	43	36	29	22
20	91	82	74	66	58	53	46	39	32	26
21	91	83	75	67	60	53	46	39	32	26
22	92	83	75	68	60	54	47	40	34	28
23	92	84	76	69	62	55	48	42	36	30
24	92	84	76	69	62	56	49	43	37	31
25	92	84	77	70	63	57	50	44	39	33
26	92	85	77	70	64					

USING A PSYCHROMETER TO DETERMINE RELATIVE HUMIDITY *(continued)*

◆ Observations

Data Table 2

	Sample Data	*Your Data*
Dry-bulb reading	21°C	
Wet-bulb reading	15°C	
Difference	6°C	
Relative humidity	53%	

1. Which of the two thermometers measures the air temperature?

The dry-bulb thermometer measures the air temperature.

2. What is the relative humidity in your classroom?

53% for the sample data; Students' data will likely be close to the outside relative humidity if the

classroom is not air-conditioned. The relative humidity in an air-conditioned room will likely be

lower than that outside.

◆ Analyze and Conclude

1. What is the relationship between evaporation and the wet-bulb temperature?

Evaporation is a cooling process. As water evaporates from the gauze around the thermometer

bulb, the temperature drops.

2. Explain your answer to question 1 in terms of energy.

Evaporation requires energy. As water evaporates from the gauze, energy is taken from the air

surrounding the gauze and then moves away from the thermometer.

3. What is the relationship between evaporation and relative humidity?

The relationship is inverse. The lower the relative humidity of the air, the faster evaporation will be.

4. Predict the difference between the dry-bulb and wet-bulb readings when the
relative humidity is 100%. Give a reason for your answer.

If the relative humidity is 100%, the surrounding air could not hold any more moisture, so

evaporation isn't possible. Therefore, both thermometers would read the same.

USING A PSYCHROMETER TO DETERMINE RELATIVE HUMIDITY (continued)

5. Predict how the relative humidity inside your classroom compares with the relative humidity outdoors. How could you test your prediction?

Predictions will vary. You could use the same equipment and take outdoor readings. Then use

the chart to determine the outdoor relative humidity.

_____

_____

◆ Critical Thinking and Applications

1. Does the air in your classroom tend to be moist, dry, or somewhere in between? Give a reason for your answer.

Answers will vary. Many indoor environments tend to be dry in winter and moist in summer.

_____

_____

_____

2. Would you feel more comfortable in a desert where the temperature is 35°C or in a rain forest where the temperature is 35°C? Give a reason for your answer.

You would likely feel more comfortable in a desert because the air would have a lower relative

humidity and would allow sweat to evaporate more quickly. The evaporation would cool your

body.

_____

_____

3. How can you tell, without using a psychrometer, whether the air is moist or dry?

Possible answers include dry skin or nose and throat irritations if the air is very dry; "sticky" or

damp feeling if the air is very moist.

_____

_____

4. Why does running a dehumidifier in your home during the summer help make you feel more comfortable?

A dehumidifier removes moisture from the air. Less humidity allows faster evaporation of sweat

and makes you feel cooler.

_____

_____

USING A PSYCHROMETER TO DETERMINE RELATIVE HUMIDITY *(continued)*

5. Antarctica is the coldest place on Earth. Explain why the parts of Antarctica not covered by glaciers are a frigid desert.

Very cold air can hold very little water vapor, therefore the air is very dry and little

precipitation falls.

◆ More to Explore

In Analyze and Conclude question 5, you predicted how the relative humidity in the classroom compares with the relative humidity outdoors. Now test your prediction. Write a procedure you can follow. You may wish to include other areas in your school in your investigation, for example, the cafeteria or gym. Be sure to make predictions for these places before testing them. Have the teacher approve your procedure before you carry out the investigation. Be sure to wear your safety goggles.

If the classroom is air-conditioned, chances are good that the relative humidity outdoors will be greater than that in the classroom. Students could make their predictions based on how high the humidity feels to them in various places. Suggest students compare their calculated relative humidity with the actual value given in a weather report.

I-3 **LABORATORY INVESTIGATION**

Investigating Weather Maps

Key Concept: Weather maps summarize weather data.

Skills Focus: Inferring, predicting, making models

Time Required: 90 minutes; You may want students to complete the lab for homework.

◆ Pre-Lab Discussion

Accurate weather forecasting requires analysis of detailed information about atmospheric conditions in many locations. In the United States, weather data from more than 300 local weather stations are used to prepare daily maps of the weather throughout the country. A detailed map may contain more than 10,000 data points. Such detailed maps are useful for making weather predictions.

Every minute of the day, weather stations, weather ships, satellites, balloons, and radar are recording temperature, pressure, wind direction, and other data and feeding them into the Global Telecommunications System (GTS). From this information, powerful supercomputers develop an image of conditions in the entire atmosphere and make forecasts for up to one week.

In this investigation, you will study how weather is presented, then prepare a simplified weather map and analyze it to discover relationships between weather and certain variables such as temperature and pressure.

1. What are three kinds of information that you could get from a newspaper weather map?

Answers might include the areas getting precipitation, the type of precipitation, temperatures in

different cities, the locations of different fronts, and areas of high and low pressure.

2. What kind of weather is associated with a low?

Clouds and precipitation

3. What kind of weather is associated with a high?

Dry, clear weather

◆ Problem

Alternative Materials: A crayon can be substituted for a colored pencil.

How can you make a weather map and use it to understand relationships between weather and certain atmospheric variables?

◆ Materials *(per group)*

Teaching Tips: Review the concepts of high- and low-pressure areas before the lab.

pencil
colored pencil

Go over one or two example stations with students before they begin Part B.

Have an overhead of the map available to use in case students have questions.

Remind students to use a light color for the shading in Part B, Step 4.

INVESTIGATING WEATHER MAPS *(continued)*

◆ Procedure

Part A

Read the following steps and study the diagrams to learn how weather data are presented on station circles.

1. Figure 1 shows the correct notation of some weather data recorded at an observation station. The circle represents the observation station. The data have specific positions inside and outside the station circle.

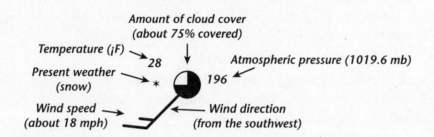

Figure 1
Station Circle

Amount of cloud cover
(about 75% covered)

Temperature (¡F) → 28

Atmospheric pressure (1019.6 mb)

Present weather
(snow) → * 196

Wind speed →
(about 18 mph)

Wind direction
(from the southwest)

2. Isobars are lines on a weather map that connect stations that report the same atmospheric pressure. These pressures are measured in millibars (mb), so isobars are labeled in millibars. To record the pressure on the station circle, use only the last three digits of the pressure and omit the decimal point. Look at the atmospheric pressure shown on the station circle in Figure 1. The atmospheric pressure is 1019.6 mb, which is recorded on the station circle as 196.

3. Think of the station circle as the point of an arrow. Attached to the station circle is a line, which is the arrow's shaft. The wind direction is represented as moving along the arrow's shaft *toward* the center of the station circle. Wind directions are given in degrees and represent the direction *from which* the wind is blowing. Figure 2 will help you determine wind direction. In Figure 1, the wind is blowing from the southwest toward the northeast.

4. Look at Figure 19 on page 103 of your textbook. It shows the data from station circles placed on a map. Compare the symbols discussed above with the symbols in Figure 19. Notice that the temperature is in degrees Fahrenheit.

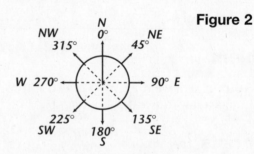

Figure 2

N
0°

NW
315°

NE
45°

W 270°

90° E

225°
SW

180°
S

135°
SE

Part B

1. The Data Table on the next page lists data collected at various weather stations on a particular day. Starting with Seattle, transfer all the data provided on the table to the appropriate observation stations on the map. Use the station circles and weather symbols discussed above. The station circle for San Francisco is done for you.

INVESTIGATING WEATHER MAPS (continued)

Data Table: Observation Stations

Weather Station	Wind Speed (mph	Wind Direction	Atmospheric Pressure (mb)	Temperature (°F)	Type of Precipitation	Cloud Cover (%)
Seattle	7	260°	1020.8	42		0
Bend	10	200°	1023.5	40		0
San Francisco	8	135°	1020.0	48	fog	25
Los Angeles	12	150°	1021.1	41	fog	25
Phoenix	11	50°	1021.1	45		0
Ely	2	15°	1025.1	37		0
Dubois	18	225°	1024.0	38		0
Helena	15	315°	1020.0	41		0
Medicine Hat	20	345°	1020.1	40		0
Bismarck	18	0°	1014.3	48		0
Casper	12	350°	1016.0	50		0
Pueblo	8	315°	1015.3	50		0
Roswell	22	350°	1016.0	48		0
Del Rio	38	315°	1012.0	50	thunderstorms	100
Galveston	5	225°	1016.0	72		25
Dallas	29	315°	1007.9	60	hail	100
Oklahoma City	45	315°	1007.7	57	thunderstorms	100
Kansas City	2	215°	1002.3	58	rain	100
Burwell	22	325°	1009.3	52	rain	100
Minneapolis	15	45°	1008.2	51	drizzle	100
Sioux Lookout	20	50°	1016.8	46		25
Chicago	10	45°	1005.2	58	drizzle	100
Little Rock	8	225°	1009.3	67		25
New Orleans	5	225°	1017.9	73		0
Nashville	5	220°	1011.1	68		25
Cincinnati	7	90°	1009.8	57	rain	100
Detroit	10	75°	1011.9	54	drizzle	100
Sault Ste. Marie	15	45°	1013.1	50	drizzle	100
Quebec	8	100°	1017.0	50		25
Boston	12	100°	1018.1	52	fog	25
Buffalo	7	75°	1016.0	52	drizzle	100
New York	10	80°	1017.6	56	fog	50
Hatteras	14	90°	1019.1	60		50
Charleston	15	225°	1017.8	70		25
Atlanta	3	225°	1014.6	70		0
Jacksonville	2	200°	1018.1	73		0
Tampa	2	230°	1018.0	74		25
Miami	8	180°	1019.8	78		0

3

INVESTIGATING WEATHER MAPS (continued)

2. On your map, find the observation station with the highest atmospheric pressure. Just above it, write *H* (for high). Find the observation station with the lowest atmospheric pressure. Just above it, write *L* (for low). Starting at this point, which is the center of a low-pressure area, sketch a cold front and a warm front. Refer to page 103 in your textbook for the way fronts should look. The cold front will be between stations where winds change from southwest to northwest and temperatures decrease suddenly. The warm front will be between stations where winds change from east to southwest and temperatures rise suddenly.

3. Draw the following isobars on your map: 1008 mb, 1012 mb, 1016 mb, 1020 mb, and 1024 mb. Label each isobar.

4. Draw a line around all the locations where precipitation has fallen. Shade the precipitation area with a colored pencil.

3 ◆ **Observations**

Weather Map

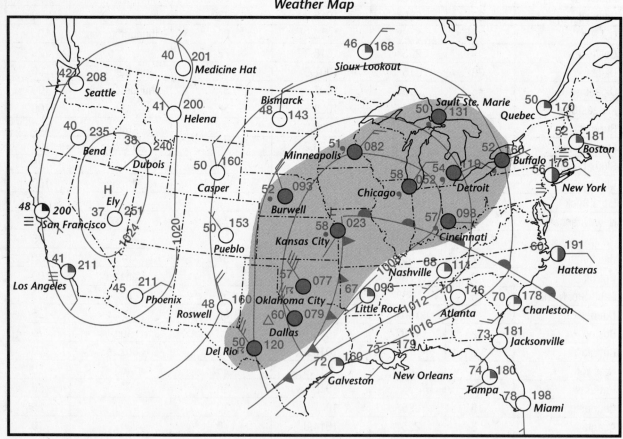

1. Which observation station reported the highest atmospheric pressure? The lowest atmospheric pressure?

Ely reported the highest atmospheric pressure, and Kansas City reported the lowest atmospheric pressure.

INVESTIGATING WEATHER MAPS *(continued)*

◆ Analyze and Conclude

1. According to your map, is precipitation usually associated with an area of low pressure or an area of high pressure?

Precipitation is usually associated with low pressure.

2. Compare wind direction around the low-pressure center with wind direction around the high-pressure center. Use clock directions in your answer.

Winds blow counterclockwise around the low-pressure center and clockwise around the high-

pressure center.

3. Compare the type and location of precipitation associated with the cold front to those associated with the warm front.

Thunderstorms and hail are associated with the cold front, while drizzle and rain are associated

with the warm front.

4. Describe changes in temperature and wind direction associated with the passage of the warm front.

When the warm front passes, temperatures rise and the wind direction shifts from east to

southwest.

5. Describe changes in temperature, wind direction, and atmospheric pressure associated with the passage of the cold front.

When the cold front passes, temperatures fall, wind direction shifts from southwest to northwest,

and the barometer rises.

◆ Critical Thinking and Applications

1. Look at your weather map. Assume that the storm center is moving in a north-easterly direction. Describe at least three changes in the weather in Cincinnati, Ohio, if the low-pressure center moves to Sault Ste. Marie.

Answers might include winds shifting to the southwest, temperature increasing, clouds

decreasing, and rain ending.

2. Can yesterday's weather map help you predict tomorrow's weather? Give a reason for your answer.

Students will probably answer yes because you can tell the direction the highs, lows, and fronts

are moving.

INVESTIGATING WEATHER MAPS *(continued)*

3. Before weather satellites existed, weather forecasts for cities on the West Coast were not as reliable as those for cities in the Midwest. Explain this difference.

In the United States, weather generally moves from west to east. Weather data could be

gathered from land stations to the west of cities in the Midwest, but there were no land stations

to the west of cities on the West Coast.

◆ More to Explore

Refer to the two maps below to answer the questions.

March 27

March 28

1. If the low-pressure area in the middle of the country on March 27 continues at its present speed and direction, where will it be centered on March 29?

The low would likely be centered over Ohio, Pennsylvania, or West Virginia.

2. Predict the weather conditions in Mississippi as the cold front moves through on March 29.

Temperatures will drop, and winds will probably become gusty out of the northwest.

Thunderstorms might occur, followed by clearing skies and higher pressure.

3. Draw a weather map that predicts the locations of the fronts, highs, and lows for March 29.

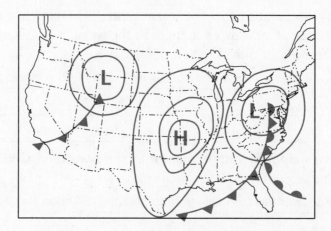

Maps will vary somewhat but should indicate a general west to east movement of all the weather features on the map.

Investigating Differences in Climate

Key Concept: Four climate types (arid, semiarid, subhumid, and humid) can be determined from P/E_p values.

Skills Focus: Inferring, making models, communicating

Time Required: 40 minutes

◆ Pre-Lab Discussion

Many factors are responsible for the different types of climates. However, each factor falls into one of two major categories: those that affect the average yearly temperature of an area and those that affect the average yearly precipitation. The amount of available energy helps to determine the temperature of a region.

One measure of energy is evapotranspiration—the total water loss from the land through evaporation and transpiration. In transpiration, the surface of leaves and other plant parts gives off moisture. In this investigation, you will use the ratio of average yearly precipitation (P) to average yearly potential evapotranspiration (E_p). This climate ratio, written as P/E_p, represents the average yearly moisture supply divided by the moisture demand, or need, at a certain location. Four different climates, based on P/E_p, are arid, semiarid, subhumid, and humid. The table below lists each climate and its ratio.

Climate Ratios

P/E_p	Climate
less than 0.4	arid
0.4–0.8	semiarid
0.8–1.2	subhumid
greater than 1.2	humid

In this investigation, you will study how the relationship between available energy and moisture affects climate.

1. What conditions produce a "dry" climate?

A climate is dry if there is less precipitation than potential evaporation.

2. Why might a cool place with low rainfall be less dry than a hotter place that gets the same amount of rain?

Because water evaporates more slowly in cool weather, the cool place would not lose as much

moisture to evaporation.

INVESTIGATING DIFFERENCES IN CLIMATE *(continued)*

◆ Problem

How can you use the ratio between precipitation and potential evapotranspiration to map different climates?

Advance Preparation: Each group needs four pencils of different colors.

Alternative Materials: Transparent markers can be substituted for colored pencils or crayons.

Teaching Tips: Point out that pages I124–I125 in the textbook have a review of climate regions.

Remind students to put a color key on their maps.

Review with students how to measure latitude prior to starting the lab.

◆ Materials *(per group)*

soft graphite pencil
colored pencils or crayons, four colors

◆ Procedure

1. Carefully examine the map of Ert, an imaginary continent. The numbers at various locations are the climate ratios for those areas. Notice that Ert is very large, extending toward the poles beyond latitudes 60° N and 60° S. Notice also the extensive mountain range along the west coast, as well as two mountain ranges along the east coast.

2. Remember the following information when you are working on your map:

   • Climate ratios greater than 1.2 are usually in regions at or near the equator. These regions are generally humid.

   • Regions at or near latitudes 30° N and 30° S are generally arid, unless influenced by mountain ranges or other factors. Climate ratios of 0.4 or less are usually found in these regions.

   • Areas at or near latitudes 60° N and 60° S are generally moist but often have climate ratios that vary a lot because of the influence of global wind systems, large bodies of water, and mountain ranges.

   • The lines of two climate types cannot cross. They tend to run parallel to each other and do not form sharp edges or acute angles. Also, these lines must be continuous; that is, they must form closed loops or run off the edges of the continent.

3. Locate the regions on Ert that are most arid and most humid. Find the mountain ranges and lines of latitude.

4. Using a soft graphite pencil, lightly connect points with a 0.4 climate ratio. Notice that two regions have this climate ratio, one in each hemisphere. The 0.4 line in the Southern Hemisphere has been correctly drawn for you.

5. Lightly draw lines connecting points that have a 0.8 climate ratio. Then draw lines connecting points that have 0.0, 1.2, and 1.6 climate ratios.

6. Darken the contour lines and identify the areas as arid, semiarid, humid, or subhumid. For example, regions between lines 0.4 and 0.8 are semiarid. Color each type of region on your map a different color. Add a color key that identifies the climate.

INVESTIGATING DIFFERENCES IN CLIMATE *(continued)*

Ert: A Continent

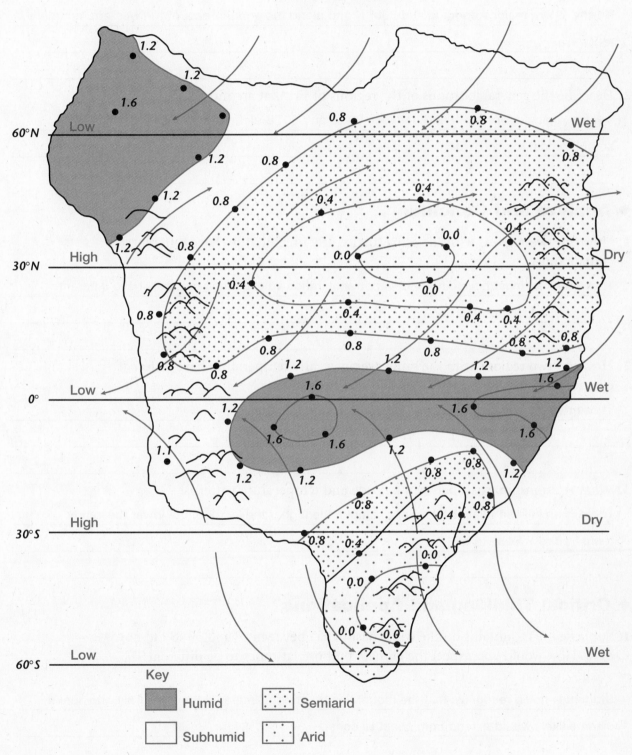

Key

▨ Humid   ⣿ Semiarid

☐ Subhumid   ⣀ Arid

INVESTIGATING DIFFERENCES IN CLIMATE *(continued)*

◆ Observations

1. Describe the general locations of the regions of Ert that are most humid.

   Northwestern regions about latitude 60° N and along the equator east of the western mountain

   range

2. Describe the general locations of the regions of Ert that are most arid.

   Central region about 30° N and between 30° S and 60° S along the east coast, which is the

   southernmost region of Ert

◆ Analyze and Conclude

1. How can two regions with the same total yearly precipitation have different climate ratios?

   These regions must have different evapotranspiration values. They probably have different

   average yearly temperatures.

2. How can two regions with the same average yearly temperature have different climate ratios?

   These regions must have different amounts of precipitation.

3. What relationship exists between latitude and temperature patterns?

   There is an inverse relationship. For example, the higher the latitude, the lower the yearly

   temperature is likely to be.

◆ Critical Thinking and Applications

1. Suppose the mountains on the west coast of Ert between 0° and 30° S did not exist. How would you expect the climate in those latitudes to be different, if at all?

   Students should recognize that the mountains do affect climate. In their absence, the humid

   climate likely would extend from coast to coast.

INVESTIGATING DIFFERENCES IN CLIMATE *(continued)*

2. What areas on Ert would you expect to be the most heavily populated? Give a
reason for your answer.

The humid and subhumid climates would most likely have the most people. The lack of water

and vegetation in the arid and semiarid areas would make them less able to support large

populations.

3. In which of the four climatic regions would you prefer to live? Give reasons for
your answer.

Answers will vary. Reasons should refer to temperature and/or precipitation.

4. How does the climate of your area in question 2 affect the type of clothing
people wear?

Answers will vary according to geographic location. Sample answers for the upper Midwest:

People wear heavy clothing and boots in winter because of cold weather and snow and

lightweight clothing in summer because of heat and humidity.

The types of plants or animals that are raised for food?

Adequate rainfall supports many food crops and animals.

The recreational activities?

Recreational activities include ice-skating and snowmobiling in winter and boating in summer.

The amount of energy consumed?

Energy consumption is fairly high to provide heat in winter and air-conditioning in summer.

4

INVESTIGATING DIFFERENCES IN CLIMATE *(continued)*

◆ More to Explore

Imagine that the continent of Ert is located on Earth. Draw on your map the directions of the global winds from above 60° N to 60° S. Also label each latitude line on your map as an area of generally high or low air pressure and wet or dry conditions. Remember that winds flow from high-pressure areas to low-pressure areas. Give reasons for the locations of the most humid and most arid regions of Ert.

Since winds flow from high- to low-pressure areas, humid climates are associated with (1) proximity to bodies of water that supply moisture brought inland by global winds; (2) low-pressure systems, as winds tend to flow toward these regions; and (3) wet weather. Arid climates are associated with (1) distance from large bodies of water; (2) high-pressure systems, as winds tend to flow away from these regions; (3) moisture loss as air moves over barriers such as mountain ranges; and (4) dry weather.

4

J-1   LABORATORY INVESTIGATION

Constructing a Foucault Pendulum

Key Concepts: One of Earth's motions is rotation. Observing the apparent movement of a pendulum can show Earth's rotation.

Skills Focus: Observing, inferring, predicting, making models

Time Required: 40 minutes

1

◆ Pre-Lab Discussion

In 1851, Jean Foucault was the first to prove that Earth rotates. He hung a heavy iron ball from a wire 67 m long. He set this pendulum swinging north and south. He knew that a free-swinging pendulum does not change direction. After about 8 hours, however, the pendulum was swinging east and west. Foucault concluded that Earth had rotated beneath the swinging pendulum.

In this investigation, you will make a device that uses the principle behind a Foucault pendulum.

1. Compare and contrast rotation and revolution.

Rotation and revolution are both motions of Earth. Rotation is spinning on an axis, and revolution

is one object moving around another object.

2. Which movement, rotation or revolution, causes day and night? Explain.

rotation, because day and night are caused by Earth's spinning on its axis

◆ Problem

How can you demonstrate that Earth rotates?

◆ Materials *(per group)*

2 ring stands
2 burette clamps
wooden dowel, about 40 cm long
board, at least 45 cm long
thread, about 30 cm
scissors
fishing sinker or several metal washers
  or nuts, 110 g or more
sheet of lined paper
tape
meterstick

Alternative Materials: Instead of a board, any sturdy, flat object, such as a cookie sheet, can be used. If student desks are movable, have students omit the board and rotate the entire desk.

Teaching Tips: Be sure there is enough room for students to move around the setup.

Encourage students to move the setup in one fluid, steady motion, so they don't disturb the pendulum's motion. If the motion is disturbed, students must start over.

Students may need a review of relative motion. Ask them to give other examples, such as how scenery appears to move when someone is in a moving car, even though it is the car and passengers that are moving.

◆ Safety   *Review the safety guidelines in the front of your lab book.*

Use caution in handling sharp scissors.

CONSTRUCTING A FOUCAULT PENDULUM *(continued)*

◆ Procedure

1. Tape a sheet of lined paper on the middle of the board. The lines should be perpendicular (at 90°) to the length of the board. Then set up the ring stands, clamps, and dowel as pictured in Figure 1.

Figure 1

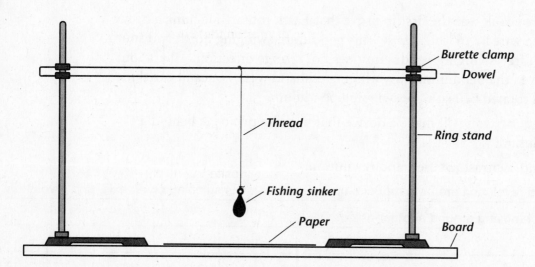

Burette clamp
Dowel
Thread
Ring stand
Fishing sinker
Paper
Board

2. Cut a piece of thread about 30 cm long. Tie the fishing sinker to one end of the thread. Tie the other end of the thread to the center of the dowel so that the sinker can swing freely like a pendulum.

3. Carefully set the pendulum swinging in the direction of the lines on the paper. Draw a two-headed arrow on the paper to show the direction the pendulum is swinging. Label the arrow A.

4. Using two students, slowly turn the whole apparatus clockwise one quarter of a full turn (90°). Be careful not to disturb the swinging of the pendulum.

5. Draw a two-headed arrow on the paper to show the direction the pendulum is now swinging. Label this arrow B. Observe how the direction of the pendulum has changed in relation to the lines on the sheet of paper.

6. Predict how the pendulum swing will compare to the arrows when the students at the ends of the board again slowly turn the whole apparatus clockwise another quarter of a turn (90°). Give a reason for your prediction.

Students will likely predict that the swing will again match the direction of arrow A, given that

arrow B was perpendicular to arrow A.

7. Turn the apparatus clockwise 90° and compare the results to your prediction.

CONSTRUCTING A FOUCAULT PENDULUM *(continued)*

◆ Observations

1. Describe how the direction of arrow A differs from that of arrow B.

Arrow A is perpendicular to arrow B.

2. Describe how the direction of the pendulum changed in relation to the lines on the sheet of paper.

The pendulum changed direction 90° in relation to the lines on the sheet of paper.

◆ Analyze and Conclude

1. If a pendulum was swinging freely on Earth, how would it appear to act if Earth rotated?

The pendulum would appear to slowly change direction opposite to the direction of Earth's

rotation.

2. How would the pendulum appear to act if Earth did not rotate?

The direction of the pendulum would appear to stay the same.

3. Think about a playground swing and how it swings with the seat empty and with someone on the seat. Why do you think it is important to use a fairly heavy weight on your pendulum?

More weight keeps the pendulum swinging longer and in a more consistent direction.

◆ Critical Thinking and Applications

1. Describe the changes in geographical direction that a pendulum would appear to undergo if it began swinging north and south.

The pendulum would slowly turn until it appeared to swing east-west. Then it would be back to

north-south. Then it would gradually return to east-west. Eventually, it would be back to

north-south.

CONSTRUCTING A FOUCAULT PENDULUM *(continued)*

2. What happens to the swing of a pendulum, or its arc, as the pendulum swings over a period of time?

The swing, or arc, gets smaller and smaller. Eventually the pendulum stops swinging.

_____

1

3. What is the reason for this change? (Hint: Think about what the pendulum weight and string move against.)

Air resistance and friction of the thread on the dowel slow the pendulum, eventually stopping it.

_____

◆ More to Explore

Construct a simple working model of a Foucault pendulum. Can this model be used to show Earth's actual rotation? Write a procedure you would follow to answer this question. Have the teacher approve your procedure before you carry out the investigation. Wear your goggles while carrying out your procedure.

See the following figure for a sample setup. Suggest where students could find a flat surface at the necessary height. Students can set up blocks around the pendulum to see the actual effects of Earth's rotation. A surface clamped on top of a 10-foot stepladder works. As Earth rotates, the orientation of the arc of the pendulum will change. This model can be used to observe Earth's actual rotation because the cord is long enough and the weight has enough mass to make air resistance less important than it is with the smaller pendulum.

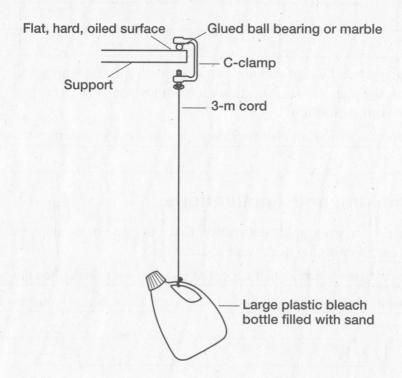

Flat, hard, oiled surface — Glued ball bearing or marble

C-clamp

Support

3-m cord

Large plastic bleach bottle filled with sand

J-2 **LABORATORY INVESTIGATION**

Measuring the Diameter of the Sun

Key Concepts: The part of the sun that is seen in a photo is the photosphere. By observing the sun indirectly, you can use proportions that involve actual size and image size to measure the photosphere.

Skills Focus: Measuring, calculating, designing experiments

Time Required: 40 minutes

◆ Pre-Lab Discussion

If you look at the full moon in the sky and a golf ball in your hand, they seem to be about the same size. However, you know that they are much different in size. They look about the same to you because they are at much different distances from you. For example, from Earth, the sun and moon appear to be about the same size because the moon is much closer to Earth than the sun is.

How can you measure the size of something as far away from you as the sun is? Although Earth is about 150,000,000 km from the sun, you can still make accurate measurements of the sun's size. In this investigation, you will construct a simple device and use it to collect data that will allow you to calculate the diameter of the sun.

1. What part of the sun do you see when you look at its image?

the photosphere

2. Why must you look at the sun indirectly instead of directly?

Eyes might be damaged by the intensity of the sun's rays.

◆ Problem

What is the diameter of the sun?

◆ Materials *(per group)*

meterstick
card, 20 cm × 25 cm
card, 10 cm × 15 cm
scissors
tape
square of aluminum foil,
    15 cm × 15 cm
drawing compass or pin

Advance Preparation: Precut the slits. You may want to precut the square hole as well.

Teaching Tips: As a safety measure, cut the slits for students with a razor blade. To ensure that the slits are straight and parallel to the sides of the cards, first mark where to cut. Carefully cut each slit in the shape of an I so that the meterstick will go through the cards without tearing them.

The foil must be tight over the hole in the cardboard so that the pinhole directs the image onto the other card.

Have one student hold the meterstick steady and another student move the card.

Have an alternative activity available in case the sun is not shining all day.

Before students do the calculations, review how to use cross products to solve a proportion.

◆ Safety   *Review the safety guidelines in the front of your lab book.*

Use caution in handling sharp objects such as the compass, pin, and scissors. Never look directly at the sun; direct sunlight can damage your eyes.

MEASURING THE DIAMETER OF THE SUN *(continued)*

◆ Procedure

1. Have your teacher cut a slit in each card in the positions shown in Figure 1 so that the meterstick can fit snugly in them.

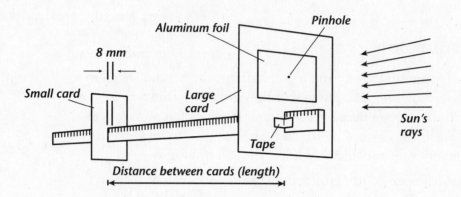

Figure 1

2. Draw two parallel lines exactly 8 mm apart near the center of the small card, as shown in Figure 1.

3. Cut a square hole, about 3 cm × 3 cm, in the larger card and cover it with aluminum foil. Use tape to hold the foil securely in place. Punch a very small hole near the center of the foil with a compass point or a pin.

4. Slide the large card near one end of the meterstick. Set the card perpendicular to the meterstick and tape it in place. Slide the small card on the other end, perpendicular to the meterstick.

5. **CAUTION:** *Never look directly at the sun. Direct sunlight can damage your eyes.* Aim the end of the meterstick with the foil-covered card toward the sun. Move the meterstick until the shadow of the large card covers the smaller card. A bright image of the sun will fall on the smaller card. Move the smaller card along the meterstick until the image exactly fills the space between the two parallel lines.

6. Make sure both cards are still perpendicular to the meterstick. Measure the distance between the two cards to the nearest millimeter. Record the distance and the diameter of the image in the Data Table below.

◆ Observations

Data Table

Distance Between Two Cards	Diameter of Sun's Image

Distance between cards will vary. The sun's image is 8 mm in diameter.

MEASURING THE DIAMETER OF THE SUN *(continued)*

◆ Analyze and Conclude

1. The diameter of the sun's image equals the distance between the parallel lines on the small card. The average distance between Earth and the sun is approximately 150,000,000 km. Using the formula below, calculate the diameter of the sun.

$$\frac{\text{diameter of the sun (km)}}{\text{distance to the sun (km)}} = \frac{\text{diameter of the sun's image (mm)}}{\text{distance between two cards (mm)}}$$

Answers will vary but should be approximately 1,391,000 km.

2. The actual diameter of the sun is 1,391,000 km. Using the formula below, determine the percentage of error in your calculated value for the sun's diameter.

$$\text{percentage of error} = \frac{\text{difference between your value and the correct value}}{\text{correct value}} \times 100\%$$

If students are careful with their observations and calculations, their calculated value should be within 10 percent of the sun's actual diameter.

3. What could account for an error in your calculated value for the sun's diameter?

Answers may vary. An average value for the distance between the sun and Earth was used, and

measurements on the small card and on the meterstick are not exact.

_____

◆ Critical Thinking and Applications

1. How could you use the technique in this investigation to make other astronomical measurements?

Sample answer: When the moon is full, its diameter could be measured. With a light-gathering

instrument such as a telescope, the diameters of some planets could be measured.

_____

_____

MEASURING THE DIAMETER OF THE SUN *(continued)*

2. A camera operates in a way similar to the setup for your experiment. Light through a small hole projects an image onto the film. A common film size is 35 mm. Some film is 11 mm. If the image projected is the size of the film, which size of film must be closer to the hole that projects the image?

The 11-mm film must be closer. The greater the distance, the larger the image.

3. How might clouds affect the accuracy of your measurement in this investigation?

If a cloud partly covers the sun, the image might appear smaller than it normally would. Total

cloud cover would probably make the image too faint to be seen and measured properly.

◆ More to Explore

New Problem What is the diameter of the moon?

Possible Materials   Students can use the hole punch to make a hole in the card. They should
  hole punch   move the card on the meterstick until the moon fills the hole as viewed
  index card   through the card. The student's eye should be at the end of the meterstick.
  meterstick   Data collected should consist of the distance from the eye to the card and the
                       diameter of the hole.

Procedure   Remind students to do this nighttime activity with adult supervision.

1. Develop a plan similar to the one you used in the investigation to determine the diameter of the moon. (Hint: Because you can observe the moon directly, you can look through a small hole directly at the moon.) Write the steps to your procedure on another sheet of paper. What data will you need to collect? What mathematical formula will you use to calculate the diameter?

2. After your teacher has approved your plan, use your setup and formula to find the diameter of the moon. (The average distance from the moon to Earth is 368,500 km.)

Observations On another sheet of paper, make a data table similar to the one in the investigation in which to record your data.

Using the formula

$$\frac{\text{Moon's diameter}}{\text{Moon's distance}} = \frac{\text{Hole's diameter}}{\text{Hole's distance}}$$

Analyze and Conclude

1. What is your calculated diameter of the moon?

student results should be close to a diameter of 3,476 km.

2. If you were given the diameter of the moon instead of its distance from Earth, how could you find the distance?

To find the moon's distance from Earth, the same formula would be used. Students would find a

cross product and divide both sides of the equation by the diameter of the hole to find the

moon's distance.

Chemical Composition and the Spectrum

Key Concepts: When compounds of certain metals are heated, the metals in them give off wavelengths of visible light. The wavelengths are different from the wavelengths produced by other elements and can be used to identify the metals.

Skills Focus: Observing, inferring, classifying, designing experiments, controlling variables

Time Required: 40 minutes

◆ Pre-Lab Discussion

Some elements—such as sodium, calcium, strontium, and potassium—are classified as metals because they conduct heat and electricity and have certain other properties in common. Metals often combine with nonmetals to form compounds. For example, the metal sodium will combine with the nonmetal chlorine to form the compound sodium chloride, which is common table salt.

When compounds of certain metals are heated, the metals give off wavelengths of visible light. Each metal gives off wavelengths that are different from the wavelengths produced by other elements.

This light is divided when you use a spectroscope—an instrument that breaks light into its component colors. By using a spectroscope to examine the light from a flame, you can tell whether certain metals are present in the flame. Scientists can learn about stars and other bodies in space by studying the spectrum of the electromagnetic waves each of these objects give off.

In this investigation, you will observe the colors produced by compounds of certain metals when they are heated. You will use a spectroscope to examine the spectrums of several different metals. Then you will design a way to determine what metals are in two unknown solutions.

1. What is a spectrum? How are spectrums useful in studying stars?

A spectrum is a range of electromagnetic waves of different wavelengths. Each element gives off

energy at a different wavelength and produces a unique set of lines on a spectrum. By studying

a star's spectrum, astronomers can infer which elements are found in that star and what the

star's surface temperature is.

2. Can humans see all types of electromagnetic waves? Give a reason for your answer.

No; many types of electromagnetic waves have wavelengths that cannot be detected by the

human eye.

◆ Problem

How can astronomers use spectrums to learn about distant stars?

CHEMICAL COMPOSITION AND THE SPECTRUM *(continued)*

◆ Possible Materials *(per group)*

paper towels

Bunsen burner

matches or igniter

hand-held spectroscope

nichrome wire loops with handles,
one per solution, dipped in
solutions of calcium chloride,
strontium chloride, potassium chloride,
and sodium chloride

colored pencils

nichrome wire loops with handles,
one per solution, dipped in unknown
solutions

Advance Preparation: Prepare saturated solutions of the listed compounds by dissolving about 30 g of each in 100 mL of distilled water. Add small amounts until no more of the compound will dissolve. Make an additional 100 mL of one of the four solutions to serve as the first unknown solution, then prepare the second unknown by mixing an additional 50 mL each of two solutions. Adjust the amount of solution according to class size. You must use distilled water and clean lab equipment to prepare the solutions. Sodium is a common contaminant. Its bright yellow flame will mask any other flame color.

Clean nichrome wire loops by dipping them in a dilute (5 percent) solution of hydrochloric acid. Consider setting up a single station for each solution to minimize the number of nichrome wire loops required.

Alternative Materials: Other salts of these metals can be used. Chlorides were chosen because they are relatively safe and soluble.

◆ Safety   *Review the safety guidelines in the front of your lab book.*

Wear lab aprons and safety goggles. Use caution when lighting and working around an open flame. Tie back long hair and loose clothing and remove dangling jewelry. Do not touch the nichrome wire loop. Wash your hands after testing each solution, and use paper towels to immediately clean up any spills.

◆ Procedure

Do not use potassium nitrate as the potassium salt. Table salt may be used for sodium chloride. Gas discharge tubes may be used to produce visible spectrums in place of salt solutions. If premade spectroscopes are not available, students can make their own, using inexpensive materials such as cardboard tubes and diffraction gratings.

Part A: Known Solutions

1. Read through the entire lab before carrying out the procedure.

2. **CAUTION:** *Put on your safety goggles and lab aprons.* Light the burner and adjust it to give a hot, blue flame.

3. Look at the flame through the spectroscope. The slit of the spectroscope should be vertical. Rotate the eyepiece to make a sharp spectrum on the side wall of the spectroscope. Each group member should observe this spectrum.

Teaching Tips: If the burner flame is yellow, increase the air supply until the flame is blue. Remind students of safety precautions near an open flame.

If students have studied the structure of the atom, inform them that when an atom is supplied with enough energy, some of its electrons jump to a higher energy level. The electrons then drop back to a lower energy level, losing energy by giving off electromagnetic waves that have wavelengths unique to that substance.

The room must be dark for students to see distinct spectral lines. As students develop their plans for Part B, be sure they identify the responding variable and manipulated variable.

CHEMICAL COMPOSITION AND THE SPECTRUM *(continued)*

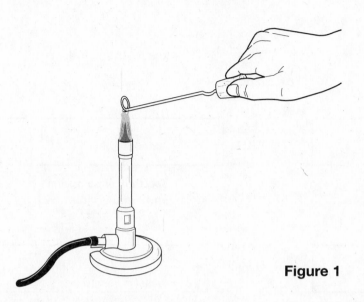

Figure 1

3

4. **CAUTION:** *Do not touch the nichrome wire loop. Hold it by the wooden or cork handle at all times. The metal will continue to be hot after it is removed from the flame.* While you are looking at the flame through the spectroscope, have a classmate carefully hold in the top of the burner flame a nichrome wire loop that has been dipped in a calcium chloride solution. See Figure 1. Be sure to look at the flame from the wire loop, not from the burner. In Observations, draw what you see through the spectroscope as the sample burns. Use colored pencils or label the colors that you see. Each group member should observe this calcium spectrum.

5. Repeat Step 4 with nichrome wire loops dipped in solutions of strontium chloride, potassium chloride, and sodium chloride. To avoid contamination, be sure to use a different nichrome wire loop for each solution. In Observations, draw the spectrum for each metal.

Part B: Unknown Solutions

1. Plan how you will find out what metal is in an unknown solution. Will you use the spectroscope? What factors must remain constant? Write down your procedure on a separate sheet of paper.

2. After the teacher has approved your plan, obtain a new nichrome wire loop that has been dipped in a solution of an unknown substance. Use your procedure to find out what metal is in the solution. Draw its spectrum and identify the metal in Observations.

3. Develop a plan to find out what metals are in a second unknown that is a mixture of two of the solutions you tested earlier. Write down your procedure on a separate sheet of paper.

4. Make sure you get the teacher's approval before carrying out your plan. Then repeat Step 2 for the mixture of solutions.

CHEMICAL COMPOSITION AND THE SPECTRUM *(continued)*

◆ **Observations**

Part A

Spectrums

Spectrum of calcium
Orange (l) and yellow (r) bands

Spectrum of potassium
Bands in the violet end

Spectrum of sodium
Strong yellow bands

Spectrum of strontium
Bands in the red end

Part B

Spectrum of Unknown Solution

Identity of Metal _____

Spectrum of Mixture of Unknown Solutions

Identity of Metals _____

Sample Data

Unknown solution: Answers should match the spectrum of the metal in the solution you supplied.

Mixture: Answers should be a combination of the spectrums of the metals in both solutions used to make the mixture.

CHEMICAL COMPOSITION AND THE SPECTRUM (continued)

◆ Analyze and Conclude

1. Why must you use a different nichrome wire loop for each substance?

You must avoid contamination to get the characteristic spectrum of the particular metal being

tested and no other metal.

2. How did the spectrums of the samples differ?

They differ in brightness, location, and color of the lines.

3. If all the bands you observed were drawn on one band, what would it look like?

It would show many spectral lines, from red at one end of the visible spectrum to violet at the

other end.

4. What might the unknown solution contain? How do you know?

Answers will vary. The unknown sample can be identified by comparing its spectrum with the

spectrums of the samples.

5. When you heated the unknown mixture of solutions, were you able to see the colors of each metal in the flame? Explain your answer.

Flames will combine the flame colors of the metals present. Stronger colors will mask less

prominent colors, so the latter may not be visible.

◆ Critical Thinking and Applications

1. How do the samples resemble stars? How can scientists tell what elements are in a distant star?

Both the stars and the samples emit light. Scientists can compare the spectrums from the stars

to the known spectrums of elements to determine what stars are made of.

CHEMICAL COMPOSITION AND THE SPECTRUM *(continued)*

2. Spectral lines are often called the fingerprints of the elements. Why?

Each person has a unique set of fingerprints. Similarly, each element has a unique set of

spectral lines.

_____

3. When you are heating the nichrome wire loops, what is the responding variable? What is the manipulated variable?

The responding variable is flame color, and the manipulated variable is the metal present.

_____

_____

◆ More to Explore

3

Do different types of light bulbs (incandescent, halogen, fluorescent, high intensity, and so forth) have different spectrums? Write a procedure you could follow to answer this question. Your teacher must approve your procedure before you carry out the investigation.

Provide a variety of light sources (incandescent, fluorescent, halogen bulbs) and suggest other feasible sources (sodium or mercury street lights, headlights). Spectrums should vary depending on the type of light bulb.

K-1   **LABORATORY INVESTIGATION**

Determining the Density of Liquids

Key Concepts: Density is the ratio of mass to volume and is a property of all matter. The density of a substance is characteristic and can be used for identification. A less dense material will float on a denser material.

Skills Focus: Observing, predicting, measuring, calculating, designing experiments

Time Required: 40 minutes

1

◆ Pre-Lab Discussion

If you've ever carried bags of groceries, you know that some bags have greater mass than others, even though the volumes of the bags are the same. Mass and volume are general properties of all matter. Density is the ratio of mass to volume. The density of a specific kind of matter helps to identify it and to distinguish it from other kinds of matter. Liquids have density, and you determine their densities in grams per milliliter (g/mL).

In this investigation, you will develop a procedure for finding density and use it to determine the density of several liquids. You will compare the densities of liquids by using a wood float.

1. A rock sinks when placed in water. Which is more dense, the rock or the water?

the rock

2. Liquid A has a mass of 32 grams and a volume of 20 milliliters. Liquid B has a density of 1.2 g/mL. Will Liquid B float on Liquid A? Explain your answer.

Yes, Liquid B will float on Liquid A because the density of Liquid B (1.2 g/mL) is less than that of

Liquid A (32 g/20 mL = 1.6 g/mL).

◆ Problem

How can you determine the density of a liquid?

Advance Preparation: Prepare a salt solution that is notably denser than fresh water by dissolving 100 g of salt in 1 L of water.

◆ Possible Materials

(per group)

4 graduated cylinders, 100 mL
balance
30 mL ethanol
salad oil
salt water
paper towels
4 wooden dowels, about 6 cm long
glass marker
salt
ruler

Alternative Materials: If large numbers of graduated cylinders are not available, use a permanent marker and 50 mL of water to calibrate transparent plastic cups. The cups should be as narrow as possible so that the wooden dowels will float without touching the bottom of the cup. Pencils can be used for wooden dowels.

Teaching Tips: Density will change slightly with a temperature change. Have all solutions at room temperature. If students don't know which formula to use, refer them to the textbook.

Watch closely for spills. Oil spills can easily cause falls, and ethanol spills can be a fire hazard.

Different dowels should be used for each liquid since the dowel will absorb some liquid, thus changing its density. This also prevents contamination.

DETERMINING THE DENSITY OF LIQUIDS *(continued)*

◆ Safety 🔲 🔲 🔲 🔲 🔲 🔲 *Review the safety guidelines in your lab book.*

Wear safety goggles and lab aprons. Never have an open flame in the same room as an open container of ethanol. Report any spills of oil or ethanol to the teacher. Ethanol is poisonous.

After the lab, ethanol can be washed down the drain with running water. Salad oil can be collected in a container, mixed with dish detergent, and washed down the drain.

1

◆ Procedure

1. Read the entire lab before continuing with the procedure.

2. With your group, design a procedure to find the density of 30 mL of water. Think about what properties of water you need to know to find its density. Your procedure should include keeping the sample of water for Step 6. Write each step of your procedure on a separate sheet of paper.

3. Finish designing the Data Table in Observations to determine the density for water and three other liquids. Add headings and columns to organize the data you will need to find and record. Change the first column if you use other liquids.

4. **CAUTION:** *Wear safety goggles and lab aprons.* After the teacher has approved your plan and Data Table, find the density of the sample of water. What mathematical formula will you use to find density? Record all your data and the density of water in your Data Table.

5. **CAUTION:** *There should be no open flames in the room where you're using the ethanol. Ethanol is a poison, so keep it away from your face.* Use your procedure to find the density of 30-mL samples of ethanol, salad oil, and salt water or other liquids you are using. Record all your data and the density of these three liquids in your data table. **CAUTION:** *Report any oil or ethanol spills immediately.*

6. Set four graduated cylinders side by side, each containing 30 mL of one of the liquids you tested. See Figure 1. Think about their differences in density. Predict how high a wooden dowel will float in each liquid, compared to the other three.

   Predictions should indicate that the greater the density of the liquid, the higher the wooden

   dowel will float.

   _____

   _____

7. On a separate sheet of paper, write a procedure for testing your prediction. Have the teacher approve your plan, and then carry it out.

   Students could use this procedure. Tilt the first cylinder and gently drop the wooden dowel into it, being careful not to spill or splash any liquid. Measure and record the height of the bottom (or top) of the dowel in the cylinder. Remove the dowel, rinse it, dry it, and repeat for the three other liquids.

DETERMINING THE DENSITY OF LIQUIDS *(continued)*

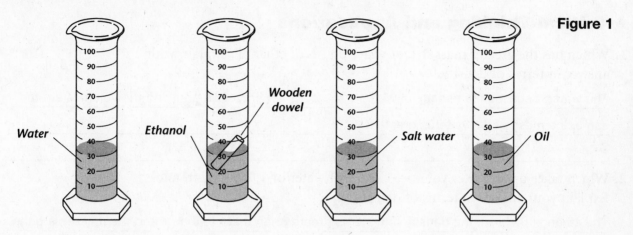

Figure 1

◆ Observations

Data Table

Data of the liquids listed should show an increasing mass and density from ethanol to oil to water to salt water.

Liquid	Mass of Empty Graduated Cylinder (g)	Mass of Graduated Cylinder and Liquid (g)	Mass of Liquid (g)	Volume of Liquid (mL)	Density of Liquid (g/mL)
Water			30.0	30	1.0
Ethanol			24.0	30	0.8
Salt water			36.0	30	1.2
Oil			27.0	30	0.9

◆ Analyze and Conclude

1. List the four liquids that you used in this experiment, in order of increasing density.

   Of the liquids listed in the Data Table, the order is ethanol, salad oil, water, salt water.

2. Were your predictions accurate? Make a statement that compares the density of a liquid to how high a wooden dowel will float in it.

   The more dense the liquid, the higher the wooden dowel will float in it.

DETERMINING THE DENSITY OF LIQUIDS *(continued)*

◆ Critical Thinking and Applications

1. Which has the greater mass, 1 L of water or 1 L of ethanol? Explain your answer in terms of density.

The water; because the density of water is greater than that of ethanol and the volumes are the same, the mass of the water is greater.

2. Which takes up a greater volume, 1,000 g of water or 1,000 g of ethanol? Explain your answer in terms of density.

The ethanol; because the density of water is greater than that of ethanol and the masses are the same, the volume of the ethanol is greater.

3. Which is more dense, 1 mL of water or 50 L of water? Give a reason for your answer.

The densities are the same. As volume changes, mass will change the same amount, so the density of water is always the same.

4. Predict what would happen if you poured into one beaker all the liquids used in this lab.

The liquids would form layers; from bottom to top they would be salt water, water, salad oil, and ethanol.

◆ More to Explore

Does the amount of salt in water affect the liquid's density? Write a procedure you would follow to answer this question. Have the teacher approve your procedure before you carry out the investigation. Use your results to explain why it is easier for a person to float in the Great Salt Lake than it is to float in a freshwater lake. Wear your safety goggles and apron and wash up afterwards.

Students could use this procedure. Put different amounts of salt in the same volume of water (for example, 25 g, 50 g, and 100 g of salt dissolved in 1 L of water), float the wood in the same amount of the solutions, and compare how high it floats. The more salt, the higher the wood floats and the denser the liquid. The water in the Great Salt Lake is denser than fresh water.

K-2   **LABORATORY INVESTIGATION**

Changes in a Burning Candle

Key Concept: A candle goes through chemical and physical changes when it burns.

Skills Focus: Observing, inferring, interpreting data, designing experiments

Time Required: 40 minutes

◆ Pre-Lab Discussion

What do you observe as you watch a candle burning? You see a bright flame and feel the heat. You may notice an odor if it is a scented candle. As you watch, the candle becomes smaller until, eventually, it is just a small stub. Some changes that occur are physical, and others are chemical. In this investigation, you will determine the physical and chemical changes in a burning candle.

In one part of the investigation, you will test for carbon dioxide, using limewater. Limewater is a mixture of water and calcium hydroxide that turns cloudy when carbon dioxide is added.

1. What is a physical change?

The form of a material changes, but the identity of the chemicals in the material does not.

_____

_____

2. What is a chemical change?

One or more substances combine or decompose to form new substances with new chemical and

physical properties.

_____

◆ Problem

What physical and chemical changes does a candle undergo as it burns?

◆ Materials *(per group)*

large birthday candle
matches
shallow metal dish
150-mL beaker
paper towel
500-mL Erlenmeyer flask
25 mL of limewater solution
solid rubber stopper
tongs

Advance Preparation: Prepare limewater by dissolving 25 g of calcium hydroxide in 1 L of distilled water. Use a large bottle so that the clear solution may be poured from the bottle without disturbing any undissolved solid on the bottom. Limewater quickly gets cloudy upon sitting. It must be prepared fresh and is always stored covered in clean glassware.

Teaching Tip: To make the water level in the flask more visible in Step 4, add a drop of food coloring to the water that students put into the metal dish. Demonstrate that limewater is an indicator for carbon dioxide by blowing through a straw into a beaker of limewater.

CHANGES IN A BURNING CANDLE *(continued)*

◆ Safety   *Review the safety guidelines in the front of your lab book.*

Use caution when working around an open flame. Tie back long hair and loose clothing. Keep the limewater away from your eyes. If you get some in your eyes, immediately tell the teacher and rinse your eyes for 15 minutes.

◆ Procedure

1. Light a candle and allow two or three drops of the melted wax to fall on the center of the metal dish. Press the candle upright onto the melted wax before the wax hardens. If the candle burns too low during the following steps, repeat this step with a new candle.

2. Observe the flame of the burning candle for a few minutes. Observe what is burning and where the burning takes place. Note the different regions of the flame. Record your observations in the Data Table.

3. Fill a 150-mL beaker with cold tap water, dry the outside, and use tongs carefully to hold it 3 cm to 5 cm above the candle flame for about 10 seconds. Record your observations.

4. Pour tap water into the metal dish to a depth of about 1 cm. Quickly lower a 500-mL Erlenmeyer flask over the candle so that the mouth of the flask is below the surface of the water. See Figure 1. Leave the flask in place for about a minute. Record your observations.

5. Hold the flask by its neck and lift it out of the water. **CAUTION:** *Lift the flask by its neck because the base of the flask may be hot.* Turn it upright, and add about 25 mL of limewater. Stopper the flask and swirl the solution for about a minute. Record your observations.

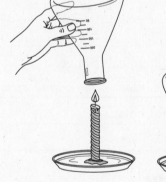

Figure 1

◆ Observations

Data Table

Procedure	*Observations*
Candle burning (Step 2)	The candle wax melts. The vapor burns. The inner part of the flame is blue and the outer part is yellow. The flame looks hollow at the bottom.
Beaker above flame (Step 3)	Water condenses on the beaker. The beaker is blackened.
Flask over candle (Step 4)	The flame goes out, and water rises inside the flask.
Limewater in flask (Step 5)	The limewater solution becomes cloudy.

CHANGES IN A BURNING CANDLE *(continued)*

◆ Analyze and Conclude

1. Which of the changes that you observed were physical?

The melting and vaporizing of the candle wax were physical changes. Some students will also

correctly include the condensation of water vapor on the beaker.

2. Which of the changes that you observed were chemical?

The burning of the candle wax is a chemical change. Some students also will correctly include

the clouding of the limewater.

2

3. One of the requirements for combustion is fuel. From your observations, what are the other requirements? Explain.

A minimum temperature (heat) and air (oxygen) are also needed. A match (heat) was needed to

start the candle burning. The flame went out when cut off from continued supply of air.

4. What are the two chemical products of combustion of the candle? How do you know?

Carbon dioxide and water vapor; Limewater turned cloudy, showing that carbon dioxide was

produced. Water condensed on the beaker above the flame.

◆ Critical Thinking and Applications

1. Why was water needed when the Erlenmeyer flask was placed over the candle?

The carbon dioxide gas produced by the combustion of the candle is heavier than air. To assure

that the gas is captured, water is needed to trap the gas.

CHANGES IN A BURNING CANDLE *(continued)*

2. You can use an equation to describe a chemical reaction. For a one-way reaction, the part of the equation to the left of the arrow gives the ingredients, and the part of the equation to the right of the arrow gives the products. For example, an equation for the chemical reaction that produces mayonnaise is

Eggs + Vinegar + Salad Oil → Mayonnaise.

Write an equation for the combustion of a candle in oxygen. Hint: There are two ingredients and two products.

Candle + Oxygen (air) → Carbon dioxide + Water

2

◆ More to Explore

New Problem What is actually burning when a candle burns?

Materials
two candles
matches
clay

Safety Follow the same cautions as in the lab when working around an open flame. Wear your safety goggles and apron.

Procedure

1. Set each candle in a lump of clay to hold up the candle. Light one of the candles.

2. Light the second candle and hold the flame about 2 cm to 4 cm to the side of the first candle. Gently blow out the first candle flame, then quickly move the flame of the second candle into the smoke from the first candle. Do not allow the second candle flame to touch the wick of the first candle.

Observations Record what happens when you move the flame of the second candle into the smoke of the first.

The first candle reignites.

Analyze and Conclude Which part of the candle burned? What is the evidence for your answer?

The vapor from the candle wax burned. This was demonstrated by the fact that the first candle was

reignited when the flame from the second candle was placed in the smoke of the first candle even

though its flame did not touch the wick of the first candle.

Name _____ Date _____ Class _____

Finding Average Mass

Key Concept: Atomic mass is the average of the masses of all atoms of the same element.

Skills Focus: Inferring, predicting, measuring, calculating, graphing, designing experiments

Time Required: 40 minutes

◆ Pre-Lab Discussion

Atoms are made up of protons, neutrons, and electrons. The neutron and proton have approximately the same mass, and both masses are very large compared to the mass of the electron. An atom's total mass is the sum of the masses of all the protons and neutrons inside it. Since each proton and each neutron is assigned a mass of 1 atomic mass unit, a particular atom's mass is always a whole number. So why is the mass of the atom in the periodic table *not* a whole number? Atoms of an element all have the same number of protons but can have different numbers of neutrons. The atomic mass in a periodic table is the average mass of all the atoms of an element.

How do you figure out the atomic mass of an element? It's like finding the average mass of all your textbooks. Each book has a different mass. To get the average mass, you add the masses of the books and then divide the total mass by the number of books. In this investigation, you will devise a procedure to determine the average mass of another group of objects.

1. Why must each atom of an element always have the same number of protons?

The number of protons in an atom defines its identity as an element. All atoms with the same

number of protons have the same identity.

2. The total mass of ten quarters is 55 grams. What is the average mass of a quarter?

total mass/number of quarters = 55.0 g/10 = 5.5 g

◆ Problem

Alternate Materials: You could use small objects other than pennies.

What is the average mass of an object in a group of similar objects?

◆ Possible Materials *(per group)*

balance
pennies or other small objects
forceps
watch glass

Teaching Tips: Any group of similar objects can be used. Pennies are easy to work with, and they won't fall off the balance. Nuts, bolts, dominoes, and jacks also work well. Forceps and a watch glass will be useful for controlling objects that are likely to roll off the balance pan.

◆ Safety *Review the safety guidelines in the front of your lab book.*

FINDING AVERAGE MASS *(continued)*

◆ Procedure

1. Read through the entire lab before starting the investigation.

2. Working with a partner, plan a way to find the average mass of an object in a group of those objects. Consider the number of objects and their shape. What equipment will you need to measure the mass of each object? Will you need equipment to contain the objects?

3. Decide how to use the Data Table to record each object and its mass. Find the mass of at least ten objects to the nearest 0.1 g.

4. Write your procedure on a separate sheet of paper. Have the teacher approve your procedure before you carry out the investigation.

◆ Observations

Data Table

Object	Mass
1	2.8 g
2	2.9 g
3	2.8 g
4	3.0 g
5	2.8 g
6	2.9 g
7	3.1 g
8	2.7 g
9	2.8 g
10	2.8 g

The distribution of masses will vary somewhat between groups. Have students speculate on the distributions and how each will affect the overall result if the masses for all groups are combined. Like all statistics, if you have a bigger population sample, the precision of the average will increase.

Scientists use special equipment to measure the masses of more than 10^{23} atoms to get the representative mass of an element. This gives an extremely accurate profile of the mass distribution of all the atoms of an element. An accurate profile gives a more exact value for the mass of an atom.

◆ Analyze and Conclude

1. Add up the masses of all the objects.

Sum of all masses = 28.6 g

FINDING AVERAGE MASS (continued)

2. Calculate the average mass.

Average mass = sum of all masses / number of pennies = 28.6 g/10 pennies = 2.86 g/penny

3. Make a bar graph showing how many of the objects have identical mass. Use increments of 0.1 g in your graph.

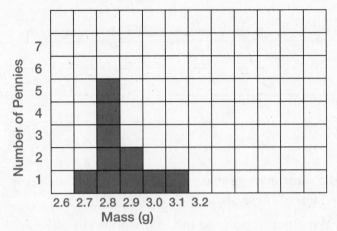

4. Were there more objects with masses greater than the average or with masses less than the average?

Answers will vary. For the sample data, there were six pennies with masses less than the average

and four with masses greater than the average.

5. All the objects look identical. Why do you think some of the objects have more mass than others, although they are all the same size?

Answers will vary. Sample answer for pennies: Although the pennies may look the same, they

may be made of different material, depending on the mint date. For example, in 1982 a zinc plug

replaced much of the copper in a penny. Also, the copper in pennies oxidizes, and the added

oxygen increases the mass. Some pennies are dirtier than others, which could change the mass.

◆ Critical Thinking and Applications

1. If you repeated this lab, what might you change in your procedure?

Answers will vary. Students might choose a different type of object. They might want to measure

the mass of all the objects in one group instead of individually.

2. A small group of neon atoms has the following masses: 20% have 21 atomic mass units (amu) and 80% have 20 amu. What is the average mass of the neon atoms? Show your calculations.

(20% × 21 amu) + (80% × 20 amu) = (0.20 × 21) + (0.80 × 20) amu = 20.2 amu

FINDING AVERAGE MASS *(continued)*

3. How does the mass you found in Question 2 compare to 20.1797 amu reported for neon in the periodic table?

The calculated mass is very close but not an exact match.

4. Do you think that the atomic mass for neon in the periodic table is more exact and closer to the true value than the answer to Question 2? Give a reason for your answer.

Sample answer: Yes, because the periodic-table value is based on averaging the masses of a

much larger group of atoms.

◆ More to Explore

New Problem Would you get the same average mass if you used fifty of the same objects as you did when you used ten of these objects?

Possible Materials Use fifty of the objects you used in the previous lab.

Procedure Predict whether the average masses will be the same, greater, or less. On a separate sheet of paper, write a procedure you would follow to test your prediction. Have the teacher approve your procedure before you carry out the investigation.

Observations Make a data table and record your observations on a separate sheet of paper.

Analyze and Conclude

1. Compare the average mass for the fifty objects to the average mass of ten objects. Was your prediction accurate? If not, give a reason for the inaccuracy.

The values should be close but not exactly the same because of the same variability in objects

observed previously.

2. Does finding the average mass of fifty objects produce a more correct value than finding the average mass of ten objects? Give a reason for your answer.

The more objects you use, the more complete picture of their masses you get. Therefore, the

average mass of the fifty objects is likely to be more correct.

The statistics will vary somewhat. The value of the average mass depends on the condition of the pennies/objects. The value will be close but may not be exactly the same.

K-4 LABORATORY INVESTIGATION

Testing Unsaturated Cooking Oils

Key Concept: An unsaturated bond will absorb iodine to make a saturated bond.

Skills Focus: Observing, inferring, classifying, measuring

Time Required: First day: 30 minutes
Second day: 15 minutes

◆ Pre-Lab Discussion

The nutrition labels on packages of food tell you how much saturated fat is in a serving. Why should you care? Fats are made mostly of saturated fatty acids. Research shows that unsaturated fatty acids are better for your health than saturated fatty acids are. Oils, which are usually liquid at room temperature, are made mostly of unsaturated fatty acids. If you are health conscious, you might choose to cook with oils rather than with solid fats.

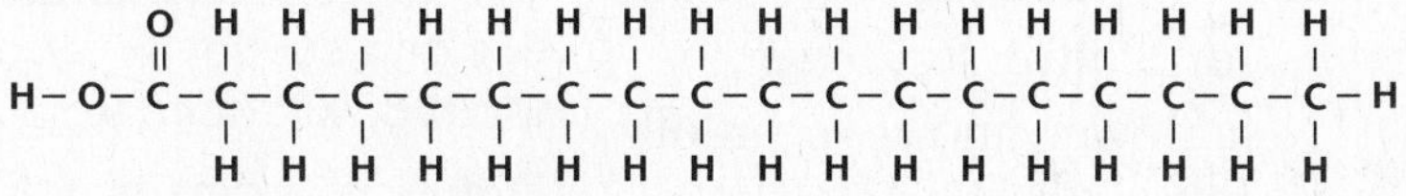

Stearic acid, a saturated fatty acid

Figure 1 shows the difference between molecules of saturated and unsaturated fatty acids. Unsaturated fatty acids have at least one double bond between two carbon atoms. Saturated fatty acids have only single bonds between carbon atoms.

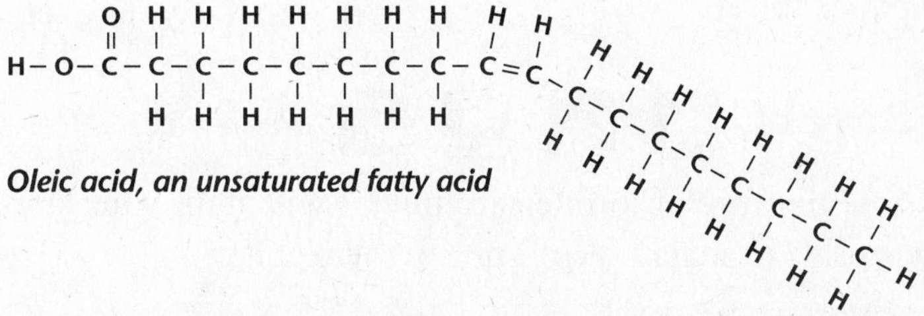

Oleic acid, an unsaturated fatty acid

Figure 1

How can you find out how unsaturated the fatty acids in a fat or an oil are? You can mix the chemical iodine with the fat or oil. As iodine reacts with the molecules of unsaturated fatty acids, it loses its color. The more iodine that disappears, the more unsaturated fatty acid is in the fat or oil. When the iodine no longer changes color, the reaction is complete.

In this investigation, you will determine the relative amount of unsaturated fatty acid in some cooking oils.

1. How does a saturated fatty acid differ from an unsaturated fatty acid?

   A saturated fatty acid has only single bonds between hydrogen and carbon. One or more double

   bonds between hydrogen and carbon make cooking oils unsaturated.

2. What is the connection between saturated fats and cholesterol?

   The two are often found in the same foods, such as animal fats.

Advance Preparation: Gather a few vegetable oils with a range of unsaturated fats and with nutrient labels. Canola and corn oils are polyunsaturated, olive oil is monosaturated, and coconut and palm oils are saturated. Tincture of iodine is used as an antiseptic and can be purchased at any drug store. You can also prepare it yourself by mixing 4 g potassium iodide and 2 g iodine in 100 mL of ethanol. Store the mixture in a dark bottle.

TESTING UNSATURATED COOKING OILS *(continued)*

◆ Problem

How can you tell how unsaturated an oil is?

Teaching Tips: Use liquid vegetable oils for this experiment rather than solid fats. Solid fats would have to be liquefied with heat or by dissolving them in an organic solvent, such as methylene chloride.

The oil's reaction with iodine is slow; it will take a few hours or overnight to occur. You may want to practice this test before the lab, so you're prepared to help students recognize and interpret the color change.

◆ Materials *(per group)*

10 test tubes
10 stoppers for test tubes
test-tube rack
balance
several vegetable oils, such as
 corn, olive, sunflower,
 safflower, and soybean oil
tincture of iodine
3 plastic droppers
glass-marking pencil
paper towels

Assign different oils for each group to test. Students will need to enter data from one other oil into their Data Table. Compile students' data on a class data table and rank the oils for amount of saturation. The following oils are in order from most unsaturated to least unsaturated: canola and safflower (about 93%); olive and sunflower (about 89%); corn, soybean, and peanut (about 80%); palm (about 50%); and coconut (about 10%).

Tincture of iodine is not readily soluble in oil and must be shaken well to mix and react with the oil. The orange color of the tincture of iodine gradually disappears as the oil absorbs the iodine. The oil absorbs the iodine as long as any carbon-carbon double bond remains. If any unreacted iodine remains, an orange color will be visible.

◆ Safety   *Review the safety guidelines in the front of your lab book.*

Handle tincture of iodine carefully; it will stain your skin and clothes. Clean up any spills immediately and notify the teacher.

◆ Procedure

1. You will be given one oil to test. Label 10 test tubes with the name of the oil. Number them 1 through 10. The number tells you how many drops of iodine to add to each test tube.

2. Add 20 drops (1 mL) of oil to each test tube. Record the color in the Data Table.

3. **CAUTION:** *Wipe up any spilled iodine immediately, especially on the outside of the test tube and stopper.* Add one drop of iodine to the first test tube and put the stopper on. Shake the test tube while holding the stopper and carefully observe the reaction of the oil and iodine. Record your observations in the Data Table.

4. Now add 2 drops of iodine to the test tube marked 2. Stopper it, shake it, and observe.

5. Add the corresponding number of drops to the remaining test tubes in order. Shake each test tube thoroughly to mix the contents.

6. Allow the test tubes to sit with stoppers on in the test tube rack overnight. The next day observe any color changes. On a separate piece of paper, record the color change for each test tube in a chart.

7. Record in your Data Table the lowest number of drops of iodine used where the color remained.

TESTING UNSATURATED COOKING OILS (continued)

8. Provide your results to your teacher so they may be shared with your class-mates. Enter the data from one additional oil into your Data Table.

9. Clean up the equipment with soapy water. Wash your hands as well.

◆ Observations

Data Table   Students need to enter data from one other oil into their Data Tables.

	Oil Soybean oil	*Oil* Canola oil
Color before adding iodine	Pale yellow	Yellow, somewhat darker than soybean oil
Color and other observations after adding iodine (first day)	At first the orange iodine didn't mix with the oil. Shaking broke up the iodine and mixed the orange solution with the oil.	Same as for soybean oil
Color after iodine color stops changing (second day)	Orange	Orange
Drops of iodine needed for permanent color change	6	8

◆ Analyze and Conclude

1. Why did the oil react with the iodine?

   The oil has unsaturated fatty acids that combine with iodine. (One of the bonds in a double bond

   breaks, and each of the two carbons bonds to an iodine atom.)

   _____

2. Which of the oils is the most unsaturated? Give evidence to support your conclusion.

   For the sample data, the canola oil is the most unsaturated. The evidence is that more drops of

   iodine reacted with the canola oil than with the soybean oil.

   _____

   _____

TESTING UNSATURATED COOKING OILS *(continued)*

◆ Critical Thinking and Applications

1. The iodine was orange when added to the oil. Why did the color disappear?

Answers should indicate that chemical changes often result in color and other changes of properties. (The color of the iodine comes from the structure of iodine as I_2. When the iodine reacts with the oil, the I_2 separates into two I atoms that attach to double bonds and the resulting product is not colored.)

2. Is the iodine-oil reaction a physical change or a chemical change? Give a reason for your answer.

It is a chemical change. The iodine combines with the oil.

3. Why did the iodine color remain when the reaction was complete?

Iodine stopped reacting when no more double bonds were left. The excess iodine colors the oil orange.

4. How can you use the data from this lab to improve your health?

From the data, students can conclude which oils are more unsaturated. They can choose these oils for cooking because unsaturated fats are more healthful than are saturated fats.

◆ More to Explore

Do the relative amounts of unsaturated fatty acids from your tests agree with the relative amounts on the nutrition labels for the oils? On a separate sheet of paper, make a data table that compares the two sets of figures. Discuss why the relative amounts are or are not comparable.

If students compared olive oil to corn oil, the olive oil is more unsaturated: 89% unsaturated fat compared to 80%. Because of measurement error, students' results may not correspond to the label if the two oils have small differences in percentages (less than 15%–20%).

L-1   **LABORATORY INVESTIGATION**

The Law of Definite Proportions

Key Concepts: The law of definite proportions states that the elements in a compound always occur in the same ratio by mass. Compounds containing the same elements will differ in properties, depending on the ratios of the elements involved.

Skills Focus: Observing, inferring, measuring, developing hypotheses

Time Required: 40 minutes

1

◆ Pre-Lab Discussion

Many compounds made of exactly the same elements have different physical and chemical properties. For example, carbon dioxide (CO_2) and carbon monoxide (CO) are both gases made of carbon and oxygen. Yet CO_2 is a virtually harmless gas found in the body and in the atmosphere, while CO is deadly when inhaled in sufficient amounts.

The law of definite proportions explains the differences between these two carbon-oxygen compounds. This law states that the elements in a compound always occur in the same ratio by mass. In other words, a CO molecule consists of only one carbon atom and one oxygen atom. A CO_2 molecule consists of one carbon atom and two oxygen atoms. The different numbers of oxygen atoms make these two compounds different from each other.

In this investigation, you will compare the physical and chemical properties of water and hydrogen peroxide, both of which consist of hydrogen and oxygen.

1. What is a ratio?

a comparison of two numbers expressed as a fraction, usually in lowest terms

_____

2. What are some signs of a chemical reaction?

Answers may include gas production, precipitates, energy change, color change, and changes in

other physical properties.

3. How does a catalyst affect a chemical reaction?

speeds it up

_____

4. What happens during a decomposition reaction?

A compound breaks into simpler compounds or its component elements.

_____

_____

THE LAW OF DEFINITE PROPORTIONS (*continued*)

◆ Problem

How can two compounds consist of the same elements yet have different properties?

◆ Materials (*per group*)

2 test tubes
test-tube rack
glass marker
graduated cylinder, 10 mL
hydrogen peroxide, 3% solution
manganese dioxide
2 wood splints
matches
tongs

Teaching Tips: If graduated cylinders are not available, have students fill the test tubes to equal levels. The quantity used is not critical as long as the amounts are the same.

Caution students not to taste either liquid.

Point out that manganese dioxide is a catalyst, not a reactant.

◆ Safety   *Review the safety guidelines in the front of your lab book.*

Hydrogen peroxide and manganese dioxide are both poisonous. Keep them away from your face, and wash your hands thoroughly after using these compounds. Wear safety goggles and lab aprons throughout the activity.

◆ Procedure

1. **CAUTION:** *Put on your safety goggles and lab apron. Hydrogen peroxide is a poison. Keep it away from your face.* Label one test tube H_2O (water) and the other H_2O_2 (hydrogen peroxide). Measure 5 mL of each liquid and pour it into the appropriate test tube.

2. Observe the physical properties of each compound and record your observations in the Data Table provided on the next page.

3. **CAUTION:** *Tie back long hair and loose clothing, in case you need to use a flame. Manganese dioxide is a poison.* Put a small amount of manganese dioxide on the tip of a wood splint and add a little of this chemical to each test tube. If you see evidence of a chemical reaction, light the unused wood splint with a match. Blow out the flame, so that the wood is glowing at the edges. Using tongs, insert the glowing splint into the test tube(s) in which a chemical reaction is occurring. Record your observations in the Data Table.

4. Wash your hands when you're finished with the lab.

THE LAW OF DEFINITE PROPORTIONS *(continued)*

1

◆ Observations

Data Table

Compound	Physical Properties	Evidence of Chemical Reaction to Manganese Dioxide
Water (H_2O)	Colorless, clear, liquid at room temperature	None
Hydrogen peroxide (H_2O_2)	Colorless, clear, liquid at room temperature	Bubbles that support combustion

◆ Analyze and Conclude

1. Compare the physical properties of water and the hydrogen peroxide solution.

All the physical properties observed in this lab are the same. Both are clear, odorless

liquids.

2. Compare and contrast the molecular formulas for the two compounds.

Both compounds consist of hydrogen and oxygen; the numbers of atoms of each differ.

3. State a hypothesis to explain why water and hydrogen peroxide have different chemical properties.

Answers should include that different compositions result in different properties.

◆ Critical Thinking and Applications

1. Hydrogen gas burns. Oxygen gas does not burn but supports the burning of other materials. What seemed to burn in the splint test? What gas did the chemical reaction in this activity produce? How do you know?

The splint starts to flame. Oxygen is the gas produced.

2. In this activity, manganese dioxide is a catalyst and is not permanently changed by any chemical reaction in which it is involved. Consider your observations and the role that manganese dioxide plays in a reaction. State a hypothesis about what happened during any chemical reaction that took place.

Hydrogen peroxide broke down into water and oxygen gas.

© Prentice-Hall, Inc.

THE LAW OF DEFINITE PROPORTIONS *(continued)*

3. The atomic mass number of hydrogen is 1.0. The atomic mass number of oxygen is 16.0. What is the ratio by mass of hydrogen to oxygen in water? In hydrogen peroxide?

2:16 or 1:8; 2:32 or 1:16

4. How does the law of definite proportions explain why water and hydrogen peroxide have different properties, although they consist of the same elements?

The elements are not in the same ratio in the two compounds, resulting in different chemical

properties.

◆ More to Explore

New Problem Do hydrogen peroxide and water react differently in bleach?

Materials You will need hydrogen peroxide, water, bleach, 2 test tubes, a test tube holder, and a medicine dropper.

Safety Wear safety goggles and aprons. Bleach can damage your clothes. It is also a poison, so keep it away from your face. Wash up after the experiment is done.

Procedure Put a test tube in a holder. Put a few drops of bleach in the test tube. Hold the test tube away from you and add a few drops of hydrogen peroxide. Make sure the tube is not pointed at anyone. Record your observations below. Predict what will happen if you repeat this investigation using water instead of hydrogen peroxide. Test your prediction.

Observations

Hydrogen peroxide and bleach:

Students should see a lot of fizzing when they combine bleach and hydrogen peroxide, and no reaction for bleach and water.

Water and bleach:

Analyze and Conclude

1. Why do you think hydrogen peroxide and bleach reacted as they did?

Bleach is a catalyst that permits very rapid oxidation of hydrogen peroxide.

2. How could you find out if bleach is used up in the reaction with hydrogen peroxide or if it is a catalyst?

You can tell bleach is a catalyst because adding more hydrogen peroxide always gets the same

reaction, which calms down rapidly when the peroxide has virtually all been oxidized.

L-2   **LABORATORY INVESTIGATION**

Testing for Hard Water

Key Concept: Hard water is a mixture of ions dissolved in water; the more ions present, the harder the water is.

Skills Focus: Observing, predicting, classifying, designing experiments, controlling variables

◆ Pre-Lab Discussion

Time Required: 40 minutes

Hard water is a common problem for many households. It can form chemical deposits that clog water pipes and damage water heaters and boilers. What causes hard water? No natural water source is 100% pure water. All sources contain other chemicals, such as calcium and magnesium compounds. These compounds form ions in water. Ions are single atoms or groups of atoms that carry an electric charge. The total amount of ions present in water is a measure of the hardness of the water.

When you add soap to hard water, the ions combine with the soap and form scum. Because some soap is being used to produce scum, fewer suds form. Therefore, you need to use more soap when you shower or wash your clothes. You can tell from the amount of soap suds how hard the water is.

In this investigation, you will test water and rate its hardness.

Figure 1

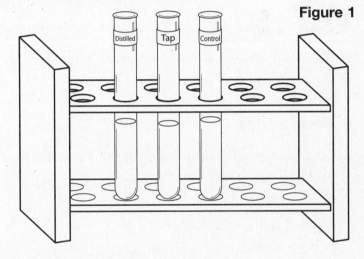

1. How does soap make it possible for water and oil to mix?

   A soap molecule has a polar end and a nonpolar end, so it attracts water (polar) and mixes with

   oil (nonpolar).

2. Why are soap and the ions in hard water attracted to each other to form scum?

   The polar end of soap molecules attracts the charged ions. These ions combine with soap to

   form a new compound (scum).

◆ Problem

Advance Preparation: You can make a standard sample of hard water by mixing 1 g of calcium chloride in 10 mL of distilled water. Prepare 200 mL of hard water for the lab.

How can you determine if water is hard?

Have some students bring a sample of tap water from home and have others get tap water from school. You could also use bottled water for comparison. Get a supply of hand soap (liquid or bar) or soap flakes. If students use bar soap or soap flakes, a pea-sized piece will be enough for a 10-mL sample. One drop of liquid soap is enough for a 10-mL sample.

TESTING FOR HARD WATER *(continued)*

◆ Possible Materials *(per group)*

distilled water
tap water
3 or 4 test tubes
test-tube rack
graduated cylinder
plastic dropper
100-mL beaker
bar soap
liquid hand soap
standard sample of hard water

Soap flakes can be used in place of liquid or bar hand soap, but you must make sure that this is soap and not detergent. Most detergents are sold as powders or flakes. Since detergents are formulated to eliminate problems from hard water, detergents are not usable for this investigation.

Teaching Tips: If you are also testing bottled water, the procedure will require four test tubes, and students should adjust data tables accordingly.

Distilled water makes lots of suds from soap; it is very soft water.

Student plans should include one sample size of water for all tests, one amount of soap for all tests, and a consistent way to mix the sample with soap (for example, shake ten times).

Students can gauge hardness from the height of the suds in the test tube and the relative amount of cloudiness. Letting the samples sit for 10 minutes accentuates the differences.

◆ Safety   *Review the safety guidelines in the front of your lab book.*

Always clean up spilled water to prevent falls.

◆ Procedure

1. Read the entire lab before starting your investigation.

2. Working with a partner or group, plan how to test the hardness of water. Consider the following:

   • What water will you test?

   • What will you use as a control?

   • Use soap to test for hardness. What will you look for as evidence of hardness? Be sure to use the same amount of soap for each sample.

   • What observations will you record? You can either use the Data Table in Observations or develop your own data table on a separate sheet of paper.

3. Once you have decided what samples you will test, predict which sample will be the hardest and which the least hard. Give reasons for your predictions.

   Students' predictions will vary. They may be based on their experience with using different kinds

   of water; for example, observations about how sudsy the water becomes when they wash their

   hands.

4. Write your procedure on a separate sheet of paper. Have the teacher approve your procedure before you carry out the investigation. Remember to wear your safety goggles and apron.

TESTING FOR HARD WATER *(continued)*

◆ Observations

Data Table

Water Type and Soap	Observations	
	Just After Mixing	**10 min After Mixing**
Distilled water	Lots of suds fill the test tube; Water is clear.	Suds fill test tube and water is clear. Suds take a long time to dissipate.
Tap water	If the water is very hard, few suds will form and the water will be cloudy. If the water is not very hard, more suds will form and the water will be clearer.	If no suds were present before, none will be now. If suds were present, there will be fewer now. Cloudiness depends on amount of scum formed.
Control Standard sample of hard water (Distilled water plus calcium chloride)	Few suds; cloudy water	Few, if any, suds; cloudy water; Suds easily dissipate.

◆ Analyze and Conclude

1. How does the soap show that water is hard?

Because soap suds will not form in hard water, absence of soap suds clearly indicates hard

water.

2. List samples in order of hardness, from most to least.

Order will vary; distilled water is always the softest. Answers should reflect students' data.

3. How do your results differ from your prediction? Explain what your results mean.

Answers will vary. Students should describe how the results differ from the prediction. Some

students may be knowledgeable about water hardness if their local water supply is notably hard.

TESTING FOR HARD WATER *(continued)*

◆ Critical Thinking and Applications

1. Did suds form in all the test tubes? If not, why?

Answers will vary. Some samples, such as the control, may have many ions in them, so they are

very hard. Soap can't make suds in very hard water.

2. The control contained calcium chloride dissolved in distilled water. What ions are present in the control?

Calcium ions, Ca^{2+}, and chloride ions, Cl^-, are present.

3. What are the disadvantages of using hard water to do laundry?

Hard water would prevent the soap from dispersing in the water, so it can't work on the dirt in the

clothes. Also, scum forms and may collect in places around the inside walls of the washing

machine.

4. What do you have to do to turn hard water into soft water?

You need to remove the dissolved calcium and magnesium ions from the hard water to make the

water soft.

◆ More to Explore

Check the labels of some laundry detergents and soaps and list the ingredients. Note any special directions about using the detergent. Use a chemical reference book to find out more about these chemicals. How does getting clothes clean in hard water differ from doing so in soft water? Write a procedure you could use to test your hypothesis. Have the teacher approve your procedure before you carry out your investigation. Remember to wear your safety goggles and apron.

Detergents are designed to be active in all water conditions. They contain synthetic soap-like molecules made from alkene benzene sulfonic acid or phosphates. These compounds do not form scum in hard water, so they work better than soap in hard water. Students may design a procedure to compare how much detergent is necessary for getting clothes clean in different types of water. Or they might compare the effectiveness of soap versus detergents. Warn students to keep laundry detergent off their skin; it is very harsh.

L-3　　　　　　　　　　　　　　　　　　**LABORATORY INVESTIGATION**

Determining Solubility

Key Concept: Solubility is a measure of how much of a given material will dissolve in a particular solvent under a determined set of conditions.

◆ Pre-Lab Discussion

Skills Focus: Inferring, measuring, calculating, graphing

Solubility is how much of a solid can dissolve in a liquid. Suppose, for example, you stir salt (the solute) into a glass of water (the solvent) a little at a time. The salt dissolves until the saltwater solution is saturated. After that, added salt crystals will no longer disappear.

Time Required: 40 minutes

Now suppose you took an identical glass of water and made a saturated solution of sugar. You could stir in a lot more sugar than salt before the solution becomes saturated. In fact, you could tell the two samples apart by observing how much of each dissolves in the same amount of water. The water has to be the same temperature, however, or your results would not be comparable. The amount of sugar that could dissolve in cold water is different than the amount that can dissolve in the same amount of warm water.

In this investigation, you will determine the amount of a solute that can dissolve in water at different temperatures.

1. What is a solution?

A solution is a homogeneous mixture of a solute dissolved in a solvent.

_____

2. What is a saturated solution?

In a saturated solution, no more solute can be dissolved in the solvent.

_____

3. How do you know when a solution is saturated?

More solute added to the solvent will not dissolve and will remain visible in the solvent.

_____

◆ Problem

How can you determine the solubility of a substance in water?

◆ Materials (per group)

small piece of paper, about
　　15 cm × 15 cm
balance
25 g potassium nitrate
water
10-mL graduated cylinder
tongs

2 test tubes
thermometer
hot plate
two 250-mL beakers
ice
spatula

Alternate Materials: You could substitute other nitrates for potassium nitrate, but they don't have as large a range of solubility over a wide temperature range.

Teaching Tips: Assign each student one temperature above room temperature and one below. The class as a whole should test a variety of different temperatures between 0°C and 100°C.

DETERMINING SOLUBILITY (continued)

◆ **Safety**   *Review the safety guidelines in the front of your lab book.*

Handle the thermometer carefully. If it breaks, tell the teacher. Use tongs or an oven mitt when handling hot objects.

◆ Procedure

1. The teacher will assign you a high and a low temperature to use in the lab.

2. Use a balance to find the mass of the small sheet of plain paper. In the Data Table, record the mass of the paper.

3. Adjust the balance so that it registers 25 g more than the mass of the paper alone. Slowly and carefully add potassium nitrate to the paper until the balance is again level. In this way, you have poured out 25 g of potassium nitrate. Record this amount in the Data Table. Add and record the total mass of the paper and potassium nitrate.

4. Pour 10 mL of water into a test tube. Put the test tube in a half-filled beaker of water. Place the beaker on the hot plate. See Figure 1. Insert a thermometer in the test tube. You will need to hold the thermometer so that the end is in the water but not touching the bottom.

5. Heat the test tube in the water bath over the hot plate until the water reaches the high temperature assigned to you. **CAUTION:** *Use tongs to hold the thermometer in the test tube.* Try to maintain this temperature during the next step by adjusting the dial on the hot plate.

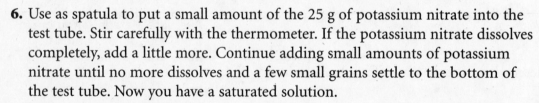

Figure 1

6. Use as spatula to put a small amount of the 25 g of potassium nitrate into the test tube. Stir carefully with the thermometer. If the potassium nitrate dissolves completely, add a little more. Continue adding small amounts of potassium nitrate until no more dissolves and a few small grains settle to the bottom of the test tube. Now you have a saturated solution.

7. In the Data Table, record the exact temperature of the solution when it has become saturated.

8. Find the mass of the paper and the remaining potassium nitrate. Subtract this amount from the mass before dissolving to find the amount of potassium nitrate you used. Record the amount used in the Data Table.

DETERMINING SOLUBILITY *(continued)*

9. Half-fill a beaker with ice. Pour 10 mL of water into another test tube. Set the test tube on the ice. Insert a thermometer so that the end is in the water but not touching the bottom. Cool the water until it reaches the second temperature assigned to you. Try to maintain this temperature during the next step by periodically removing the test tube from the ice.

10. Repeat steps 6–8.

11. Report your data to the teacher, who will compile all the information obtained by the class. In this way, you will find out how much potassium nitrate dissolves in 10 mL of water over a wide temperature range.

12. Graph the class's results on the grid provided in Observations.

◆ Observations

Data Table   Sample Data

Mass of paper	4.3 g
Mass of potassium nitrate	25.0 g
Mass of paper and potassium nitrate before dissolving	29.3 g
Temperature of heated solution when saturated	100°C
Mass of paper and potassium nitrate after saturation	6.3 g
Mass of potassium nitrate used to saturate	23.0 g
Temperature of cooled solution	0°C
Mass of paper and potassium nitrate before dissolving	6.3 g
Mass of paper and potassium nitrate after saturation	5.0 g
Mass of potassium nitrate used to saturate	1.3 g

DETERMINING SOLUBILITY *(continued)*

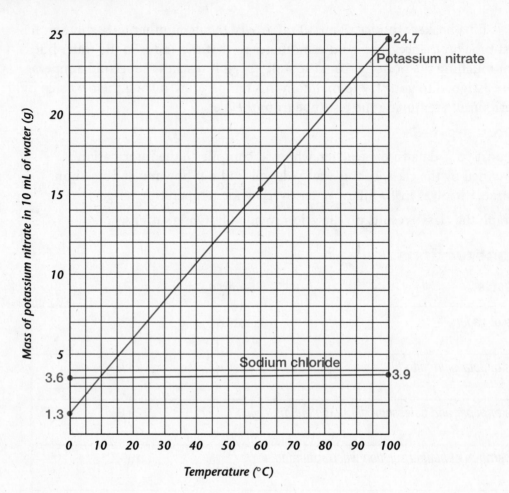

◆ Analyze and Conclude

1. What effect does temperature have on the amount of potassium nitrate that can dissolve in a given amount of water?

More potassium nitrate can dissolve in warmer water.

2. From your graph, predict how much potassium nitrate would dissolve in 10 mL of water at 60°C.

Answers will vary somewhat. For the sample data, 15.3 g of potassium nitrate would dissolve.

3. How much potassium nitrate do you think could dissolve in 100 mL of water at 60°C? Show your calculations.

The volume of water increases by a factor of 10, so the amount of solute will increase by about the same factor. For the sample data, this will be 153 g of potassium nitrate, or ten times the amount in 10 mL of water at 60°C.

DETERMINING SOLUBILITY (*continued*)

4. What temperature would 10 mL of water have to be for 14 g of potassium nitrate to just dissolve completely?

reading from the graph of the sample data, 54°C

◆ Critical Thinking and Applications

1. If the temperature of a saturated solution of potassium nitrate dropped, what would you see?

The solubility of potassium nitrate would decrease, and some would precipitate on the bottom of

the test tube.

2. Based on the graph, how much potassium nitrate do you think would dissolve in 190 mL of water at 100°C? Show your calculations.

For the sample data, 24.7 g of potassium nitrate will dissolve in 10 mL of water at 100°C.
Therefore, 19 × 24.7 g = 469 g of potassium nitrate will dissolve in 190 mL of water at 100°C.

3

3. Suppose you measured the solubility of potassium nitrate only at 10°C and at 90°C. Would this affect the accuracy of your solubility graph? Give a reason for your answer.

A graph of two points is a straight line. If the mathematical relationship is not linear and some

curvature is actually present, the two data points won't show this relationship, and the graph

would be inaccurate. In addition, the more data points you have, the less likely it is that

measurement errors will result in an incorrect graph.

4. If 10 mL of a saturated solution of potassium nitrate cooled from 60°C to 10°C, how much potassium nitrate would be on the bottom of the test tube? Show your calculations.

15.3 g at 60°C minus 3.6 g at 10°C = 11.7 g

DETERMINING SOLUBILITY *(continued)*

◆ More to Explore

New Problem What is the solubility of sodium chloride under the same conditions as in this lab? Does its graph differ from the graph for potassium nitrate?

Materials Use the same equipment as in this lab.

Safety Handle the thermometer carefully. If it breaks, tell your teacher. Use tongs or an oven mitt when handling hot objects. Wear your safety goggles and apron.

Procedure Decide how, if at all, you should adjust the previous procedure to solve this new problem. Have the teacher approve your procedure before you carry out the investigation.

Observations Plot the data on the same graph in Observations.

Analyze and Conclude

1. How does the solubility graph for sodium chloride compare to the graph for potassium nitrate?

   Compared to potassium nitrate, more sodium chloride dissolves in water at 0°C, and less

   dissolves in water at 100°C. So the line has a much flatter slope.

2. Use your graph to find the temperature at which sodium chloride and potassium nitrate have the same solubility.

   using the sample data, 10°C

   Sodium chloride is much more soluble in water at lower temperatures than potassium nitrate is. But it is much less soluble than potassium nitrate at higher temperatures. Sodium chloride's solubility in water differs very little between 0°C and 100°C.

L-4   **LABORATORY INVESTIGATION**

Separating Plastics

Key Concepts: Plastics must be separated before they can be recycled and made into useful products. Their varying densities allow them to be separated by floating in different-density liquids.

Skills Focus: Observing, communicating, measuring, controlling variables

◆ Pre-Lab Discussion

Time Required: 40 minutes

Schools, stores, and sports arenas make special containers available for disposal of aluminum cans. Trash collectors pick up recyclable materials separated from the rest of the trash.

More and more, people are recycling resources so they can be used again. Along with metals, glass, and paper, a variety of plastics can be recycled. If you look at a soft-drink bottle, plastic wrap, a cottage-cheese container, and a plastic pipe, you can see some of the different properties plastics can have. Because of these differences, plastics must be separated by type before recycling. Often a number in a triangle on the bottom of the item indicates the type of plastic, as shown in Data Table 1 below.

Data Table 1: Recyclable Plastics

Plastic	Some Uses	Recycling Code	Products Made from Recycled Plastic
Polyethylene terephthalate (PETE)	Soft-drink bottles, detergent containers	♺1	Carpets, skis, paintbrushes, fiberfill
High-density polyethylene (HDPE)	Milk jugs, some grocery bags, crates	♺2	Piping, toys, fencing, garden furniture
Polyvinyl chloride (PVC)	Shampoo bottles, credit cards, shrink wrap	♺3	Fencing, flooring, piping, wiring insulation
Low-density polyethylene (LDPE)	Food wrap, trash bags, some grocery bags	♺4	Trash bags, insulation
Polypropylene (PP)	Drinking straws, caps, lids	♺5	Batteries, industrial parts
Polystyrene (PS)	Fast-food containers, disposable cups and plates, egg cartons, meat trays, packing material	♺6	Office equipment, insulation

SEPARATING PLASTICS *(continued)*

Plastic containers can take up a lot of space, so waste-handling facilities prefer to shred them as they arrive. Unfortunately, shredding makes separating the plastic more difficult because identifying codes get lost. In this investigation, you will find a way to separate these pieces of different types of plastic by comparing their densities. Remember that less dense materials float in more dense materials, and more dense materials sink in less dense materials.

1. Plastic is a type of polymer. What is a polymer?

A polymer is a large, complex molecule made by joining smaller molecules, called monomers.

2. Explain the difference between a natural polymer and a synthetic polymer.

A natural polymer occurs in nature: it is not human-made. A synthetic polymer does not occur in

nature but is made in a laboratory or factory.

4 ◆ Problem

How can different types of shredded plastic be separated?

◆ Materials *(per group)*

sheet of paper
2 or 3 pieces of polystyrene
2 or 3 pieces of PETE (polyethylene terephthalate)
2 or 3 pieces of HDPE (high-density polyethylene)
2 or 3 pieces of polypropylene
2 plastic or paper cups, 8-oz
water
100-mL graduated cylinder
forceps
isopropyl (rubbing) alcohol 91%
tablespoon
plastic spoon

Advance Preparation: Collect samples of polystyrene (Styrofoam), PETE (soft-drink bottles), HDPE (plastic milk containers), and polypropylene (shampoo bottles). You can check for additional examples of each type by finding plastic with the indicated recycling code on it. (See Data Table 1.) Avoid having students work with cutting tools by precutting the samples into pieces about 1 cm × 1 cm.

Alternative Materials: If polypropylene is not readily available, students will get the same results with LDPE (cottage-cheese containers). Provide metric measuring cups instead of graduated cylinders. You could substitute laboratory-grade alcohol for rubbing alcohol, but rubbing alcohol is adequate and less expensive. You'll need about a quart of rubbing alcohol for a class, or less laboratory-grade alcohol.

◆ Safety   *Review the safety guidelines in your lab book.*

SEPARATING PLASTICS *(continued)*

◆ Procedure

1. Fold a sheet of paper in fourths. Unfold the paper. Write the name of a different type of plastic from the materials list in each of the four sections.

2. Get two or three pieces of each type of plastic. When you are not using them, keep the plastic pieces on their section of the paper to help you keep track of their identity.

3. Write a description of each plastic in Data Table 2.

4. Predict which plastic is the most dense and which is the least dense. Give reasons for your predictions.

   Answers will vary. The relative densities probably won't be obvious from the small pieces used

   in the lab, but students may be able to make accurate predictions based on their experiences

   with larger items.

   _____

5. Add 100 mL of water to one cup. Put two or three pieces of polystyrene in the water. Use a spoon to gently stir the water. Push the pieces underwater as you stir. Record in Data Table 2 whether the polystyrene floats in water.

6. Use forceps to remove the plastic from the water. One type at a time, test the other plastic samples to see whether they float in water. Record your results in Data Table 2.

7. Add 100 mL of rubbing alcohol to the other cup. **CAUTION:** *Do not get alcohol near your mouth or eyes. Be sure no open flame is anywhere in the room when you are using alcohol.*

8. Repeat steps 5 and 6, using the alcohol instead of water to test any samples that floated in the water.

9. Return to the cup containing the water. Add one piece of each type of plastic that floated on the water but sank in the alcohol.

10. Add one tablespoonful of the alcohol from Step 7 to the water, then stir.

11. Keep adding alcohol, one tablespoon at a time, to the cup until one of the samples sinks. Keep track of how many tablespoons of alcohol were added. Record this information in Observations question 1 and your results in Data Table 2.

12. Rinse the plastic pieces in water and give them to the teacher to recycle. Pour the alcohol-water mixture down the drain, accompanied by plenty of water. Return any unused alcohol to the teacher.

Teaching Tips: Before starting the procedure, review the concept of density. At this point, a qualitative understanding is adequate. Demonstrate simple examples of objects floating or sinking due to differences in density, such as oil floating on water, wood floating in water, a helium balloon rising in air, or a rock sinking in water. Students must understand that a less dense material floats in a more dense fluid and a more dense material sinks in a less dense fluid.

Samples from colored soft-drink and shampoo bottles make observation easier.

Students can see the plastics better if they use colorless, transparent plastic cups.

Use the alcohol in a well-ventilated area.

SEPARATING PLASTICS (continued)

◆ Observations

Data Table 2

Plastic	Description of Plastic	Floated or not, if tested		
		In Water	In Alcohol	In Mixture
Polystyrene	Lightweight, white, seems to contain air	Yes	Yes	X
PETE	Clear, thin	No	X	X
HDPE	White, somewhat thin, translucent	Yes	No	Yes
Polypropylene	Opaque, may be colored	Yes	No	No

1. How many tablespoons of alcohol did you add in steps 10 and 11 before one
piece of plastic sank? What type was it?

Sample data: 9 tablespoons for the polypropylene

_____

◆ Analyze and Conclude

1. Why wasn't it necessary to test all the plastics with the alcohol (in Step 8) and
the alcohol-water mixture (in steps 9–11)?

A plastic's unique ability to float in water and/or alcohol allows it to be separated from other

materials. Once a plastic's unique ability to float is established, no further testing is needed.

_____

_____

2. Rank the following from least dense to most dense: water, alcohol, water-
alcohol mixture. Give a reason for your answer.

Alcohol, water-alcohol mixture, water; some plastics floated in water but sank in alcohol. The

plastics' behavior in the mixture was between their behavior in water and that in alcohol.

_____

_____

SEPARATING PLASTICS *(continued)*

3. Rank the plastics you tested from least dense to most dense. Give reasons for your answer.

   Polystyrene, HDPE, polypropylene, PETE. Explanations should reflect students' data. The

   plastics most likely to float are least dense; those least likely to float are most dense.

◆ Critical Thinking and Applications

1. Were your predictions in Step 4 correct? What difficulties did you face in making a prediction?

   Answers will vary. The small size of the samples makes it difficult to determine relative densities.

   Students may not have had enough experience with all the types of plastic to judge densities.

2. Describe a procedure that a recycling center could use to separate small pieces of different types of plastic.

   A recycling center could separate the pieces by floating or sinking them using liquids of different

   densities.

3. Think about the densities of gold, water, and soil. Explain how panning for gold uses differences in density.

   Gold is the most dense. It sinks to the bottom of the pan, while other materials wash off the top.

4. Metals are extracted from ores that are mined. A limited amount of ore is available, so it's important to recycle metals and conserve ore. Plastics, on the other hand, are human-made. Why is it important that they be recycled?

   Even though plastics are human-made, they are made from natural raw materials such as

   petroleum. These resources are limited and need to be conserved. Also, most plastics do not

   biodegrade rapidly and can accumulate in the environment.

SEPARATING PLASTICS *(continued)*

◆ More to Explore

Look at the plastic coding system in Data Table 1. Examine plastic items around your home. Which types of plastic do you dispose of most often? Contact a local recycling operation and find out which of these plastics it collects and recycles. If your community doesn't recycle all types of plastics, find out why not.

Students will discover that many recycling centers recycle only categories 1 and 2. Not recycling the others is a result of economics, not conservation. The high cost of sorting and processing limits the market for many recycled plastics.

M-1   **LABORATORY INVESTIGATION**

Measuring Speed

Key Concept: Average speed is equal to the total distance divided by the total time.

Skills Focus: Observing, communicating, measuring, calculating, creating data tables, designing experiments, controlling variables

Time Required: 50 minutes

◆ Pre-Lab Discussion

Perhaps you've heard about the race between the tortoise and the hare. The hare was a fast runner but kept taking breaks because it was so sure of winning. The tortoise could only walk but never took a break. The hare lost the race.

These two racers demonstrate the difference between speed at one particular instant and average speed. To find a person's speed, you need an accurate measurement of the distance he or she travels and how long it takes the person to cover the distance.

In this investigation, you will design and use a plan to find the average speed of a pedestrian.

1. What is the formula used to calculate speed?

Speed = Distance/Time

2. If you calculated the average speed of a runner in a marathon, would the runner be moving at that speed at every point in the race? Give a reason for your answer.

No, a runner does not maintain a constant speed throughout the race. On hills a runner might

slow down, for example.

◆ Problem

Advance Preparation: Check with your school principal about setting up a course near the office, where foot traffic during class time is more likely.

If you use tape measures, be sure they are metric.

How can you find the average speed of a pedestrian?

◆ Possible Materials (*per group*)

tape measure or meterstick
masking tape
3 stopwatches

Alternative Materials: If stopwatches are not available, watches with second hands can be used. If students want to set up a course outside the building, you might suggest they use chalk rather than tape to mark the course.

◆ Safety 🦺 *Review the safety guidelines in the front of your lab book.*

Don't get in the way of the people whose speed you are measuring. Don't create hazards in the walkway.

Teaching Tips: The best group size for this lab is four students.

If students can't set up a course outside the classroom, have them set it up in the classroom with students measuring the times of other members of the group walking the course.

Students should agree on when to stop their stopwatches. For example, will they stop when the person's foot crosses the tape mark, or will they stop when the person's torso crosses the mark?

MEASURING SPEED (*continued*)

Encourage students to practice their timing skills before beginning the investigation. Tell them to start their stopwatches on your hand signal. Give a second hand signal to stop the watches. Have students compare their results. Repeat this activity a few times.

◆ Procedure

1. Read through the entire lab now.

2. Develop a procedure to find out how fast pedestrians move. Consider the following variables and questions as you develop your procedure.

   • Choose a place that gets a lot of pedestrian traffic. It should have room for you to work without getting in the subjects' way.

   • How long should the course be?

   • How will you mark the beginning and end of the course?

   • When does a subject officially enter the course and leave it?

   • How will you get accurate beginning and ending times for the course?

   • How many people will you need to do the timing?

   • Include a way to check whether the pedestrian's rate is variable or constant. For example, you could have timers at the quarter mark, halfway point, and at the three-quarters mark. A fourth person could signal all the timers to begin timing, and each would stop their stopwatch as the pedestrian passed by.

   Write your procedure on a separate sheet of paper.

3. Decide what data you will need to collect. You should gather enough data to be able to show whether the subject speeds up or slows down. Time at least 5 subjects. Adjust the Data Table on the next page so that you can use it with your procedure. You may want to add columns and headings.

4. After the teacher has approved your plan and data table, go ahead with the experiment. Practice your timing technique before trying to record data. You may need to adjust the length of the course.

5. After you collect your data, answer the questions in Observations.

◆ Observations

1. Which pedestrian had the fastest average speed over the entire course? What was it?

   See students' data table. For the sample data: Subject E; 2.1 m/s

2. Which pedestrian had the slowest average speed over the entire course? What was it?

   See students' data table. For the sample data: Subject D; 1.0 m/s

MEASURING SPEED *(continued)*

Data Table   Sample Data

Course Length: __60 m_____

Subject	First Quarter (15 m)		Second Quarter (15 m)		Third Quarter (15 m)		Fourth Quarter (15 m)		Total Time (s)	Average Speed (m/s)
	Time (s)	Speed (m/s)	Time (s)	Speed (m/s)	Time (s)	Speed (m/s)	Time (s)	Speed (m/s)		
A	10	1.5	12	1.3	13	1.2	10	1.5	45	1.3
B	8	1.9	10	1.5	9	1.7	7	2.1	34	1.8
C	11	1.4	12	1.3	14	1.1	11	1.4	48	1.3
D	13	1.2	15	1.0	14	1.1	16	0.9	58	1.0
E	7	2.1	7	2.1	7	2.1	7	2.1	28	2.1

Students should record data for 5 or more people. The data table should record times for each pedestrian for parts of the course and for the entire course, speed for parts of the course and average speed for the entire course. Typical walking speeds are between 1 and 2 m/s.

◆ Analyze and Conclude

1. Did any of the pedestrians speed up while walking the course? How do you know?

   Students can determine if any of the pedestrians were speeding up only if they divided the

   course and timed travel through each part. If pedestrians speeded up, their average speeds over

   the segments would increase.

2. Did any of the pedestrians slow down while walking the course? How do you know?

   See answer to question 2. If any of the pedestrians were slowing down, their average speeds

   over the segments of the course would decrease.

MEASURING SPEED *(continued)*

◆ Critical Thinking and Applications

1. How accurate do you think the measured times are? Suggest a method that would allow you to get more accurate results in this experiment.

Answers will vary. One method to improve accuracy would be to have more than one timer at

each station and to average their results.

2. Would the results of your investigation have been different if you had timed vehicles on a street rather than people walking? Would it have been easier or more difficult to get accurate results? Give a reason for your answer.

Students should expect the average speed of vehicles to be faster than that of pedestrians. It

would be more difficult to time vehicles because they are moving faster.

3. If you were going to repeat the investigation using vehicles, would you be more likely to get accurate results with a longer course or a shorter course? Give a reason for your answer.

A longer course would probably give more accurate results because of the faster speed of the

cars.

◆ More to Explore

Do you know what your average walking speed is? It probably varies, depending on circumstances, such as whether you're late or early for school. How could you use your walking speed to measure distance? On another sheet of paper, write a procedure you would follow to answer this question. Include a way to check the accuracy of your measurements. Have the teacher approve your procedure before you carry out the investigation. How could you improve the accuracy of your measurements?

One way to use time to measure distance is to find how long it takes you to walk a measured distance, for example, 10 meters. Then time how long it takes to walk somewhere, divide by the time it takes you to walk 10 meters, and multiply by 10 to get the distance in meters. A way to check accuracy could be to have another person measure the distance by walking it and compare results; if it's a short distance, measure it with a tape measure. A way to improve accuracy is to walk and time yourself on 10 meters several times and take the average, before measuring an unknown.

M - 2   LABORATORY INVESTIGATION

Weight and the Force of Gravity

Key Concept: The force on a spring increases as the mass attached to it increases.

Skills Focus: Observing, inferring, predicting, measuring, calculating, graphing, forming operational definitions

Time Required: 40 minutes

◆ Pre-Lab Discussion

If you've ever seen astronauts floating in a spacecraft, you've observed that mass and weight are different properties. The astronauts' mass doesn't change, but their weight decreases so much that they appear to float.

Mass and weight are certainly different, yet they are related. The mass of an object is the amount of matter it contains. You can use a balance to measure mass. The weight of an object is the force of gravity on its mass. To measure weight, you can use a spring. Because weight is the downward force of gravity on an object, a weight on a spring stretches the spring. The greater the weight of the object, the more the spring stretches.

If known masses are attached to a spring, you can use the amount of stretch (weight) to compare the weights of the unknown masses. In this investigation, you will measure how much a spring stretches with different numbers of washers. You will use these data to find the relationship between mass and weight.

1. What is gravity?

Gravity is the force of attraction between objects that have mass.

2. How would your mass and weight change if you went to the moon, which has much less mass than Earth?

Your mass would not change, but your weight would be less because of the lower gravity on the

moon.

◆ Problem

How can you measure the force known as weight?

Advance Preparation: The springs must be able to support 100 g without permanent distortion. Test the springs with the washers you plan to use to be sure that they stretch enough. You may need to use larger or smaller washers.

◆ Materials *(per group)*

ring stand	clamp
large ring	2 large paper clips
spring	15 washers
meterstick	100-g mass

Alternative Materials: Fishing sinkers can take the place of washers. If springs are not available, hang large rubber bands from the ring with a large paper clip. Note, however, that rubber bands stretch out easily.

Teaching Tip: Discuss student conceptions of weight and mass before the lab. Are mass and weight the same? When are they different? Why does a balance measure mass, while a spring measures weight? Use examples to show that mass is invariable, while weight is variable (on Jupiter, under water, etc.).

Discuss the calculation used to answer Critical Thinking and Applications question 3.

WEIGHT AND THE FORCE OF GRAVITY *(continued)*

◆ **Safety** 👓 ⛏ *Review the safety guidelines in the front of your lab book.*

Wear safety goggles during this activity. To prevent slips or falls, immediately pick up any dropped washers.

◆ Procedure

1. Attach the ring to the ring stand and hang the spring from it. Clamp the meterstick to the ring stand, so that the 100-cm mark is on the tabletop and the spring is close to, but not touching, the meterstick. Bend the large paper clip into an S and hang it on the bottom of the spring. See Figure 1.

2. Note the number on the meterstick, to the nearest tenth of a centimeter, that is just even with the bottom of the spring. Record this reference point in Data Table 1.

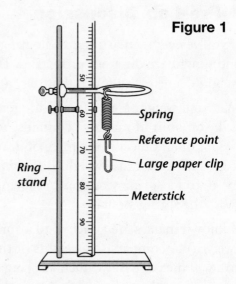

Figure 1

3. Hang 5 washers on the paper clip and note the number on the meterstick that is just even with the bottom of the spring. Record this number in Data Table 1.

4. Repeat Step 3 with 10 washers and with 15 washers on the paper clip.

5. If you removed washers five at a time, predict whether the spring's length will be the same or different from its length when you added washers. Give a reason for your prediction.

Predictions will vary. Some students may predict that the spring will become stretched out. They

will discover during the lab that readings are about the same.

6. Remove 5 washers. Note the number on the meterstick that is just even with the bottom of the spring. Record the number in Data Table 1. Do this twice more, removing 5 washers each time.

7. To find the change in the length of the spring, find the difference between each particular meterstick reading and the previous reading. Calculate this change to complete Data Table 1.

8. Note the reference point, as you did in Step 2. Record this number in Data Table 2.

9. Hang a 100-g mass from the spring and note the number on the meterstick that is just even with the bottom of the spring. Record this number in Data Table 2. Calculate and record the change in length of the spring.

WEIGHT AND THE FORCE OF GRAVITY *(continued)*

◆ Observations

Be sure students understand how to calculate the numbers in Column 3 from those in Column 2. Example: 68.2 – 67.5 = 0.7

Data Table 1

Number of Washers	Reading of Meterstick (cm)	Stretch Length (cm) (Change in Length of Spring Compared to Previous Measurement)
0	67.5	
5	68.2	0.7
10	68.9	0.7
15	69.6	0.7
10	68.9	0.7
5	68.2	0.7
0	67.5	0.7

Sample Data: The change in the length of the spring with the 100-g mass attached will vary from spring to spring.

Data Table 2

Reference point (cm)	67.5
Meterstick reading with 100-g mass (cm)	77.5
Change in length of spring (cm)	10.0

◆ Analyze and Conclude

1. Use the grid at the right to graph your results in Data Table 1. Label the vertical axis *Stretch length (cm)* and the horizontal axis *Number of washers.*

   Graphs should be close to a straight line.

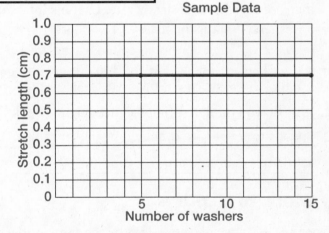

Sample Data

2. How much did the length of the spring change as each group of 5 washers was added?

   Answers will vary, but should show a fairly consistent increase for every 5 washers added.

3. How much did the length of the spring change as each group of 5 washers was removed?

   Answers will vary, but should show a fairly consistent decrease for every 5 washers removed.

WEIGHT AND THE FORCE OF GRAVITY *(continued)*

4. How do your answers to questions 2 and 3 compare? Explain why they are the same or different.

The increase in length as 5 washers are added should equal the decrease in length as 5 washers

are removed. The weight of those washers is the same, and that is what the spring measures.

5. How does the shape of your graph illustrate your answers to questions 2 and 3?

The graph is a straight line. This shows that the stretch increased and decreased by the same

amount each time as the same number of washers was added or removed.

2

◆ Critical Thinking and Applications

1. What forces act on the objects you attach to the spring?

Gravity is the downward force on the objects. The spring exerts an upward force. If the object is

at rest, the two forces are equal and in opposite directions.

2. In terms of force, explain why the spring stretched as more washers were added.

The mass increased as more washers were added, so the force of gravity on the washers

increased. The force of the spring also increased, shown by its greater stretch. The longer it

stretches, the more upward force it exerts.

3. In Data Table 2, you put a 100-g mass on the spring and recorded the amount the spring stretched. From your graph, you know that mass and stretch length increase together at a steady rate. Use this information to calculate the mass of 5 washers. What is the mass of 1 washer?

Answers will vary depending on the washer size. Sample answer:

If 5 washers stretch 0.7 cm and 100 g stretch 10 cm, then 5 washers stretch 0.7 ÷ 10 = 0.07 of
the 100-g stretch. Then 0.07 of 100 grams = 7 g. So 5 washers = 7 g; 1 washer = 7 ÷ 5 = 1.4 g.

4. Why do you think a spring balance might give different results at different times?

Springs may not always stretch by the same amount when weights are added, particularly if they

have been overstretched. They may also be affected by temperature.

◆ More to Explore

Does an object weigh more, less, or the same under water as it does in air? Write a procedure you would follow to answer this question, and predict the results. Have the teacher approve your procedure before you carry out the investigation. Was your prediction correct? If not, do some research to find out why you had surprising results.

One procedure is to weigh an object dry, place a beaker of water under the spring scale, and weigh the object when it's submerged. An object under water will weigh less than an object in the air, because of the buoyant force of the water. Students might find it interesting that astronauts train in water as a way to simulate weightlessness.

Raising a Sunken Ship

Key Concept: Buoyancy and density control whether an object floats or sinks.

Skills Focus: Predicting, making models, measuring, calculating, posing questions, designing experiments

Time Required: 90 minutes

◆ Pre-Lab Discussion

Why does a ship float? Ships float because they are buoyant. Buoyancy is related to the density of the ship. A ship will float if its density is less than the density of the water in which it floats.

Many ships carrying valuable cargo have sunk over the centuries. Some went down because great holes in their hulls let in water that destroyed their buoyancy. Suppose you have been hired by a salvage operation that has discovered a sunken ship. The ship is not too badly damaged, and the salvage crew hopes to raise it intact. The rumor is that this vessel was carrying valuable cargo when it went down 100 years ago. You might make a lot of money if you could get the vessel to the surface of the ocean. In addition, the historical significance could be great. You have some ideas on how to raise the ship, but you need to try them on a model first.

In this investigation, you will try to raise a model of a sunken ship.

1. Define density.

Density is the ratio of the mass of an object to its volume.

_____

2. How can a ship that weighs many tons float when the metal it is made of would sink if in a solid block?

Ships have hulls that are filled with air. This spreads the mass of the ship over a large

volume. This design reduces the total density of the ship, so that it is less than that of water.

_____

_____

◆ Problem

How can you change the buoyancy of a ship sunk in deep water so that it floats to the surface?

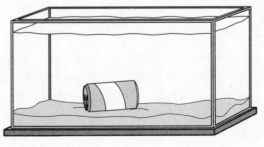

Advance Preparation: Fill soda cans with water and sink them in water-filled buckets or aquariums. To make a more realistic sea bottom, add sand or stones to the bottom and let the water-filled can sink to the bottom.

RAISING A SUNKEN SHIP *(continued)*

◆ Possible Materials *(per group)*

soda can or other container
    that will float when empty
aquarium or large bucket
handheld air pump
plastic or rubber tubing,
    various lengths
tongs or forceps
tape
clay
balloons
string
plastic straws
balance
graduated cylinder, 100 mL

Teaching Tips: Here is a recommended procedure for the lab. Attach the tubing to the air pump. Using tongs, push the open end of the tubing into the hole in the can. Pump air into the can to displace the water. Keep pumping as the can floats to the surface. Remove the tubing and put a piece of tape over the hole or plug the hole with clay so that the can won't refill and sink.

Students may also try to attach balloons to the cans with strings. As the can has a smooth surface, students will have to create a noose and put it around the can. Then they will have to inflate the balloons to get them to float. Another way to use a balloon is to attach a ballooon to the air pump tubing, push it into the can with a straw and then inflate it with the pump.

Students may want to use a winch and a magnet to lift the can. Clearly, this wouldn't work with an aluminum can. If students choose this method, they need to figure out how to attach magnets to the can.

◆ Safety   *Review the safety guidelines in the front of your lab book.*

Always wear safety goggles. To prevent slips or falls, immediately wipe up any water spilled on the floor.

◆ Procedure

1. Observe the can at the bottom of the container of water. The can represents the sunken ship. Working with a partner or in a group, decide on a plan to float the can. Because the sunken ship is supposed to be in very deep water, you may not touch the can with your hands or put your hands in the water until the can is at the surface. You may only use the tools and materials listed above to get the can to float. What property of the can has to change before it will float?

   Its density has to change.

2. Write down your selected procedure on a separate sheet of paper. Have the teacher approve your procedure before you carry out the investigation. Follow your procedure to float the can.

3. After the can floats to the surface, remove the can from the water and dry it. Find the mass of the empty can and record it in the Data Table on the next page.

4. Fill the can with water and find the mass of the filled can. Record the value.

5. Measure the volume of the water in the can, using a graduated cylinder. If the amount of water is more than 100 mL, measure the first 100 mL, empty the graduated cylinder, and measure the remaining water. Add the numbers and record the volume in the Data Table.

RAISING A SUNKEN SHIP *(continued)*

◆ Observations

Data Table   Sample Data

Mass of empty can	15.5	g
Mass of can plus water	387.2	g
Volume of water	371	mL

◆ Analyze and Conclude

1. If the volume of the water in the can is 350 mL, what is the volume of the can when it is empty (that is, contains only air)?

350 mL

2. Calculate the density of the can when it is empty.

Answers will vary. Using the sample data,
mass of empty can/volume of water = 15.5 g/371 mL = 0.0417 g/mL.

3. Calculate the density of the water-filled can.

Mass of water-filled can/volume of water = 387.2 g/371 mL = 1.04 g/mL.

4. How do the densities of the empty can and the water-filled can compare to the density of water, which is 1.0 g/mL?

The density of the empty can is less than the density of water, and the density of the water-filled

can is greater than the density of water.

RAISING A SUNKEN SHIP *(continued)*

◆ Critical Thinking and Applications

1. Would you expect the empty can to float? Give a reason for your answer.

Yes, the empty can would float because its density is less than the density of water.

_____

_____

2. Use the data you collected on mass and volume to explain why the water-filled can sank.

The water-filled can sank because its density was greater than the density of water.

_____

_____

3. Would you expect a can that is half-filled with water to float? Use the data that you collected on mass and volume to solve this problem.

Using the sample data, a half-filled can would have a mass of 201.4 g ([371.7 g water/2] + 15.5 g [mass of can]). The density of this can would be 201.4 g/371 mL = 0.542 g/mL. You would expect this can to float because its density is less than the density of water.

4. Calculate the maximum amount of water that the can could hold and still float. (Hint: To barely float, the can and water must have a density slightly less than the density of water, which is 1.0 g/mL.)

Use a value of 99.9% of 1.0 g/mL, or 0.999 g/mL, as the target density. Because the volume of the can is 371 mL and the mass of the can is 15.5 g, the mass of water needed is

0.999 g/mL = (mass of water + 15.5 g)/371 mL

Mass of water = (0.999 g/mL × 371 mL) − 15.5 g = 355 g.

◆ More to Explore

Consider how you would raise an artifact from the sea floor, such as a 225-kg cannon or a 5,000-kg section of the *Titanic*. What problems would you encounter? Write a procedure you would follow to answer this question. Present your procedure to the class and compare it to other students' ideas.

The problems might include how to contain the air (perhaps in balloons), how big the flotation balloons would have to be, how many would be needed, how they would be attached, and whether air would be the best gas to use.

M - 4   **LABORATORY INVESTIGATION**

Pulleys as Simple Machines

Key Concept: The number and arrangement of pulleys determine the mechanical advantage.

Skills Focus: Observing, making models, measuring, calculating

Time Required: two periods of 45 minutes; a possible breakpoint is after Step 5.

◆ Pre-Lab Discussion

Pulleys are simple machines that lift objects in a variety of ways. The simplest kind of pulley is a grooved wheel around which a rope is pulled. Pulleys can change the direction of an applied force. For example, a pulley fixed to the top of a flagpole lets you raise a flag *up* by pulling *down*.

A combination of fixed and movable pulleys is a pulley system, or block and tackle. A pulley system multiplies input force to lift heavy objects. Pulley systems are commonly seen on construction sites.

In this investigation, you will use different pulley systems and determine the mechanical advantage of each.

1. Define the mechanical advantage of a machine.

The mechanical advantage of a machine is the number of times a machine multiplies a force

exerted on it.

2. Why is a pulley considered a machine?

A machine makes work easier by changing the direction or amount of force needed to

accomplish a task. Pulleys and pulley systems do both of these.

◆ Problem

Advance Preparation: Cut 1 m of fishing line for each group.

How do pulleys help raise objects? How can you find the actual mechanical advantage of a pulley or pulley system?

Alternative Materials: If standard 500-g masses are not available, substitute large washers tied together that approximate the same mass.

◆ Materials *(per group)*

2 single pulleys
2 double pulleys
nylon fishing line, 1 m
ring stand
large ring
1,000–g spring scale
500-g mass

Teaching Tips: Have students refer to the section on pulleys in their textbook before performing the lab.

In most cases, the scale spring stretches somewhat before the mass itself begins to move. Tell students to pull down on the scale until the mass just starts to move, then take the reading on the scale.

Some students may have trouble visualizing and setting up the complex pulley systems. Have a model of each pulley system available for students to inspect.

◆ Safety *Review the safety guidelines in the front of your lab book.*

The weight of a 500-g mass is approximately 5 N.

PULLEYS AS SIMPLE MACHINES *(continued)*

◆ Procedure

1. Calibrate the spring scale so that it reads zero when no masses are attached to it.

2. Find the weight of the mass you are using by attaching it directly to the spring scale. Record this weight in the Data Table in Observations as the output force for all the pulley arrangements.

3. Set up a single fixed pulley as shown in Figure 1. Pull down on the spring scale to lift the mass. The reading on the scale shows the amount of input force needed to lift the mass. Record this number in the Data Table.

4. Set up a single movable pulley as shown in Figure 2. Lift the mass by pulling up on the spring scale. The reading on the scale shows the amount of force needed to lift the mass. Record this number in the Data Table.

5. Set up the single fixed and single movable pulley system shown in Figure 3. Measure the amount of force needed to lift the mass and record it in the Data Table.

6. Set up the pulley systems shown in figures 4 and 5. For each pulley system, measure the amount of force needed to lift the mass and record it in the Data Table.

7. Calculate the actual mechanical advantage for each pulley and record it in the Data Table.

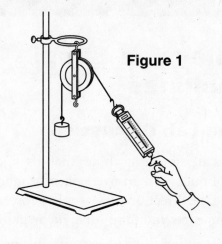

Figure 1

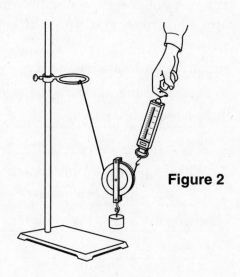

Figure 2

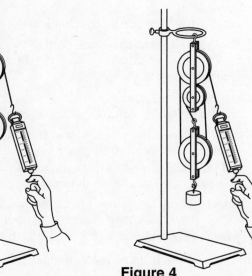

Figure 3

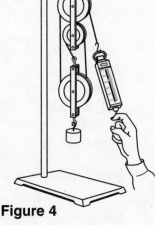

Figure 4

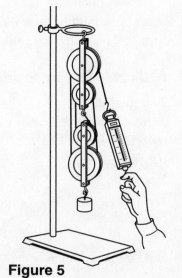

Figure 5

4

PULLEYS AS SIMPLE MACHINES *(continued)*

◆ Observations

Data Table   Sample Data

Pulley Arrangements	Output Force (O)	Input Force (I)	Actual Mechanical Advantage (O ÷ I)
Single fixed	5 N	5 N	1
Single movable	5 N	2.5 N	2
Single fixed and single movable	5 N	2.5 N	2
Double fixed and single movable	5 N	1.7 N	3
Double fixed and double movable	5 N	1.3 N	4

◆ Analyze and Conclude

1. Was there a difference in the mechanical advantages you calculated for the single fixed pulley and the single movable pulley? Give a reason for your answer.

   Yes. The single fixed pulley has an ideal mechanical advantage of 1; the ideal mechanical

   advantage of the single movable pulley is 2. Actual mechanical advantage for these pulleys will

   probably be somewhat different because of friction and measurement error.

2. As you added pulleys to the system, what happened to the amount of input force needed to raise the mass?

   Less input force was needed with more pulleys.

3. What factors determine the mechanical advantage of pulley systems?

   The number and arrangement of the pulleys determine what the mechanical advantage will be.

◆ Critical Thinking and Applications

1. If a simple machine has a mechanical advantage of 1, input force is not multiplied. Which type of pulley has an ideal mechanical advantage of 1? What is the practical use of this pulley?

   The single fixed pulley has an ideal mechanical advantage of 1. Its practical use is to change the

   direction of effort.

PULLEYS AS SIMPLE MACHINES *(continued)*

2. To determine the ideal mechanical advantage of a pulley or pulley system without calculations, count the number of sections of rope that support the weight. The end section, which is attached to the spring scale, counts as a supporting section *only when pulled upward.* Using figures 1 through 5, determine the number of supporting rope sections for each type of pulley.

    a. Figure 1: ____1____   **c.** Figure 3: ____2____   **e.** Figure 5: ____4____

    b. Figure 2: ____2____   **d.** Figure 4: ____3____

3. Do the values from question 2 agree with the actual mechanical advantage calculated for the Data Table? Why or why not?

Mechanical advantage for a pulley system is the same no matter how it is calculated. However,

measurements of actual mechanical advantages will vary because of friction and measurement

error.

4. Draw an arrangement of two double pulleys that would give you a mechanical advantage of 6.

Diagrams should show six supporting sections of rope.

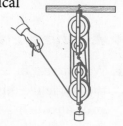

5. When using any simple machine, you never get something for nothing. Although the amount of input force needed to lift a mass is usually less in a pulley system, something else increases. What must increase as the input force decreases?

The distance through which the input force moves increases.

6. Explain your answer to question 5 in terms of work input and work output.

In a machine, work output can never be greater than work input. Because work input is input

force times distance, if the input force decreases, the distance must increase.

◆ More to Explore

In this investigation, you calculated mechanical advantage by dividing the output force by the input force. How could you use distances moved by the output and input forces to calculate mechanical advantage? Write a procedure you would follow to answer this question. Have the teacher approve your procedure before you carry out the investigation. How do these mechanical advantages compare with the ones you calculated earlier? Is one method better than the other for calculating mechanical advantage?

If the input force and the output force move the same distance, the pulley system will have a
mechanical advantage of 1. If the input force moves a greater distance than the output force moves,
the pulley will have a mechanical advantage greater than 1.

M-5　　　　　　　　　　　　　　　　　　　**LABORATORY INVESTIGATION**

Winding Up With Wind

Key Concept: A windmill can convert wind energy to mechanical energy.

Skills Focus: Making models, communicating, measuring, calculating, designing experiments

Time Required: 60 minutes to design and construct the windmill; 30 minutes to test its power

◆ Pre-Lab Discussion

Wind power is an ancient energy source. The earliest ships used the wind to carry them across seas. The first windmills were built in Persia (now Iran) in the sixth century A.D. They raised water from rivers. Later, windmills were used to turn a large stone wheel that ground grains.

Today, huge windmills, or wind turbines, generate electricity. The wind turbines are grouped in clusters called wind farms. Most wind farms are in California, located in windy mountain passes. California wind farms produce enough electricity to power all the homes of San Francisco. By the middle of the twenty-first century, experts think wind power could supply up to one-fifth of the electricity used in the United States.

In this investigation, you will design blades for a windmill, build a model windmill, and measure its power output.

1. What kind of energy does wind have? Give a reason for your answer.

Wind has kinetic energy because wind is moving air.

2. How do you calculate power?

Divide the amount of work done by the amount of time to do the work.

◆ Problem

Alternative materials: A half-gallon milk container may be used as a windmill base. A hairdryer can be used instead of an electric fan to produce wind.

How can you design a windmill and test its power output?

◆ Possible Materials *(per group)*

windmill base	thumbtacks
electric fan	string
scissors	cloth
poster board	sandpaper
cardboard	thread
balsa wood	paper clips
white glue	stopwatch
masking tape	meterstick
transparent tape	balance
pushpins	plastic straw

Advance Preparation: Make a simple windmill base for each group. For each base, you will need an empty wood spool, a piece of plastic straw about 1 cm longer than the spool, a 2-inch #10 sheet-metal screw, and a 6-inch piece of two-by-four. Put the screw through the straw, and the screw and straw through the spool. Attach the screw to the narrow side of the two-by-four at one end, until it tightens against the piece of straw. The spool should turn freely.

Gather miscellaneous craft supplies that students can use to construct their windmills.

WINDING UP WITH WIND *(continued)*

◆ **Safety** *Review the safety guidelines in the front of your lab book.*

Keep your fingers and other objects away from the moving blades of the fan.

> Teaching Tips: Use small, battery-powered fans, if they are available, to produce wind in Step 5.
>
> If you want to provide low-temperature glue guns, set up one or two stations where they are available.

◆ Procedure

Part A: Design Blades

1. Brainstorm a list of features that you need to consider in designing windmill blades. Look at pictures of different types of windmills, both old and modern in design. See Figure 1.

2. Choose the materials you will use for your windmill blades.

3. Design the blades for your windmill. (Hint: Consider the tilt of each blade.) On a separate sheet of paper, draw and describe how you will construct the blades and attach them to the windmill base. Have the teacher approve your design.

4. Construct your windmill blades and attach them to the base.

5. Try out the windmill, using an electric fan for wind. Hold the windmill about 30 cm from the fan.

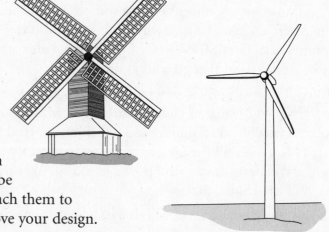

Figure 1

Part B: Measure Power Output

6. Tape a piece of thread, about 75 cm long, on your windmill's spool. Attach a paper clip to the other end of the string, as shown in Figure 2.

7. Place your windmill at the edge of your lab bench so that the paper clip is suspended in air. See if your windmill can lift the paper clip by winding up the thread on the spool.

8. Add more paper clips until you reach the maximum capacity for your windmill.

9. Measure the length of the thread, from the spool to the top of the paper clips. Record this length in the Data Table on the next page. Use a stopwatch to time how long it takes to lift the paper clips. Record the time.

10. Remove the paper clips and find their mass. Record the mass in the Data Table.

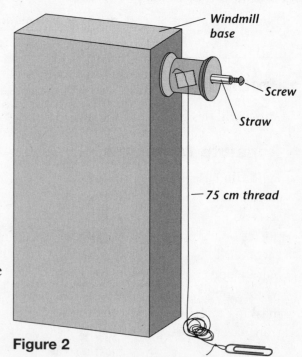

Figure 2

WINDING UP WITH WIND *(continued)*

◆ Observations

Data Table   Sample Data

Length of thread	75 cm
Time for paper clips to be lifted	5.9 s
Mass of paper clips	4.1 g (3 large paper clips)

(margin note:) Have a utility knife handy to help students with tricky cuts if they are using balsa wood. Make these cuts yourself.

Students may need to give the blades a slight push to get them started, but then they should turn on their own.

◆ Analyze and Conclude

1. Calculate the potential energy that the paper clips gained when they were lifted. Use the formula

$$\text{Gravitational potential energy} =$$
$$\text{Mass (g)} \times \text{Gravitational acceleration (980 cm/s}^2) \times \text{Height (cm)}.$$

Divide your results by 10,000 and the units of your result will be mJ (millijoule, a thousandth of a joule).

Answers will vary. The cgs unit for energy is the erg. Since students will not be familiar with this unit, they should convert their result to millijoules.

Sample calculation: $PE = (4.1 \text{ g} \times 980 \text{ cm/s}^2 \times 75 \text{ cm})/10,000 = 30.1 \text{ mJ}$

5

2. Calculate the power that gave the paper clips this energy. Use the formula

$$\text{Power} = \text{Work (mJ)} \div \text{Time (s)}.$$

The units of your result will be mW (milliwatt, a thousandth of a watt).

Answers will vary. Sample calculation: $P = 30.1 \text{ mJ} \div 5.9 \text{ s} = 5.1 \text{ mW}$

3. Did your design work well? Which features of your design do you think were most important?

Answers will vary. The most important design aspects of the blades are tilt and balance. If the

blades are not tilted, there is no force pushing them to the side. If the blades are unbalanced,

unnecessary friction results as the spool bangs around on the axle.

WINDING UP WITH WIND *(continued)*

◆ Critical Thinking and Applications

1. Was gravitational potential energy the only kind of energy that the paper clips got from the windmill? Give a reason for your answer.

The paper clips moved as they were lifted, so they had kinetic energy as well.

_____

_____

_____

2. Look at the fan you used in the investigation, especially at its blades. Could it be used for a windmill? How could you prove this?

Yes, the fan could be used as a windmill. You could prove this by exposing the fan to a strong

wind, perhaps from another fan, and the fan blades would turn.

_____

_____

3. In terms of energy conversion, what is the difference between an electric fan and a windmill that generates electricity?

An electric fan converts electrical energy into kinetic energy, and a windmill that generates

electricity converts the kinetic energy of the wind into electrical energy.

_____

_____

◆ More to Explore

Try to improve your windmill by changing one feature of your design. Have the teacher approve your new design before you build it. Construct your new design and test your windmill as you did before. Compare your new results to those of your original design. Which generated more power?

Depending on students' original design, they might change the number of blades, the material of which the blades are made, the tilt of the blades, or the balance of the blades. The power test will improve if the windmill is more effective.

Combustion Heat of a Candle

Key Concept: A calorimeter is a tool for determining the heat capacity of materials and the energy content of foods.

Skills Focus: Measuring, calculating, controlling variables

Time Required: 40 minutes

◆ Pre-Lab Discussion

During combustion, fuel burns, which produces heat and light. The combustion heat of a candle is the heat released when a candle burns. You can measure the amount of heat released by using a calorimeter. The calorimeter holds water and measures changes in the water's temperature. You heat the water with a candle and can calculate the combustion heat of the candle by using the mass and the temperature change of the water.

In this investigation, you will find out how much heat it takes to raise the temperature of a certain amount of water and what the combustion heat of candle wax is.

1. Why do you think that water is used in the calorimeter?

Water has a high heat capacity and can absorb a large amount of heat without changing

physical state.

_____

2. Do all candles have the same combustion heat? Give a reason for your answer.

As long as all the candles are made of the same material, their combustion heat will be the same.

If the candles are made of different materials, they will likely have different combustion heats.

_____

◆ Problem

What is the combustion heat of a candle?

◆ Materials *(per group)*

bottle and can opener	large can, open at both ends
small can, open at one end	matches
thin wooden dowel	metric ruler
ring stand and ring	balance
candle	water
can lid	graduated cylinder, 100 mL
Celsius thermometer	ice cubes

You may want to create the vent holes in the large cans before the lab. An unsharpened pencil may be used in place of the wooden dowel.

Advance Preparation: Ten-ounce soup cans and 46-ounce fruit-juice cans work well for this lab. Collect enough of these cans for the whole class. Remove one end of the small cans and both ends of the large cans. Use a hammer, large nail, and wooden block to make two holes in opposite sides of the small can near its open end. Fill a bucket with water and let it come to room temperature.

6

COMBUSTION HEAT OF A CANDLE (continued)

◆ Safety   *Review the safety guidelines in the front of your lab book.*

Handle the thermometer carefully. If it breaks, tell the teacher. Use tongs or an oven mitt when handling hot objects. Always wear safety goggles when heating objects. Be careful of raw, sharp edges on the cans and can lid.

◆ Procedure

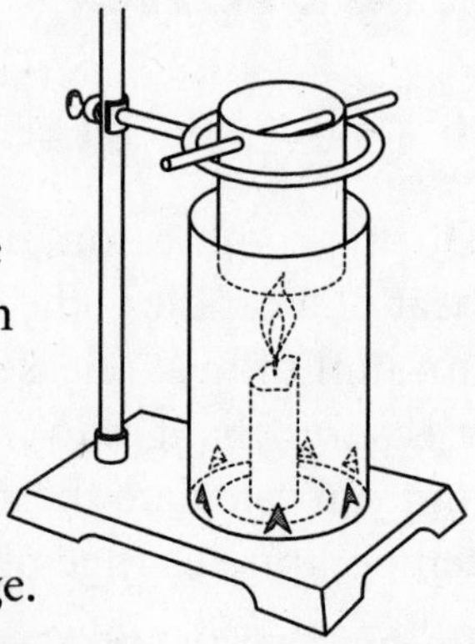

1. Insert the wooden dowel through the two holes in opposite sides of the small can. Hang the small can by the dowel on a support ring, as shown in Figure 1.

2. Attach the unlit candle to a small can lid or tray with a few drops of melted wax. Record the combined mass of the candle and the can lid to the nearest 0.1 g. Record this value in the Data Table on the next page.

3. Set the unlit candle under the hanging can. Adjust the ring so that the bottom of the can is 5 cm above the top of the candle. Remove the small can from the ring stand and take the wooden dowel out.

Figure 1

4. Using the can opener, make several air vents near one end of the large can. See Figure 1. Set the large can around the candle, with the air vents at the bottom.

5. Use the graduated cylinder to fill the small can approximately half full of water. In the Data Table, record the volume of water you use.

6. Measure the temperature of the water in the small can. Cool the water with some ice enclosed in a plastic bag until the temperature drops 10° to 15°C below its initial temperature. Remove the bag of ice. In the Data Table, record the temperature of the water after cooling to the nearest 1°C.

7. **CAUTION:** *Be extremely careful when lighting and working with an open flame. Put on goggles and tie back long hair and any loose clothing.* Insert the wooden dowel through the holes in the small can. Light the candle. Immediately hang the can of water on the ring.

8. Stir the water gently with the thermometer and observe the temperature change.

9. When the water temperature is about the same number of degrees above its initial temperature as it was below when the ice was added, blow out the candle.

10. Continue observing the water temperature. In the Data Table, record the highest temperature reached by the water. Calculate the change in water temperature (the difference between the cooled water and the heated water).

11. Find the mass of the candle and the lid after burning and record it in the Data Table. Calculate the mass of candle that burned.

12. Repeat steps 5–11. Compare your two sets of results. Note that the mass of the candle and lid before burning in Trial 2 is the same as the mass of the candle and lid after burning in Trial 1.

COMBUSTION HEAT OF A CANDLE *(continued)*

◆ Observations

Data Table   Sample Data

	Trial 1	Trial 2
Mass of candle and lid before burning	45.3 g	
Mass of candle and lid after burning	44.2 g	
Mass of candle burned	1.1 g	
Volume of water in can	320 mL	
Temperature of water after cooling	16°C	
Temperature of water after heating	37°C	
Change in temperature	21°C	

◆ Analyze and Conclude

1. Use the specific heat of water to calculate the amount of heat absorbed by the can of water. Use the following formula:

   Heat (in joules) = Volume of water (mL) × Temperature change (°C) × 4.18 J/g°C × 1 g/mL water

   Heat = 320 mL × 21°C × 4.18 J/g°C × 1g/mL water = 28,000 J

2. Calculate the combustion heat by dividing the heat that the can of water absorbed by the mass of the candle burned.

   Combustion heat (in joules) = 28,000 J/1.1 g = 26,000 J/g

3. Do you think the water absorbed all of the heat released by the candle? Give a reason for your answer.

   No. The metal of the can absorbed some of the heat.
   _____

   _____

◆ Critical Thinking and Applications

1. A candle has a mass of 30 grams. How much heat will be released when the candle burns to one-third its original height? Use the combustion heat of wax from question 2 in Analyze and Conclude. Show your calculation. (Hint: How many grams of wax burned?)

   Heat = 20 g × 26,000 J/g = 520,000 J

COMBUSTION HEAT OF A CANDLE *(continued)*

2. How many joules would it take to heat 1000 mL of water at 25°C to a temperature of 30°C? Show your calculation.

   Joules needed = 1,000 mL × 5°C × 4.18 J/g°C × 1g/mL water = 21,000 J

3. How many grams of candle wax would be needed to heat the water in the previous question? Show your calculation. (Hint: Use the combustion heat of wax from question 2 in Analyze and Conclude.)

   Mass of candle wax burned = 21,000 J/26,000 J/g = 0.81 g wax

4. Based upon this investigation, describe how you could determine the energy content of foods.

   Burn the food to transfer energy to the water in a calorimeter. Determine the amount of heat

   released and divide that value by the mass of food burned.

◆ More to Explore

New Problem If the small can contained a different liquid, such as a soft drink, would the heat required to raise the temperature be the same?

Possible Materials Decide which liquid you will use. Use materials as in the previous lab.

Safety Handle the thermometer carefully. If it breaks, tell the teacher. Use tongs or an oven mitt when handling hot objects. Always wear safety goggles when heating objects.

Procedure Develop a procedure to measure the combustion heat of the candle, using the new liquid. Write the steps on a separate sheet of paper. Have the teacher approve your procedure before you carry out the investigation.

Observations On a separate sheet of paper, make a data table like the one in the lab, in which you record your observations.

Analyze and Conclude

1. Compare the heat required to raise the temperature of the new liquid to the heat required to raise the temperature of water. Would you expect the two values to be the same?

   Students may think incorrectly that, because the candle is used to heat both liquids, the amount

   of heat would be the same.

2. If the new liquid is not water, would you use the value 4.18 J/g°C as the specific heat?

   The value 4.18 J/g°C is the specific heat of water. All materials have different specific heats. You

   would use a different value for the specific heat of the new liquid in your calculations. You can

   find the specific heat of many common liquids in a chemistry handbook.

N-1   **LABORATORY INVESTIGATION**

Electromagnetism

Key Concept: Electric current can increase the magnetic properties of a ferromagnetic material.

Skills Focus: Observing, inferring, measuring, posing questions, controlling variables

Time Required: 40 minutes

◆ Pre-Lab Discussion

When charges move in an electric current, they create a magnetic field. It's possible to make an electromagnet with a magnetic field that is stronger than any permanent magnet. The magnetic field of an electromagnet is produced by the current in the wire and the magnetized core. You can also turn an electromagnet on or off, which makes it a useful tool. The drawback is that an electromagnet is useless without a supply of electricity.

In this investigation, you will make an electromagnet and find out what affects the strength of its magnetic field.

1. How is an electromagnet different from a regular magnet?

An electromagnet uses an electric current and can create a stronger magnetic field. It can also

be turned on and off.

2. How could you use an electromagnet?

Answers will vary, and may include junkyard cranes and doorbells.

◆ Problem

What affects the strength of an electromagnet?

◆ Materials *(per group)*

dry cell, D cell or larger
5 iron nails, 10 cm long
small piece of aluminum foil
penny
nickel
dime
other test objects
bell wire, 2 m with ends stripped
15–20 paper clips

Advance Preparation: Assemble a variety of small test objects, including some made of wood and of iron or iron alloys. You could include toys, small tools, and desk objects.

Teaching Tips: Warn students that magnetism can damage magnetic storage devices, including computer disks, cassette tapes, credit cards, and watches.

Remind students not to leave the electromagnet connected to the dry cell. It will rapidly drain the cell's power.

ELECTROMAGNETISM *(continued)*

◆ **Safety** *Review the safety guidelines in the front of your lab book.*

Computer disks, audiotapes, videotapes, and watches can be ruined by strong magnets. Keep them away from the lab area.

◆ Procedure

1. Hold the five nails in a bunch. Touch the bunch of nails to each test object to check for magnetic attraction between the nails and the object. Record your results in the Data Table.

2. Hold the five nails together and neatly wrap about 25 cm of wire around them in a single layer. See Figure 1. Do not overlap the coils. Leave about 50 cm of wire at one end and about 125 cm of wire at the other end.

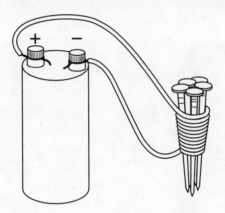

Figure 1

3. Attach the shorter end of the wire to one terminal of the dry cell.

4. Momentarily touch the 125-cm end of the wire to the other terminal of the dry cell. **CAUTION:** *Do not operate the electromagnet for more than a few seconds at a time. Otherwise it will rapidly use up the dry cell's power.* When the electromagnet is on, test each material for magnetic attraction. Record your results in the Data Table.

5. Give the electromagnet power again and find out how many paper clips it can hold. Record the number in the Data Table. Disconnect the longer end of the wire from the dry cell.

6. Use the 125-cm end of the wire to wrap another 25 cm of wire around the nails. You should have a single layer of windings. Repeat Steps 4 and 5.

7. Wind a second layer of wire over the first winding, using the 100-cm end of wire. You should have about 50 cm of unwound wire remaining.

8. Repeat Steps 4 and 5.

9. Take apart the electromagnet. Use just two nails to make an electromagnet with two layers of wire windings. Repeat Steps 4 and 5.

ELECTROMAGNETISM *(continued)*

◆ Observations

Sample Data

Test	Object	Attraction
Five nails alone	aluminum foil	no
	penny	no
	nickel	no
	dime	no
	wood	no
Number of paper clips held = 0	steel	no
Five nails, 25 cm of wire	aluminum foil	no
	penny	no
	nickel	no
	dime	no
	wood	no
Number of paper clips held = 2	steel	yes
Five nails, 50 cm of wire	aluminum foil	no
	penny	no
	nickel	a little
	dime	no
	wood	no
Number of paper clips held = 5	steel	yes
Five nails, two layers of wire	aluminum foil	no
	penny	no
	nickel	a little
	dime	no
	wood	no
Number of paper clips held = 10	steel	yes
Two nails, two layers of wire	aluminum foil	no
	penny	no
	nickel	no
	dime	no
	wood	no
Number of paper clips held = 4	steel	yes

◆ Analyze and Conclude

1. Which materials did the electromagnet attract? Which materials did the electromagnet not attract?

Steel or iron objects and the paper clips were strongly attracted. The nickel was weakly

attracted. The aluminum foil, the penny, the dime, and the wood were not attracted.

ELECTROMAGNETISM *(continued)*

2. Why were some objects attracted by the electromagnet? Why were other objects not attracted?

Materials that were attracted have electrons that align with the magnetic field of the magnet.

Materials that were not attracted do not have electrons that align with the magnetic field.

3. How did increasing the number of turns of the wire affect the strength of the electromagnet? Why did it have this effect?

The magnetic attraction increased. The extra turns of the wire reinforce and strengthen the

magnetic field, increasing the magnetic attraction.

4. How did removing some of the nails affect the strength of the electromagnet? Why did it have this effect?

The magnetic attraction decreased. The result is a weaker magnet.

◆ Critical Thinking and Applications

1. List the common properties of the materials attracted to the magnet.

The materials are all iron or iron alloys.

2. Why are magnets a hazard for audiotapes, videotapes, and computer disks?

Audiotapes, videotapes, and computer disks have information encoded with magnetic fields. A

magnet could scramble the coding.

3. Explain how you might construct an electromagnet that could hold more paper clips than your electromagnet in this lab was able to hold.

Answers may vary. Two possibilities are increasing the number of nails or the layers of wire.

◆ More to Explore

Consider what goes into an electromagnet and enhances the magnetic field. How can you increase or decrease the strength of an electromagnet without making any changes to the arrangement of wire or nails? Write a procedure you would follow to answer this question. Have the teacher approve your procedure before you carry out the investigation.

To increase the strength of the electromagnet without changing the arrangement of the nail core or the wire coils, increase the electric current to the magnet. You could use a dry cell that has a higher voltage, or wire two or more cells into the circuit.

Building Electric Circuits

Key Concept: Current and voltage are different in series and parallel circuits.

Skills Focus: Observing, making models, measuring

Time required: Part A — 40 minutes
Part B — 40 minutes

2

◆ Pre-lab Discussion

An electric circuit allows the flow of electrons from a power source to make a complete round trip back to the power source. Every circuit has a source of electrical energy, a device that is run by electrical energy such as a lightbulb, and a switch. In a series circuit, only one path is available for electrons to flow through. In a parallel circuit, two or more paths are available for the electrons to flow through. In this investigation, you will construct several series and parallel circuits, and then measure and compare their current and voltage.

1. What instrument can you use to measure the current in an electric circuit?

Current can be measured with an ammeter.

2. What instrument can you use to measure the voltage in an electric circuit?

Voltage can be measured with a voltmeter.

3. How is current related to voltage in electric circuits? (Hint: Think of Ohm's law.)

Voltage equals current multiplied by resistance, or $V = I \times R$.

◆ Problem

How do current and voltage compare between two types of circuits—a parallel circuit and a series circuit?

Advance Preparation: Check to make sure that your voltmeters and ammeters are in good working order and have fresh batteries if batteries are necessary. Use 1.5-V lightbulbs.

◆ Materials *(per group)*

3 small bulbs with sockets
1.5-V dry cell
17 connecting wires
ammeter, 0–1A range
voltmeter, 0–3V range
knife switch

Alternate Materials: The bulbs are used to provide a visible indication of the working of the circuits. Other electronic components may be substituted if you desire. Use wires with alligator clips at each end to make connections easier.

This lab setup can also be assembled from breadboard kits available from Radio Shack and other suppliers. If these kits are used, explain the operation of the breadboard and connecting posts that are part of this kit. Explanations are provided in the kit directions. The posts are usually springs that can allow easy connection of the wires.

◆ Safety   *Review the safety guidelines in the front of your lab book.*

Wear safety goggles throughout the activity. Be careful when handling electric circuits to avoid shocks.

BUILDING ELECTRIC CIRCUITS (continued)

◆ Procedure

Teaching Tips
You may want to do Part A one day and Part B the following day.

Part A: A Parallel Circuit

Be sure to check students' setups before going on to Step 2.

1. Use the dry cell, connecting wires, and knife switch to connect the three bulbs in parallel. See Figure 1. Be sure to connect the bulbs to the dry cell and knife switch exactly as shown. Each of the round dots represents a connection between two wires. Make sure the knife switch is open. The switch connects to the negative terminal of the dry cell. When you have finished, have the teacher check the circuit.

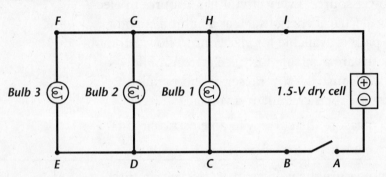

Figure 1

You may need to dim the lights or pull window shades so that students can tell if the bulbs are lit and can assess the brightness of the bulbs. If you have trouble getting the room dark enough, have students shield the bulbs with their hands as they make their observations.

2. Close the switch and record your observations in Data Table 1.

3. Unscrew bulb 2. Record your observations in the same data table.

4. Retighten the bulb. Open the switch. Measure the total voltage of the circuit by placing the voltmeter as shown in Figure 2. Using the two remaining wires, connect the positive terminal of the voltmeter to position I, and connect the negative terminal of the voltmeter to position B. Momentarily close the switch to see if the needle deflects to the right. If the needle deflects to the left, reverse the voltmeter connections. Close the switch and record the total voltage (V_T) in Data Table 2. Open the switch.

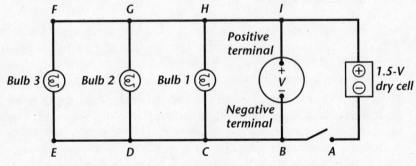

Figure 2

In Part A Step 4, you may wish to show students how to reconnect the wires so that the voltmeter is connected correctly in the circuit.

In Part A, Step 8, you may wish to show students how to connect the wires so that the ammeter is connected correctly in the circuit.

5. Measure the voltage across bulb 1 by connecting the positive terminal of the voltmeter to position H and the negative terminal of the voltmeter to position C. Close the switch and record the voltage (V_1) in Data Table 2. Open the switch.

BUILDING ELECTRIC CIRCUITS *(continued)*

6. Measure the voltage across bulb 2 by connecting the positive terminal of the voltmeter to position G and the negative terminal to position D. Close the switch and record the voltage (V_2) in Data Table 2. Open the switch.

7. Measure the voltage across bulb 3 by connecting the positive terminal of the voltmeter to position F and the negative terminal to position E. Close the switch and record the voltage (V_3) in Data Table 2. Open the switch and remove the voltmeter.

8. Measure the total current by removing the connecting wire between positions H and I and attaching the positive terminal of the ammeter to position I and the negative terminal of the ammeter to position H. See Figure 3. Momentarily close the switch. If the needle deflects to the left, open the switch and reverse the ammeter connections. Close the switch and record the total current (I_T) in Data Table 2. Open the switch.

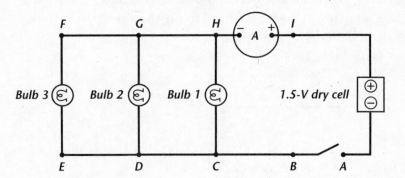

Figure 3

9. Disconnect the ammeter and replace the connecting wire between positions H and I. Disconnect the wire at position H that leads to bulb 1. Do not disconnect the wire at the lamp. Connect the negative terminal of the ammeter to the wire that is connected to the lamp. Connect the positive terminal of the ammeter to position H. See Figure 4. Close the switch and record the current (I_1) through bulb 1 in Data Table 2. Open the switch, disconnect the ammeter, and reconnect the wire to position H.

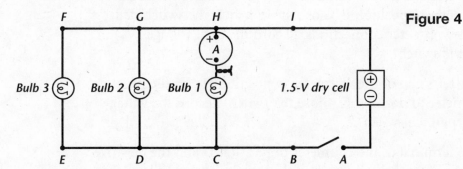

Figure 4

BUILDING ELECTRIC CIRCUITS *(continued)*

10. Disconnect the wire from bulb 2 at position G. Do not disconnect it at the bulb. Connect the negative terminal of the ammeter to the wire and the positive terminal of the ammeter to position G. Close the switch and record the current (I_2) through bulb 2 in Data Table 2. Open the switch, disconnect the ammeter, and reconnect the wire to position G.

11. Disconnect the wire from bulb 3 at position F. Do not disconnect it at the bulb. Connect the negative terminal of the ammeter to the wire and the positive terminal of the ammeter to position F. Close the switch and record the current (I_3) through bulb 3 in Data Table 2. Open the switch, disconnect the ammeter, and reconnect the wire to position F.

Part B: A Series Circuit

1. Connect the three bulbs in series by removing the connecting wires between positions G and H, between positions E and D, and between positions C and B. Insert a connecting wire between positions E and B. Your circuit should now look like Figure 5. Have the teacher check your circuit. Close the switch and record your observations in Data Table 1.

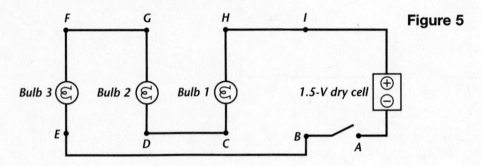

Figure 5

2. Unscrew bulb 2 and record your observation in the same data table. Retighten the bulb and open the switch.

3. Connect the positive terminal of the voltmeter to position I and the negative terminal of the voltmeter to position B. Close the switch. If the switch deflects to the left, reverse the voltmeter connections. Record the total voltage (V_T) in Data Table 2. Open the switch.

4. Connect the positive terminal of the voltmeter to position H and the negative terminal of the voltmeter to position C. Close the switch. Record the voltage (V_1) across bulb 1. Open the switch.

5. Connect the positive terminal of the voltmeter to position D and the negative terminal of the voltmeter to position G. Close the switch. Record the voltage (V_2) across bulb 2. Open the switch.

BUILDING ELECTRIC CIRCUITS *(continued)*

6. Connect the positive terminal of the voltmeter to position F and the negative terminal of the voltmeter to position E. Close the switch. Record the voltage (V_3) across bulb 3. Open the switch and remove the voltmeter.

7. Measure the total current by removing the connecting wire between positions H and I and connecting the positive terminal of the ammeter to position I and the negative terminal of the ammeter to position H. Close the switch. If the needle deflects to the left, reverse the ammeter connections. Record the total current (I_T) in Data Table 2. Open the switch, remove the ammeter, and replace the connecting wire between positions H and I.

8. Disconnect the wire from bulb 1 at position C. Do not disconnect this wire at the bulb. Connect the positive terminal of the ammeter to the wire and the negative terminal of the ammeter to position C. Close the switch and record the current (I_1) through bulb 1. Open the switch, disconnect the ammeter, and reconnect the wire to position C.

9. Disconnect the wire from bulb 2 at position G. Do not disconnect this wire at the bulb. Connect the positive terminal of the ammeter to the wire and the negative terminal of the ammeter to position G. Close the switch and record the current (I_2) through bulb 2. Open the switch, disconnect the ammeter, and reconnect the wire to position G.

10. Disconnect the wire from bulb 3 at position E. Do not disconnect this wire at the bulb. Connect the positive terminal of the ammeter to the wire and the negative terminal of the ammeter to position E. Close the switch and record the current (I_3) through bulb 3. Open the switch, disconnect the ammeter, and reconnect the wire to position E.

◆ Observations

Data Table 1   Sample Data

Circuit	Switch Closed	Bulb 2 Unscrewed
Part A: Parallel	All three bulbs are equally bright.	The remaining bulbs are still lit.
Part B: Series	All three bulbs are dimly lit.	No bulbs are lit.

BUILDING ELECTRIC CIRCUITS *(continued)*

Data Table 2   Sample Data

Circuit	Voltage (volts)				Current (amps)			
	V_T	V_1	V_2	V_3	I_T	I_1	I_2	I_3
Part A: Parallel	1.5	1.5	1.5	1.5	0.45	0.15	0.15	0.15
Part B: Series	1.5	0.5	0.5	0.5	0.05	0.05	0.05	0.05

2

◆ Analyze and Conclude

1. Add the currents I_1, I_2, and I_3 in the parallel circuit. Is the total current, I_T, approximately equal to the sum of the three individual currents in the parallel circuit?

Yes. I_T = 0.45 A while the sum, I_1 + I_2 + I_3 = 0.15 A + 0.15 A + 0.15 A = 0.45 A

2. Add the voltages V_1, V_2, and V_3 in the parallel circuit. Is the total voltage approximately equal to the sum of the individual voltages in the parallel circuit?

No. V_T = 1.5 V, while the sum, V_1 + V_2 + V_3 = 1.5 V + 1.5 V + 1.5 V = 4.5 V

3. In the parallel circuit, how does the total voltage compare with the individual voltages?

The total voltage has the same value as the individual voltages.

4. Add the currents I_1, I_2, and I_3 in the series circuit. Does the total current approximately equal the sum of the individual currents in a series circuit?

No. I_T = 0.5 A, while the sum, I_1 + I_2 + I_3 = 0.5 A + 0.5 A + 0.5A = 1.5 A

5. How does the total current compare with the individual currents in a series circuit?

The total current has the same value as the individual currents.

6. Add the voltages V_1, V_2, and V_3 in the series circuit. Is the total voltage approximately equal to the sum of the individual voltages in a series circuit?

Yes. V_T = 1.5 V, while the sum, V_1 + V_2 + V_3 = 0.5 V + 0.5 V + 0.5 V = 1.5 V

BUILDING ELECTRIC CIRCUITS *(continued)*

◆ Critical Thinking and Applications

1. In which circuit would a burned-out bulb cause all the other bulbs to go out? Why?

A series circuit. This circuit offers only one path for the current to flow. If a burned-out bulb

closes this path, no current can flow and none of the other bulbs will light.

_____

2. Voltage is the force, or "push," that gets electrons moving. Based on your data, explain why the bulbs in a series circuit burn dimmer than the bulbs in a parallel circuit.

In a series circuit, each bulb receives only a fraction of the voltage, equivalent to the total voltage

divided by the number of bulbs in the circuit. However, in a parallel circuit, each bulb receives the

total voltage. Because of this, the bulbs in the parallel circuit burn brighter.

3. What would happen to the current in a parallel circuit if all the bulbs were not the same size?

If one bulb had greater resistance, the current would decrease in that branch. If one bulb had

lesser resistance, the current would increase in that branch. The sum of the currents in each bulb

would still equal the total current.

◆ More To Explore

You have been given the job of designing the electrical circuits to supply the power to a house. You have the following information.

House Electrical Requirements

Room	Number of Lights Needed	Circuit Breaker Number
Kitchen	4	1
Bathroom	1	2
Laundry	1	2
Family room	2	3
Bedroom	1	3

You must design the correct circuits to accommodate the needs of the house. In each circuit, identify the position of lights in the circuit and identify the presence of a circuit breaker by a switch. (Hint: Each circuit breaker is wired in parallel with the house power supply and all the other circuit breakers. Also, all lights in a particular circuit must be in parallel.)

BUILDING ELECTRIC CIRCUITS *(continued)*

Use the information in the table of electrical requirements to determine the number of lights in each circuit and to find out how many series and parallel circuits are needed for the house.

Make a drawing of your circuits and locate all the lights in the circuit. Identify the circuit breakers with switches in the drawing.

In this exploration, students make a drawing of the circuits needed to meet the needs of their design house. The correct drawing is shown.

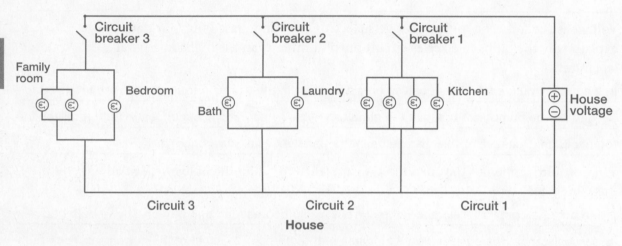

House

1. How many circuits are in the house? What kind are they?

There are three main parallel circuits. Each parallel circuit has several smaller branches, which are also in parallel.

2. Assume that you have a working model of the circuit and that all the lights are on. What happens when you open each circuit-breaker switch?

When you open the circuit-breaker switch, all of the lights on that circuit will go out.

3. As a designer, why would you not want all of the lights in the house to be connected in series?

If all the lights were on one series circuit, whenever one light would go out, all the lights would go out. By not having all the lights on one series circuit, if one light goes out, the other lights will stay lit.

4. Under what circumstances would all of the lights in the house go out?

All of the lights would go out if all the power to the house was lost or if all of the circuit breakers were opened.

Electricity From a Lemon

Key Concept: An electrochemical cell can be made by using a lemon as a source of the electrolyte and using coins of different types as electrodes.

Skills Focus: Observing, inferring, making models, measuring

◆ Pre-lab Discussion

Time required: 40 minutes

Chemical reactions can generate electricity. That's how an electrochemical cell works. Cells and batteries can be made from different kinds of materials. As you have read, Alessandro Volta produced the first battery by stacking zinc and silver plates with moist paper between them.

In this investigation, you will build a simple electrochemical cell using a lemon and two types of coins. You will determine if your cell works by testing to see if the needle of a voltmeter moves when you complete a circuit that includes your electrochemical cell.

1. What are the components that make up an electrochemical cell?

The components of the electrochemical cell are the metal electrodes and an electrolyte, which

conducts electric current.

2. What is the difference between a wet cell and a dry cell?

In a wet cell, the electrolyte is a liquid. In a dry cell, the electrolyte is a paste.

3. A voltmeter needle will deflect when current flows through it. How can you make the needle deflect more?

You can increase the deflection by increasing the voltage. The voltage can be

increased by adding more electrochemical cells in series to the circuit.

◆ Problem

Advance Preparation: Obtain one lemon for each group.

How can you make an electrochemical cell using a lemon and two coins?

◆ Possible Materials *(per group)*

coins of different types
sandpaper, steel wool,
   or metal cleaner
lemon
scissors

small cardboard box
voltmeter
bell wire
tape

Alternate Materials: If lemons are not available, oranges or other citrus fruit will work as well. Electrochemical cells may also be constructed with pieces of different metals, rather than coins, inserted into the fruit. A penny and a dime work well as the two coins.

ELECTRICITY FROM A LEMON (continued)

◆ **Safety**   *Review the safety guidelines in the front of your lab book.*

Always wear safety goggles. Be careful when handling scissors or any strong chemicals, such as metal cleaner. Wash your hands after using chemicals.

◆ Procedure

1. Read the entire lab before starting your investigation.

2. Design an electrochemical cell using the materials listed or similar materials. As you design the electrochemical cell, consider the following questions.
   • What metal or metals will you use for the electrodes?
   • Should the electrodes be made of the same or different metals?
   • Do you need to do anything to prepare the electrodes?
   • What will you use for an electrolyte?
   • Does the electrolyte need any special preparation?
   • How will you insert the electrodes into the electrolyte?
   • How should the electrodes be oriented in relation to each other?
   • How far apart should the electrodes be?

   On a separate sheet of paper, draw your design and show it to the teacher for approval. Then build your electrochemical cell.

3. Prepare your voltmeter so that you can see if your electrochemical cell generates a current. Consider these questions.
   • Where should you place the voltmeter in relation to the electrochemical cell?
   • How will you complete your circuit?
   • How will you turn the current on and off?

4. Prepare your lemon to act as an electrolyte by gently rolling it back and forth on a table or bench to release the juice inside.

5. To insert electrodes into the lemon, use scissors to carefully make two parallel slits in the lemon skin. In the left column of the Data Table, record what you used for electrodes.

6. Complete your circuit using your electrochemical cell and the wires. Observe any movement of the voltmeter needle including the direction and amount of movement. Record your observations in the right column of the Data Table.

7. If your electrochemical cell worked, go on to Step 8. If it did not work, consider how you could change your electrochemical cell and try again.

8. Reverse the connecting wires of your electrodes. Again observe and record any movement of the compass needle.

© Prentice-Hall, Inc.

ELECTRICITY FROM A LEMON (continued)

◆ Observations

Data Table Sample Data

Electrodes	Wire Connections	Observations of Compass
Penny and dime	Forward	Voltmeter needle moves right.
Penny and dime	Reversed	Voltmeter needle moves left.

Demonstrate how to release the juice in the lemon by rolling it back and forth on a table or flat surface while applying slight pressure. You can show students that the juice has been released by comparing a rolled lemon with one that has not been rolled, cutting both open, and showing how the juice flows more easily from the rolled lemon.

For the electrochemical cell to work best, the coins should be aligned parallel and placed about 1 centimeter apart. Also, the coins need to be cleaned of oils and oxides.

Students can use a metal polish to do the cleaning, or they can sand the surface with sandpaper or steel wool. If students use metal polish, they should follow the directions on the bottle and wash their hands carefully afterwards. Because most pennies are made from zinc coated with copper, if students rub too hard, they will expose the zinc and have difficulty making the electrochemical cell work properly.

◆ Analyze and Conclude

1. What are the components of an electrochemical cell? Which of these correspond to the items used in this experiment?

To produce an electric current, you must have two electrodes of different kinds of metal that are

connected to each other. The electrodes must be partially inserted into an electrolyte. The two

electrodes are the coins. The bell wire connects these electrodes. The lemon juice is the electrolyte.

2. Why was the voltmeter important in this experiment?

The movement of the voltmeter needle indicates that a potential difference exists between the

two electrodes and that current is flowing between them.

3. Did your lemon electrochemical cell generate electricity on your first attempt? If so, what made it work? If not, how did you change your cell to make it work?

Answers will vary, depending on the coins students choose. Students who choose two different

coins of different metals should be able to construct electrochemical cells that work. Students

who initially used the same type of coins will have electrochemical cells that do not work and

should have redesigned their cells using coins of different types of metals.

ELECTRICITY FROM A LEMON *(continued)*

4. With a working electrochemical cell, what happened to the voltmeter when you reversed the wires? Why does this happen?

When the wires are switched, the voltmeter needle moves in the opposite direction from the way

it did the first time. This is because the current flows in the opposite direction.

◆ Critical Thinking and Applications

1. Did you make a wet cell or a dry cell? Explain your answer.

The electrochemical cell is a wet cell because the lemon juice, which is the electrolyte, is a liquid.

2. You may have found that scrubbing or cleaning the coins was an important factor in whether your electrochemical cell worked. How did cleaning the coins help your electrochemical cell work?

Scrubbing or cleaning the coins removes oils, dirt, and metal oxides that can build up on the

coins' surfaces and inhibit the flow of charges.

3. How might using an old, dried-out lemon have affected your experiment? Explain.

There probably would not be enough juice in a dried-out lemon to be an effective electrolyte, so

the electrochemical cell probably would not work.

◆ More To Explore

How can you increase the strength of the current to get the voltmeter needle to move even more? Consider what was needed to generate the electric current and think about how these factors could be enhanced. Form a hypothesis and write a procedure for testing your hypothesis. Have the teacher approve your procedure before you carry out your investigation. Be sure to wear your safety goggles and apron.

To increase the strength of the magnetic field, the strength of the electric current must be increased. This can be accomplished by using multiple lemons in series. Insert a penny and a dime into each lemon and connect the dime from one lemon to the penny of the next lemon by a piece of wire. Current can also be increased by alternating pennies and dimes in the same lemon.

Constructing a Simple Computer Circuit

Key Concept: All computer information is stored as binary numbers.

Skills Focus: Observing, making models, creating data tables

Time Required: 40 minutes

◆ Pre-Lab Discussion

Computers use combinations of off-on switches to perform their various functions. A circuit that is closed and through which current flows is said to be "on" and represents the number 1. A circuit that is open and through which current does not flow is said to be "off" and represents the number 0.

In this investigation, you will construct an electric circuit that will show base-10 numbers as binary (base 2) numbers.

1. What is the binary system?

This is the mathematical system of units based on two. There are only two units in the system,

0 and 1. Various combinations of these units identify all other numbers.

_____

2. How do you know if a number is 0 or 1 in a binary electric circuit?

When the circuit has a current flowing through it, the number is 1. If no current is flowing through

the circuit, the number is 0.

◆ Problem

How can off-on switches model how a computer circuit converts base-10 numbers to binary numbers?

◆ Materials (per group)

three 1.5-V bulbs with sockets
1.5-V dry cell
3 knife switches, single pole–single throw
knife switch, double pole–single throw
connecting wires
pegboard
machine screws
12 clips or screws for connecting wires

Advance Preparation: If the ends of the connecting wires are covered with a little solder, the leads will last indefinitely.

Alternative Materials: This lab can be assembled from breadboard kits available from Radio Shack. Use wires with alligator clips at each end or screw-type components if you are not using pegboards for connections.

Teaching Tips: You may want to refer students to the text for information on binary numbers.

Name ______________________ Date __________ Class ______________

CONSTRUCTING A SIMPLE COMPUTER CIRCUIT *(continued)*

◆ Safety

Review the safety guidelines in the front of your lab book.

The amount of electricity you will be using in this lab cannot hurt you. If you feel components of a circuit getting warm, open the circuit. Examine it carefully for a short circuit.

◆ Procedure

1. Connect the bulbs, switches, and dry cell on the pegboard as shown in Figure 1. Note that you must use a double-pole switch for switch 3, so that it can be connected to both bulb 1 and 2.
2. Have the teacher check your circuit before you proceed.
3. Switches 1, 2, 3, and 4 correspond to the base-10 numbers 1, 2, 3, and 4. Close switch 1 and record in the Data Table which bulbs are on and which remain off. For example, if only the middle bulb is on, record off, on, off.
4. Open switch 1.
5. Close switch 2 and record which bulbs are on and which remain off.
6. Open switch 2.
7. Close switch 3 and record which bulbs are on and which remain off.
8. Close switch 3
9. Close switch 4 and record which bulbs are on and which remain off.
10. Open switch 4.

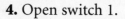

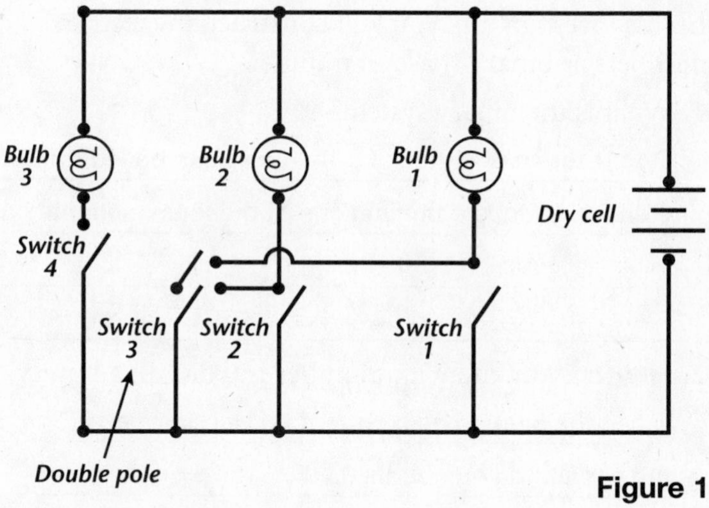

Figure 1

4

◆ Observations

Data Table

Switch Closed	Bulb 3	Bulb 2	Bulb 1
1	off	off	on
2	off	on	off
3	off	on	on
4	on	off	off

CONSTRUCTING A SIMPLE COMPUTER CIRCUIT *(continued)*

◆ Analyze and Conclude

1. Use the data in your Data Table to help you show base-10 numbers as binary (base 2) numbers. In the table below, for base-10 numbers 1, 2, 3, and 4, record "1" if a bulb is lit and "0" if a bulb is off. For example, if only the middle switch is lit, record 010. Examine the pattern and then complete the table for base-10 numbers 5, 6, and 7.

Base-10 Number	Binary Number
1	001
2	010
3	011
4	100
5	101
6	110
7	111

2. Your circuit models only how a computer shows the first four base-10 numbers as binary numbers. How could you show the following base-10 numbers as binary numbers using your circuit: 5, 6, 7? If time permits, try these numbers on your circuit.

To show 5, close switches 4 and 1. To show 6, close switches 4 and 2. To show 7, close switches

4 and 3, or close switches 4, 2, and 1.

◆ Critical Thinking and Applications

1. What is the largest base-10 number your circuit can show? Give a reason for your answer.

Seven is the largest number, represented by the binary code 111. This code means that all three

lamps are lit, the maximum possible in a three-lamp circuit.

CONSTRUCTING A SIMPLE COMPUTER CIRCUIT *(continued)*

2. How would you have to modify your circuit to go beyond the number from question 1?

Add more lamps and switches to the circuit.

_____

3. What number do you get if you add the binary numbers 101 and 001? Write your answer as a binary number.

The binary number 001 is the base-10 number 1 and the binary number 101 is the base-10

number 5. The sum of these numbers is 6, which is represented by the binary number 110.

4. What is the base-10 value of the binary number 111101?

1(32) + 1(16) + 1(8) + 1(4) + 0(2) + 1(1) = 61

◆ More to Explore

Write a hypothesis that explains how the bulb circuit you used for the lab relates to the operation of a computer that uses binary numbers to represent 256 characters. Begin by considering how many bulbs would be needed to accommodate all of the characters used by the computer. Then devise a way to get all of these characters represented by the fewest binary digits. (Hint: Try to find a pattern instead of writing out all the binary numbers.)

If you were to attempt to represent all of the characters using a bulb circuit, what is the minimum number of bulbs that would be needed?

8

Look at a computer keyboard. Why do you think that it's necessary for a computer to use so many binary numbers?

It is necessary to distinguish between uppercase and lowercase letters and between

letters and other symbols.

All of the characters can be represented by various combinations of eight digits. Computers use these eight digits, called bytes, to perform all of the functions for mathematics and other functions such as word processing. The computer also stores this information in bytes.

O-1   **LABORATORY INVESTIGATION**

Making Waves

Key Concept: The speed of a wave is defined by the wavelength and the frequency of the wave.

Skill Focus: Observing, predicting, making models, measuring, calculating, controlling variables

◆ Pre-Lab Discussion

Time Required: 40 minutes

The speed of a wave is how far the wave travels in one unit of time. The speed also equals the wavelength multiplied by the wave's frequency. If you know any two of the quantities in the speed formula—wavelength, frequency, or speed—you can calculate the third.

In this experiment, you will model waves and investigate the relationship of the frequency and length of the wave to its speed.

1. Write the equation for the speed of a wave.

Speed = Wavelength × Frequency

2. Define wavelength.

Wavelength is the distance between two corresponding parts of successive waves such as

between two crests or two troughs.

3. If a wave travels 6 m in 2 s, what is its speed?

Speed = 6 m/2 s = 3 m/s

If the same wave has a frequency of 10 Hz, what is its wavelength?

Wavelength = (3 m/s)/(10/s) = 0.3 m

◆ Problem

How does a wave's speed relate to its frequency and wavelength?

◆ Materials *(per group)*

Alternative Materials: You can use 2 or 3 layers of newspaper instead of brown paper.

meterstick
ruler
masking tape
plain brown paper
paper cup
pencil

string
graduated cylinder, 100-mL
water
stopwatch or clock with a second hand
marker

◆ Safety 🖐

Review the safety guidelines in the front of your lab book.

To prevent slips or falls, immediately wipe up any water spilled on the floor.

MAKING WAVES (*continued*)

◆ Procedure

1. Work with two other students. Measure off 4 m on the floor. Mark the starting and end points with masking tape. Lay the brown paper on the floor between the two marked points.

2. Poke a tiny hole in the bottom of a cup with a pencil point. Poke two larger holes near the top of the cup on opposite sides.

3. Thread a string through the holes near the top of the cup and attach the string to the pencil. See Figure 1. The pencil acts as a handle that lets the cup swing freely.

4. Read Steps 5–9 before continuing with the investigation.

5. Have a classmate stand at the end point with a stopwatch or a clock with a second hand. That student will time how long it takes the second student to walk the measured distance.

6. Stand behind the starting point and hold the pencil ends so the cup can swing freely.

7. Have a second classmate hold the cup while plugging the bottom hole with one finger. That student should fill the cup with 100 mL of water and hold the cup 5 cm to one side, so that the cup will swing from side to side when it is released.

Keep the bottom hole small, or the water will come out too fast.

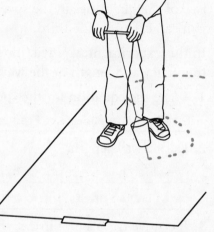

Figure 1

8. When the first student gives a signal, he or she should start the stopwatch, and the second student should let go of the cup. At the same time, walk at a steady pace along the marked distance, holding the pencil away from your body. As you walk, the cup will swing from side to side, and the water will drain through the hole. The water will trace a wave on the paper.

9. When you reach the end point, the first student should stop the stopwatch. In the Data Table provided on the next page, record the time it took to walk the 4 m. Properly dispose of any water remaining in the cup.

10. If necessary, use the marker to retrace the wave on the paper. Measure the wavelength and count the number of crests in 4 m. Record these values in the table.

11. Calculate the frequency of the wave—the number of complete waves per second. Round off your number to the nearest complete wave. Record this value in the table.

12. Predict whether you would have more or fewer crests if you repeated the experiment while walking faster. Give a reason for your prediction.

Have students add a drop of food coloring to the water to make the water more visible as it drips on the paper. Have a container at the end of the course to collect the leaking cups.

Accept any prediction with a supporting reason. In fact, there would be fewer crests because there's less time for the cup to swing.

MAKING WAVES *(continued)*

13. Check your prediction by repeating Steps 5–11, but at a faster pace than in the first trial. Record your results in the Data Table.

14. Predict whether you would have more or fewer crests if you repeated the experiment while walking slower than at first. Give a reason for your prediction.

> Remind students to release the cup from the same side as before.

Accept any predictions with a supporting reason. In fact, there would be more crests because there's more time for the cup to swing.

15. Check your prediction. Record your results in the Data Table.

◆ Observations

Data Table   Sample Data

Trial	Time (s)	Wavelength (m)	Waves in 4 m	Frequency (Hz)
1	4	0.90	4	1
2	2	1.90	2	1
3	8	0.50	8	1

◆ Analyze and Conclude

> Answers will vary. Answers given apply to the sample data in the Data Table.

1. Calculate the speed of each wave from the distance traveled and the time.

   Trial 1: speed = distance/time = 4 m/4 s = 1.00 m/s
   Trial 2: speed = distance/time = 4 m/2 s = 2.00 m/s
   Trial 3: speed = distance/time = 4 m/8 s = 0.50 m/s

2. Calculate the speed of each wave from the frequency and the wavelength.

   Trial 1: speed = wavelength × frequency = 0.90 m × 1 Hz = 0.90 m × 1/s = 0.90 m/s
   Trial 2: speed = wavelength × frequency = 1.90 m × 1 Hz = 1.90 m × 1/s = 1.90 m/s
   Trial 3: speed = wavelength × frequency = 0.50 m × 1 Hz = 0.50 m × 1/s = 0.50 m/s

3. Compare the speeds you calculated for Questions 1 and 2.

   The values for the speeds should be about the same.

4. Compare the frequencies and the wavelengths of each wave. What would happen if the frequency increased?

   If the frequency increased, the wavelength would decrease.

MAKING WAVES (*continued*)

◆ Critical Thinking and Applications

1. Was your first prediction in the Procedure correct? Explain why the number of crests changed.

The cup swings at a constant rate, and you cover the distance in less time. The result is that when you walked faster, the cup made fewer swings and therefore fewer waves.

2. If you made more crests over a given distance by walking at a different speed, did the wavelength increase? Why or why not?

No, the wavelength decreased because there are more crests in the same distance. This occurs when you walk more slowly.

3. Blue light has a higher frequency than red light. Does blue light travel faster than red light in the same medium? Give a reason for your answer.

No, the speed of blue light is the same as the speed of red light. Blue light has a higher frequency and a shorter wavelength. Red light has a lower frequency and a longer wavelength. When you multiple the frequency by the wavelength for both types of light, you will get the same speed.

◆ More to Explore

New Problem What would happen to the speed of the wave if you repeated the experiment with waves that have a greater amplitude?

Possible Materials Use the materials from this lab.

Safety To prevent slips or falls, immediately wipe up any water spilled on the floor.

Procedure Develop a procedure to solve the problem. Think about how you could increase the amplitude of the waves. Write your procedure on a separate sheet of paper. Have the teacher approve your procedure before you carry out the investigation.

Observations On a separate sheet of paper, make a data table similar to the one in this lab to record your observations.

Analyze and Conclude What effect did changing the wave's amplitude have on its speed?

Students can double the amplitude by starting the cup 10 cm to one side and their wave traces won't go off the newspaper. Wave speed depends only on the frequency and the wavelength. Amplitude affects the energy of the wave and the power that the wave carries but not the speed.

0-2   **LABORATORY INVESTIGATION**

Tuning Forks

Key Concept: Sound is a disturbance that travels through a medium as a longitudinal wave.

Skills Focus: Observing, inferring, predicting

Time Required: 40 minutes

◆ Pre-Lab Discussion

If you could live in outer space, you'd have a very quiet life. Why is that?

The energy of a sound wave disturbs the molecules in a medium, making them rock back and forth in time with the wave frequency. When the disturbance reaches your ears, you hear sound. When the vibrations are very fast, you hear a high-pitched sound. When the vibrations are slow, the pitch is low. Sound can also travel through solids and liquids. The speed of the sound depends on the temperature, the elasticity, and the density of the medium. If there's no medium, as in the vacuum of outer space, there's no sound.

In this investigation, you will use two tuning forks that vibrate at the same frequency. You will test how sound affects and is affected by different media, different speeds, and interference.

1. What does sound do to the surrounding medium?

Sound waves cause the molecules in the medium to vibrate at the same frequency as the wave.

This sets off a series of vibrations, creating a longitudinal wave.

_____

_____

_____

_____

2. What property of a sound wave changes as it gets louder?

The amplitude gets larger.

_____

_____

◆ Problem

How does sound interact with a medium?

◆ Materials *(per group)*

2 tuning forks, 320 Hz
beaker, 400-mL
water
rubber band
resonance box

Alternative Materials: To prevent accidental breakage, use plastic beakers. The 320-Hz forks provide a good mid-range frequency. Forks of other frequencies will work also.

Teaching Tips: You could have several students listen from different distances from the activity to note any changes in sound. These students would record their observations and compare them with the other participants. Have them discuss what they heard and speculate on why they heard what they did.

© Prentice-Hall, Inc.

2

TUNING FORKS *(continued)*

◆ **Safety** 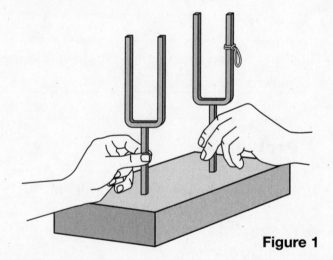 *Review the safety guidelines in the front of your lab book.*

Be careful when you strike the tuning forks against an object. Strike them against unbreakable objects (such as the heel of your shoe) and with just enough force to start them vibrating.

◆ **Procedure**

Work with a partner. Take turns performing each of the six tests below and note any differences between your observations. Read through all six tests before you perform them. Always strike the tuning fork against the heel of your shoe.

1. **Vibration in a medium:** Strike a tuning fork and insert the prongs into a beaker of water. Observe what happens. In the Data Table provided on the next page, record your observations.

2. **Similar vibration:** Strike a tuning fork and bring it within a few centimeters of a second tuning fork with the same frequency. Bring the second tuning fork to within a few centimeters of your ear. Observe what happens. Record your observations.

3. **Resonance:** Strike a tuning fork and note the loudness of the sound. Strike the tuning fork again and touch the base of its stem to the top of the resonance box. Note the loudness of the sound. Record your observations.

4. **Interference:** Strike a tuning fork and bring one of the prongs to within 2 or 3 cm of your ear. Slowly rotate the tuning fork completely. Carefully note any change in the loudness of the sound. Record your observations.

5. **Beats:** Fasten a rubber band securely on the middle of one prong of a tuning fork. See Figure 1. Using a second tuning fork of the same frequency, strike both forks. Touch the bases of the stems of the forks on the resonance box. If the sound is constant, reposition the rubber band and try again. Carefully note the sound emitted by the forks. Record your observations.

6. **Moving source:** Make sure you have plenty of room to swing your arm to the side. Strike a tuning fork extra hard. Rapidly move the tuning fork in a wide arc from your side to over your head. Note and record what you hear. Repeat this experiment with your partner standing several meters away. Does your partner observe any difference in sound at a greater distance? Record your observations and those of your partner.

Figure 1

TUNING FORKS *(continued)*

◆ Observations

Data Table   Sample Data

Test	Loudness Change	Pitch Change	Effect
Vibration in a medium	Yes	No	Interference patterns in water. Volume is dampened by water.
Similar vibrations	Yes	No	The second tuning fork starts vibrating slightly.
Resonance	Yes	No	The sound gets louder with the resonance box.
Interference	Yes	No	As the fork turns, the volume rises and falls.
Beats	Yes	No	A series of volume changes, louder and softer.
Moving sound	Yes	Yes	As the fork comes closer, pitch rises. As it goes away, pitch falls.

◆ Analyze and Conclude

1. Did the loudness of the sound change in some tests? If so, give examples and explain why the loudness changed.

Sample answer: Yes, in the resonance test, the loudness increased when constructive

interference increased the amplitude of the sound wave. In the vibration in a medium test, the

loudness decreased when the water decreased the amplitude of vibration of the tuning fork.

_____

2. How did the pitch change in the moving-source test? Explain this observation.

The movement of the tuning fork toward the listener decreases the distance between the

listener and the fork, which increases the frequency of the waves. This results in a higher pitch.

When the fork moves away, the frequency decreases. This results in a lower pitch.

_____

3. Why did you experiment with two tuning forks that vibrate at the same frequency?

All objects vibrate naturally. If the frequency of a sound wave exactly matches the frequency of

an object, the object will vibrate, or resonate. The vibration of the first tuning fork causes the

second to vibrate.

_____

_____

TUNING FORKS *(continued)*

◆ Critical Thinking and Applications

1. How does one vibrating object make another object vibrate, when they're not touching? What is true of both objects' vibrations when this happens?

The sound wave transmits vibration from an object to a medium, which can transmit vibration to

a second object. The two objects must vibrate at the same frequency.

2. Why does sound get louder with the use of the resonance box?

The sound wave makes the resonance box vibrate at the frequency of the sound wave. The

resonance box enhances the sound wave by creating constructive interference. The amplitude of

the resulting wave is much greater that that of the single wave and so it sounds louder.

3. How are beats produced by two similar tuning forks?

When two sounds are close in frequency, they combine and constructively interfere with each

other at regular intervals to make beats. The resulting sound gets louder and softer at regular

intervals. The rubber band changes the frequency of one of the tuning forks just slightly to

generate this effect.

4. Bats bounce sound waves off objects to get information about prey and obstacles. If a bat makes a constant-frequency sound and the sound bounces back with a different frequency, what does that change tell the bat about an object?

If the frequency is higher, the bat knows the object is getting closer. If the frequency is lower, the

bat knows the object is going away.

◆ More to Explore

How might a change in the resonance box affect the sound that you heard from the resonance test? For example, what would happen to its resonance if the box were a different size or shape? What if it were filled with a gas other than air or a liquid medium? Choose one of the following variables:

- size of resonance box
- shape of resonance box
- substance within resonance box

Changes to the resonance box could affect the frequency or pitch. Consider the size of a violin versus a string bass. The violin has high notes, while the bass has low notes.

Write a procedure you would follow to test that variable. Include a hypothesis about how that variable affects the sound from the box. Have the teacher approve your procedure before you carry out the investigation.

2

O-3   **LABORATORY INVESTIGATION**

In the Heat of the Light

◆ Pre-Lab Discussion

Key Concept: Fluorescent and incandescent lights work in different ways.

Skills Focus: Observing, measuring, interpreting data

Time Required: 45 minutes

Fluorescent and incandescent lights use electricity to produce light in two different ways. However, the two types of light bulbs have some common characteristics that let you make comparisons between them. They each give off a specific amount of light, called luminosity, or light output, which is measured in lumens. They each use energy at a certain rate, a characteristic called power, which is measured in watts. They each last for about a certain amount of time, often called the average life of the bulb, which is measured in hours of use. This kind of information, plus the costs of power and of the light bulb, can help you determine which type of bulbs you should buy.

In this investigation, you will compare the light given off and the power used by incandescent and fluorescent light bulbs.

1. Compare the way that incandescent and fluorescent light bulbs work.

Incandescent lights give off all colors of the visible spectrum along with infrared radiation

(heat) when an electric current flows through the bulb's filament. Fluorescent lights contain a gas

that emits mostly ultraviolet light when an electric current passes through it; when the ultraviolet

light hits the coating inside the bulb, visible light is given off.

◆ Problem

Important Note: Part A is written as a demonstration that you perform. If you wish to have students perform this activity, you will need to modify the Procedure accordingly. Be sure to provide guidance on safety procedures.

How do fluorescent and incandescent bulbs that produce the same amount of light compare in their use of energy?

Advance Preparations: Prepare each carton by cutting a large hole (diameter about 4 cm) for the socket and a small hole (diameter about 8 mm) for the thermometer, as shown in Figure 1.

◆ Materials *(per group)*

cardboard carton (approximately
    25 cm × 25 cm × 30 cm)
masking tape
15- and 60-watt incandescent bulbs
light socket   only 1 15-watt bulb per class
black electrical tape
thermometer

aluminum foil
graph paper   only 1 25-watt bulb per class
15- and 25-watt fluorescent bulbs
bulb packaging for 15-watt fluorescent
    and 60-watt incandescent bulbs
scissors
watch or clock with second hand

Alternative Materials: For Part B, students can compare any incandescent and fluorescent bulbs that produce approximately the same number of lumens. Also, you can provide the information about lumens, watts, and bulb lifetime in place of the bulb packaging.

IN THE HEAT OF THE LIGHT *(continued)*

◆ **Safety**   *Review the safety guidelines in the front of your lab book.*

Use caution in handling scissors. Handle the thermometer carefully. If it breaks, tell the teacher. Be careful not to touch a light bulb while it is on or shortly after turning it off. In Part A, look at the lighted bulbs for only a few seconds at a time.

◆ Procedure

Part A: Investigating the Brightness of Light Bulbs

1. If you compare a 15-watt fluorescent bulb and a 15-watt incandescent bulb, do you think one would be brighter, or would they look about the same? How would the brightness of a 25-watt fluorescent bulb compare with that of a 60-watt incandescent bulb? On a separate sheet of paper, write a prediction about the brightness of each of these four light bulbs, ranking them in order from brightest to least bright.

2. In a darkened room, compare the brightness of a lighted 15-watt fluorescent bulb and of a 15-watt incandescent bulb. Which bulb is brighter?

   the fluorescent bulb

3. In a darkened room, compare the brightness of a 25-watt fluorescent bulb and of a 60-watt incandescent bulb. Which bulb is brighter?

   the fluorescent bulb

4. Observe any other combinations needed to test your prediction.

   Usual order of brightness: 25-watt fluorescent, 15-watt fluorescent, 60-watt incandescent,

   15-watt incandescent

> Do Part A together as a class. You need to set up two lamps without shades at the front of the classroom. Dim the overhead lights in the room. For Step 2, turn on a 15-watt fluorescent and a 15-watt incandescent bulb. Let the students compare the brightness of each bulb, and record their observations. For Step 3, use a 25-watt fluorescent and a 60-watt incandescent bulb.

For Part B, if the bulbs have been used by a previous class, be sure they have cooled down before the next student group uses the materials. In this part of the lab, one student can be the timekeeper, a second can take the thermometer readings, and a third can record the temperatures.

Part B: Comparing Energy Use by Bulbs of the Same Brightness

1. Prepare a Data Table like the one shown on the next page. Then your teacher will give you a carton with two holes cut out. One hole will be large enough for a light socket. The other hole will be large enough for a thermometer.

2. Use aluminum foil to line the inside of the carton, including the two long flaps on top. Use masking tape to hold the foil in place. Use scissors to create two holes in the foil to match the holes in the carton.

3. Fasten a sheet of foil across part of the carton as a divider. It will shade the thermometer from direct light while still allowing air to circulate in the carton. See Figure 1 on the next page.

IN THE HEAT OF THE LIGHT (continued)

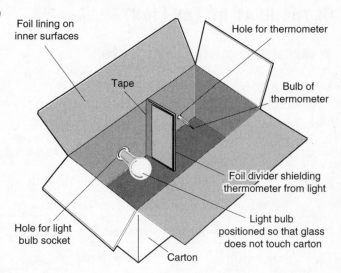

Foil lining on inner surfaces

Hole for thermometer

Tape

Bulb of thermometer

Foil divider shielding thermometer from light

Hole for light bulb socket

Light bulb positioned so that glass does not touch carton

Carton

4. Insert a light socket through the large hole, and seal it in place with black electrical tape. If necessary, support the socket outside the carton so it is stable.

5. Examine the labels on a 60-watt incandescent bulb and its packaging. In the Data Table, record the number of watts, lumens, and predicted hours of life.

6. Insert the incandescent bulb into the socket. Make sure the light bulb does not touch any part of the cardboard or aluminum foil. Test the bulb to make sure it works, and then turn it off.

7. Insert a thermometer through the other hole in the carton. Wait about one minute, and then observe the temperature inside the carton. Record that temperature for Time 0 in the first column in the Data Table.

8. On a separate sheet of paper, write a prediction about the amount of temperature change you expect when the light is turned on.

9. Close the carton so that the foil-covered lids are on the inside. Turn on the light, and for 10 minutes, record the temperature in the Data Table every half minute.

10. Turn off the light, and open the carton. **CAUTION:** *Do not touch the hot light bulb or its base.* Allow the bulb and its base to cool down for at least two minutes. When the light is cool, and the temperature of the carton reaches the original temperature, carefully remove the light bulb.

11. Repeat Steps 5 through 10 using a 15-watt fluorescent light bulb.

◆ Observations

Using the Data Table below as a model, on a separate sheet of paper create a complete Data Table. Include rows for 21 entries, one every half minute, for a total of 10 minutes.

Data Table

Sample Data:
In 10 minutes, the incandescent bulb increased the temperature from 22°C to 78°C; the fluorescent bulb increased the temperature from 22°C to 34°C.

		Incandescent Bulb _60_ Watts _840_ Lumens _1,250_ Hours of Life	Fluorescent Bulb _15_ Watts _900_ Lumens 10,000 Hours of Life
	Time (min)	Temperature (°C)	Temperature (°C)
	0		
	0.5		

Continue for 21 rows.

IN THE HEAT OF THE LIGHT (*continued*)

◆ Analyze and Conclude

1. Make a graph of your data, placing time on the horizontal axis and temperature on the vertical axis. Which light bulb heated up the inside of the box more? Explain.

   The incandescent bulb; for the sample data, the temperature in the carton increased by about

   50 Celsius degrees compared with only about 10 Celsius degrees for the fluorescent bulb.

2. Which bulb gave off more light for the amount of energy used? How do you know?

   For the sample data, the fluorescent bulb gave off more than four times as much light per watt

   as the incandescent bulb. The fluorescent bulb gave off (900 lumens) ÷ (15 watts), or

   60 lumens/watt, while the incandescent bulb gave off (840 lumens) ÷ (60 watts), or 14 lumens/watt.

◆ Critical Thinking and Applications

3

1. Which gives off more visible light, a 15-watt fluorescent bulb or a 15-watt incandescent bulb? What happens to the energy that is not given off as visible light?

   A 15-watt fluorescent bulb; fluorescent lights change more of the energy from electricity into

   light than incandescent bulbs do. Incandescent bulbs convert more energy into heat.

2. In people's homes, incandescent bulbs commonly use 60 to 100 watts. Fluorescent bulbs only use between 15 and 25 watts. Why do you think this is so?

   Compared to incandescent bulbs, fluorescent bulbs use less energy to produce the typical

   amount of light that people want.

More to Explore

You can use the information from this lab along with information about costs to determine which light bulbs to buy. For example, the cost to operate a light bulb is about 10 cents per kilowatt hour. That equals $0.0001 for each watt for one hour. Assume that a 15-watt fluorescent bulb costs $15.00, and the 60-watt incandescent bulb costs 50¢. Assume that you will use each type of light bulb about 4 hours per day.

1. Determine the average cost of operating a 15-watt fluorescent bulb for one year.

   15 watts X $0.0001/watt per hour X 4 hr/day X 365 days = $2.19

2. Determine the average cost of operating a 60-watt incandescent bulb for one year.

   60 watts X $0.0001/watt per hour X 4 hr/day X 365 days = $8.76

3. If you consider the initial cost of the bulbs, the cost of operating them, and their average lifetimes, which bulb is less expensive to use? Explain your reasoning and show your work.

   Students may use different strategies, including estimation, to solve this problem. Sample: 4 hr/day X 365 days/yr = 1,460 hr of use per year; thus, a typical incandescent bulb will last for 1,250 hours, or for most of one year. One fluorescent bulb will typically last (10,000 hr) ÷ (1,460 hr/year), or about 7 years; thus the $15 cost of the fluorescent bulb averages out to about $2 per year.

   The total annual cost of the incandescent bulb is about $.50 for the bulb + $8.76, or about $9 per year. The total annual cost of the fluorescent bulb is about $2.00 for the bulb + $2.19, or about $4 per year.

O-4   **LABORATORY INVESTIGATION**

Plane-Mirror Images

Key Concept: Images in a plane mirror are virtual images.

Skills Focus: Observing, measuring, making models

Time Required: 40 minutes

◆ Pre-Lab Discussion

When light strikes an object, the light can be reflected, absorbed, or transmitted. When the reflected light from an object strikes a mirror, the light reflects off the coating, and an image forms in the mirror. The image formed by a plane, or flat, mirror seems to be exactly like the object. But is the image really an exact copy of the object? And how does a mirror produce an image?

In this investigation, you will see how a plane mirror forms an image and how that image compares with the object.

1. What is an image?

An image is a copy of an object formed from reflected or refracted rays of light.
_____

2. When you look in a plane mirror, what size image do you see? How far away does the image appear to be?

You see an image of yourself that is the same size as you are and that appears to be the same

distance behind the mirror as you are in front of the mirror.
_____

4

◆ Problem

How is an image produced by a plane mirror?

◆ Materials *(per group)*

cardboard (approximately 30 cm × 30 cm)
unlined paper
small mirror and support
metric ruler
3 straight pins
protractor

Teaching Tips: Have students refer to the text on plane mirrors and how images are formed (page 114).

◆ Safety   *Review the safety guidelines in the front of your lab book.*

Handle the mirror carefully. If it breaks, tell the teacher. Do not pick up broken glass.

PLANE-MIRROR IMAGES *(continued)*

◆ Procedure

1. Lay the paper on the cardboard. Stand the mirror in the center of the paper and draw a line along the edge of the mirror. Stick a pin in the paper and cardboard about 4 cm in front of the mirror. Draw a small circle around the pin position and label it "Object." See Figure 1.

2. Bend down so that your head is near the lower right corner of the paper. Look at the mirror with one eye closed and observe the image of the pin. Do not look at the real pin. Stick a pin in the paper so that it hides the image of the pin in the mirror. Draw a small circle around the pin position and label it "1."

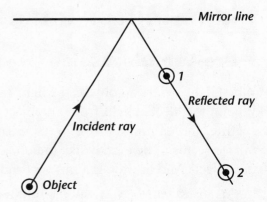

Figure 1

3. From the same position on the right-hand side of the paper, stick a second pin in the paper so that it hides the real pin at position 1 and the image of the object pin. Draw a small circle around the pin position and label it "2."

4. Remove the pins from positions 1 and 2. Use them to repeat steps 2 and 3 from the lower left corner of the paper. Draw circles around these pin positions and label them "3" and "4."

5. Remove the mirror and all of the pins. Using the ruler, draw a solid line through pin positions 1 and 2 and extend it as far as the mirror line. This line represents a reflected ray. Draw a line from the object position to the point where the reflected ray leaves the mirror. This line represents the incident ray. Label each ray and draw an arrow on the ray to show its direction.

6. Repeat Step 5 for positions 3 and 4.

7. Draw a line perpendicular to the mirror line at each of the two points where the incident rays and the reflected rays touch. These lines are the normals. See Figure 2. Label and measure the angle of incidence and the angle of reflection

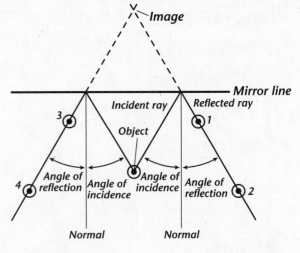

Figure 2

for the rays coming from the left and right corners of the paper. Record your measurements in the Data Table.

8. Using the ruler, draw two dashed lines extending the two reflected rays beyond the mirror line. Continue your dashed lines just beyond the point where they cross. This point is the position of the image of the pin in the mirror. Label this point "Image."

   Include your completed drawing when you hand in this lab to the teacher.

PLANE-MIRROR IMAGES *(continued)*

◆ Observations

Data Table

	Angle of Incidence	Angle of reflection
Left-side rays	30°	30°
Right-side rays	30°	30°

◆ Analyze and Conclude

1. At what distance is the object from the mirror line?

about 4 cm

2. At what distance is the image from the mirror line?

about 4 cm

3. Compare the distance of the object and of the image from the mirror.

They should be the same.

4. Compare the measures of the angle of incidence and the angle of reflection for the rays from the left side of the paper.

The angle measures should be the same.

5. Compare the measures of the angle of incidence and the angle of reflection for the rays from the right side of the paper.

The angle measures should be the same.

◆ Critical Thinking and Applications

1. Follow the path of an incident ray and its reflected ray. If the incident ray enters from the left, toward what direction does the reflected ray leave? If the incident ray enters from the right, toward what direction does the reflected ray leave?

right; left

2. Based on your answer to Question 1, how does the image compare with the object?

The image and the object appear to be the same. However, the image is reversed.

4

PLANE-MIRROR IMAGES *(continued)*

3. If the angle of incidence were not equal to the angle of reflection, would that affect the image's appearance? Give a reason for your answer.

The image would be shifted or skewed and would not appear to be the same as the object.

4. Why does the image seem to be inside or behind the mirror?

Light rays reflected by the mirror are picked up by the human eye. The human brain assumes the

light is traveling in a straight line even though the light rays are reflected. The brain is fooled into

seeing the image as if it were an object behind the mirror.

◆ More to Explore

New Problem How do convex and concave mirrors form images?

Possible Materials Consider which materials you can use from the previous part of this lab. What else will you need?

Safety Handle the mirrors carefully. If they break, tell the teacher. Do not pick up broken glass.

Procedure Develop a procedure to solve the problem. Write your procedure on a separate sheet of paper. Have the teacher approve your procedure before you carry out the investigation.

Observations On a separate sheet of paper, make a data table like the one in the previous part of this lab in which to record your data.

Have students refer to the text on concave and convex mirrors, which discusses focal points and how they affect the formation of an image. Have several convex and concave mirrors available for students to use, as well as clay, which can be used to hold up the mirrors.

4

Analyze and Conclude

1. How do the images formed by these curved mirrors compare to the actual objects?

For a concave mirror, if the object is farther from the mirror than the focal point, the image is

real and inverted. If the object is between the focal point and the mirror, a magnified

virtual image forms. For a convex mirror, the image is always virtual and appears to be smaller

than the object.

2. Suggest some practical applications for these mirrors.

Concave mirrors can focus lights and are used in car headlights. Because they produce

magnified images, they are used in makeup mirrors. Convex mirrors are used as passenger-side

rearview mirrors.

Common SI Units

Measurement	Unit	Symbol	Equivalents
Length	1 millimeter	mm	1000 micrometers (µm)
	1 centimeter	cm	10 millimeters (mm)
	1 meter	m	100 centimeters (cm)
	1 kilometer	km	1000 meters (m)
Area	1 square meter	m^2	10 000 square centimeters (cm^2)
	1 square kilometer	km^2	1 000 000 square meters m^2)
Volume	1 milliliter	mL	1 cubic centimeter (cm^3 or cc)
	1 liter	L	1000 milliliters (mL)
Mass	1 gram	g	1000 milligrams (mg)
	1 kilogram	kg	1000 grams (g)
	1 ton	t	1000 kilograms (kg) = 1 metric ton
Time	1 second	s	
Temperature	1 Kelvin	K	1 degree Celsius (°C)

Metric Conversion Tables

When You Know	Multiply by	To Find			
			When You Know	Multiply by	To Find
inches	2.54	centimeters	centimeters	0.394	inches
feet	0.3048	meters	meters	3.281	feet
yards	0.914	meters	meters	1.0936	yards
miles	1.609	kilometers	kilometers	0.62	miles
square inches	6.45	square centimeters	square centimeters	0.155	square inches
square feet	0.093	square meters	square meters	10.76	square feet
square yards	0.836	square meters	square meters	1.196	square yards
acres	0.405	hectares	hectares	2.471	acres
square miles	2.59	square kilometers	square kilometers	0.386	square miles
cubic inches	16.387	cubic centimeters	cubic centimeters	0.061	cubic inches
cubic feet	0.028	cubic meters	cubic meters	35.315	cubic feet
cubic yards	0.765	cubic meters	cubic meters	1.31	cubic yards
fluid ounces	29.57	milliliters	milliliters	0.0338	fluid ounces
quarts	0.946	liters	liters	1.057	quarts
gallons	3.785	liters	liters	0.264	gallons
ounces	28.35	grams	grams	0.0353	ounces
pounds	0.4536	kilograms	kilograms	2.2046	pounds
tons	0.907	metric tons	metric tons	1.102	tons

When You Know		
Fahrenheit	subtract 32; then *divide* by 1.8	to find Celsius
Celsius	multiply by 1.8; then *add* 32	to find Fahrenheit